THE CITY & GUILDS TEXTBOOK

LEVEL 2 NVQ DIPLOMA
BEAUTY THERAPY

INCLUDES NAIL SERVICES

Publications

For information about or to order City & Guilds' support materials, contact 0844 534 0000 or centresupport@cityandguilds.com. You can find more information about the materials we have available at www.cityandguilds.com/publications.

Every effort has been made to ensure that the information contained in this publication is true and correct at the time of going to press. However, City & Guilds' products and services are subject to continuous development and improvement and the right is reserved to change products and services from time to time. City & Guilds cannot accept liability for loss or damage arising from the use of information in this publication.

City & Guilds
1 Giltspur Street
London EC1A 9DD

T 0844 543 0033
www.cityandguilds.com
publishingfeedback@cityandguilds.com

Mum, dad and Lauren: this is for you. Thank you for always believing in me and for always supporting every decision I have ever made throughout my Beauty Therapy career. Without your continued encouragement and pushing me to achieve my dreams I would never have got to where I am today.

To Terry: thank you for instilling a passion in me for this amazing industry all those years ago.

To Stephen: thank you for your unconditional patience and support throughout this entire project.

Samantha

CONTENTS

ACKNOWLEDGEMENTS

City & Guilds would like to sincerely thank the following.

For invaluable beauty knowledge
Anita Crosland, Sarah Farrell and Andrea Plimmer

For invaluable nails knowledge
Carole Whitehead and Samantha Watkinson

For their help with the cover photoshoot
William Wilson at Goldwell (hairdresser), Andrew Buckle (photographer), Claudia Cooper (model), Lauren Mathis (make-up artist) and Hasselblad for the loan of a Hasselblad H4D-40 (40 megapixel) with a Hasselblad 120 mm macro lens.

For their help with taking pictures
Lisa Rudge at Walsall College, Helen Beckmann at Hebe Salon, Kim Ponting at The London College of Beauty Therapy, Lukia Riley at Hertford Regional College, Julie Goacher at Central Sussex College, Marisol Martinez-Lees at Leicester College, Samantha Watkinson at Derby College, Amanda Gillett at The Folkestone Academy.

Picture credits
Every effort has been made to acknowledge all copyright holders as below and the publishers will, if notified, correct any errors in future editions.

Aircare Europe Ltd: p255; **Alexandra House Spa, Huddersfield:** p389; **Anthony Braden:** pp299, 303; **Aquamanda (www.aquamanda.co.uk):** pp381, 386; **BaByliss Pro:** pp148, 151, 183; **Baglioni Spa by SPC (www.baglionispa.co.uk):** p55; **Barnet College/Photography by Mark Phillips:** p316; **Blink+Go:** p117; **Bluestone National Park Resort:** pp384, 387, 389, 390; **Bobbi Brown:** pp301, 315; **Caflon:** p352; **Camera Press London: Alain Benainous/Gamma:** p294; **Capital Hair & Beauty:** pp28, 80; **Carlton Group:** pp39; **Central Sussex College:** pp40, 58, 121, 137, 161, 172, 173, 174, 177, 178, 179, 180, 181, 182, 183, 186, 239, 240, 241, 242, 243, 244, 246, 248, 249, 250, 260, 264, 265, 266, 267, 268, 269, 270, 271, 272, 273, 274, 275, 277, 278, 282, 339, 367, 372, 374, 375, 377; **Cetuem Cosmetics Ltd.:** p284; **Champneys Health Resorts (www.champneys.com):** pp33, 57 330, 331, 333, 337; pp49, 208; **Collin UK:** p100; **Corinthia Palace Hotel & Spa:** p383; **Covermark® and Farmeco®.** Covermark® and Farmeco® are registered EU Community Trademarks: pp365, 367, 369, 370, 376; **Creative Nail Design:** pp256, 258, 269, 351, 435, 436; **Dermalogica:** pp60, 87, 88, 96, 110; **Derby College:** pp241, 243, 245, 247, 248, 249, 250, 251; **Dermacolor:** pp298, 373; **Elemis:** pp54, 92, 95, 95, 96, 107; **Ellisons:** pp39, 194, 196, 341; **EzFlow:** pp253, 259, 279, 280; **Fotolia:** © Alan Stockdale p31, © Jenny Thompson p31; **Germaine de Capuccini:** p82; **Getty images:** CMSP pp49, 208; **Guinot:** p62; **Hebe Salon:** pp35, 80 97, 98, 122, 132, 133, 134, 145, 150, 162, 197, 321, 322, 323, 353, 354, 357, 358, 359, 360, 362; **Hertford Regional College:** pp24, 25, 26, 27, 30, 34, 62, 78, 85, 93, 100, 101, 103, 104, 105, 129, 150, 153, 154, 155, 156, 158, 176, 289, 291, 315, 326, 333, 334, 335, 337, 338, 343, 345, 368, 380; **IBD:** p191, 200; **IIAA College Programme:** p76; **iStock:** © 4x6 p91, © Abel Mitja Varela p306, © ampyang p 99, © Andrew J Shearer p346, © Appeal Group p143, © Atomic Sparkle p359, © CAP53 p294, © Cathy Britcliffe p257, © Chris Gramly p295, © christianpound p211, © cjp p134, © claire222 p114, © Clayton Cole p50, © D4 Fish Photography p133, © Dana Bartekoske p123, © Dodz Larysa pp123, 296, © drbimages p319, © Dr Bouz p138, © Edward Bock p297, © Ekaterina Monakhova p164, © Emma K. Studio p120, © Fatal Sweets p141, © felixcasio p357, © George Peters p210, © gruizza pp293, 294, © Hadel Productions p91, © hoyaboy p238, © Hüseyin Tuncer p48; © Iconogenic pp89, 113, 147, 308; © Inga Ivanova pp91, 136; © IngramPublishing p1, © Ivanchecko p361, © Jacob Wackerhausen p309, © James Brey p337, © Jenny Swanson p371, © Joel Carillet p46, © Knape p134, © kristian sekulic p337, © Lee Pettet 346, © Liv Friis – Larsen p55, © Larysa Dodz p294, © Marguerite Voisey pp26-27, © Mark Richardson p32, © Mikael Damkier p346, © Nancy Nehring p355, © Nicky Gordon p37, © Pete Fleming p347, © Quavondo pp307, 356, © Rob Friedman p327, © Roberto A Sanchez p188, © Sara Sanger p294, © SavchenkoJulia p132, © Scott Harms p46, © scottjay p42, © Sheryl Yazolino Griffin p293, © Shoots imaging p126, © Simon Ivarsson 209, © Spiderstock p293, © Stéphane Bidouze p208, © swetta p146, © syagci p293, © Sze Fei Wong 349, © Valua Vitaly pp149, 160, 184, 325, © www.danielbendjyphotography.com p169, © zhang bo p83, © Ziga Lisjak p210, ZTS p160; **Jane Iredale the Skincare Make-up:** pp299, 304; **Janice Brown at Hof Beauty:** p144; **JML:** pp161, 184; **Joyce Connor, founder of Brides and Beauty (www.bridesandbeauty.co.uk):** p91; **Lash Perfect:** p124; **Leicester College:** pp135, 136; **Lush:** p93; **Lycon wax strip distribution:** p150; **M·A·C:** pp288, 298, 300, 305; **Maria Retter:** p311; **Mediscan:** p50; **Melissa Jenkins (www.melissajenkinsphotography.com):** pp171, 327, 438; **Michael Barnes:** p287; **Mundo (www.mundoproducts.co.uk):** p40; **Nail Delights (www.naildelights.com):** pp236, 237, 251, 259; **Nails by Gigi Rouse, Image Courtesy of Sweet Squared LLP:** p189; **Nail Systems International:** p276; **Natural Health Spa (www.budockvean.co.uk):** p388; **naturasun:** p57; **Orly:** pp200, 213, 232, 233; **Palms Extra:** pp258, 283; **Professionails:** pp60, 226, 232, 233, 235, 244, 285; **Professional Beauty:** p71; **Renscene:** p39; **Salon System:** p124; **Science Photo Library:** 42, 44, 50, Alain Dex, Publiphoto Diffusion p48, B. Boissonnet p8, CNRI pp45, 371, David Parker p42, Dr Chris Hale pp7, 43, 44, Dr Harout Tanielian pp7, 8, Dr H.C.Robinson p6, Dr P. Marazzi pp7, 42, 43, 44, 46, 47, 49, 50, 166, 167, 208, 209, 214, 361, Dr Zara / BSIP p45, James Stevenson p46, Joti pp44, 47, Life in View p47, Medical Photo NHS Lothian p49, St Bartholomew's Hospital p6, Tony McConnell p7, Western Ophthalmic Hospital p43; **Scratch Magazine:** p240; **Simon Hylton:** p393; **Sterex:** pp111, 168; **Studex:** pp352, 361; **The British Association of Skin Camouflage:** p369; **The Folkestone Academy:** p135; **The London College of Beauty Therapy:** pp28, 30, 53, 54, 56, 57, 59, 61, 65, 66, 68, 69, 70, 71, 72, 73, 74, 75, 80, 190, 204, 239, 290, 315, 319, 324, 326, 329, 330, 331, 332, 335, 336, 339, 340, 347; **The Sanctuary, Covent Garden:** p379; **United Beauty:** pp242, 244; **Walsall College:** pp51, 64, 80, 81, 84, 86, 87, 88, 98, 99, 101, 105, 106, 109, 115, 116, 118, 119, 123, 125, 127, 128, 130, 131, 139, 146, 149, 150, 152, 155, 156, 157, 163, 169, 191, 192, 193, 195, 198, 201, 202, 212, 217, 218, 219, 221, 222, 223, 224, 225, 227, 228, 229, 230, 231, 254, 257, 260, 338, 339, 340, 341, 348, 364, 366; **www.hiveofbeauty.com:** p128.

For further information on the M·A·C PRO Student programme and student kits please contact **mvasovic@mac-cosmetics.co.uk**
To order M·A·C products please contact M·A·C Mail-order on 0870 034 2676.

I experienced my first ever beauty treatment – a back massage – at the age of 13 and knew there and then that this was what I wanted to do. The thought of having the power in my hands to change a person's emotional wellbeing for the better made me realise that this was the career for me. So I immediately asked if they had any vacancies and worked there every Saturday for two years earning £10 a week until I began my Beauty Therapy course.

After qualifying with an NVQ Level 3, I found myself in Greece as a spa therapist in a small hotel. It was only a six-month contract but I got to meet some amazing people and, luckily, once it was over I was transferred to Antigua where I was given more responsibilities. I returned to the UK to study and worked part time as assistant manager at a local salon where I was responsible for staff training and meeting targets. Balancing a full-time course with a part-time job was such hard work, but I enjoyed it because I met people who became friends for life.

Towards the end of my further training my course leader encouraged me to go into teaching, and I'm truly glad I did because I absolutely love it! My students make each day interesting; to see them progress is so rewarding. I love the fact that I am passing my passion on to others and hope that I will be passing some on to you as you use this book throughout your NVQ Level 2. In my opinion, this is one of the best industries to get into as you will never stop learning!

Samantha Raybould

I have been working in the professional nail industry since 1986 and opened a 'nails only' salon with a business partner in 1988. That's a long time dedicated to nails! During that time I have worked in almost all areas of the industry, including teaching at a further education college, writing textbooks and developing training programmes for beginners and improvers. Now I spend most of my time working on photographic shoots, often for the advertising of cosmetic brands and designer labels. I also have a team that works with me on fashion shows in London and Paris.

I am chairperson of the Nail Services Forum for Habia and have been involved in the development process of the National Occupational Standards and assessment strategy for many years. Learning in a college or other type of training provider is just the beginning! Dedicated and successful nail technicians need to continue learning to update their skills. It is a fascinating industry to work in, so make the most of your foundation learning and, with dedication, you will have a rewarding career for life.

Marian Newman

Congratulations on choosing to make a career out of Beauty Therapy! It's a really exciting and rewarding industry, where qualified therapists have opportunities to advise and treat clients with a huge range of fabulous services. It's also an ever-changing industry – you can work in a variety of job roles in the UK or abroad, such as land-based salons and spas, as well as cruise ships sailing the world and training/teaching for beauty companies and colleges.

A City & Guilds NVQ in Beauty Therapy is a strong certification recognised by many major employers. It demands ability, focus, commitment and excellent results. This book will help you to achieve those results through its understandable text, step-by-step procedures and illustrations.

I also did a City & Guilds in Beauty Therapy, and chose it as a career because it allowed me to work in a variety of job roles at the top of an industry that I absolutely love! I now work as Head of Training at Steiner, which allows me to travel the world as well as pass on my knowledge to others.

The key to becoming a great beauty therapist is good communication, confidence and a commitment to your skill. You must also have a strong business awareness and a desire to exceed your clients' expectations and to make a difference to their lives. Use your textbook, work hard and practise, practise, practise!

Good luck and be the best you can possibly be!

Penny Hallworth

Steiner Training

INTRODUCTION – HOW TO USE THIS TEXTBOOK

You will find that your City & Guilds NVQ/SVQ Level 2 Beauty Therapy and Nails Services textbook is laid out in the same way as your City & Guilds NVQ/SVQ Level 2 Beauty Therapy logbook to aid your navigation and understanding of both.

Each chapter in your textbook covers all of the knowledge and outcomes you will need to understand in order to complete your qualification.

The units in your logbook and in this textbook are divided into 'generic' units, 'beauty' units and 'nails' units. Units that start with 'G' are generic units, units that start with 'B' are beauty units, and units that start with 'N' are nails units. There is only one spa unit – S1. There is also an anatomy and physiology chapter at the beginning of the book.

Throughout this textbook you will see the following features:

HANDY HINTS

Toner is also available as a spray which is ideal for male clients as it eliminates the risk of getting cotton wool caught in facial hair. It is also more cost effective to use toner in a spray format.

Handy hints are particularly useful tips that can assist you in your revision or help you remember something important.

Strip lashes
Very dramatic artificial lashes that are applied to the length of the eye.

Words in bold in the text are explained in the margin to aid your understanding.

WHY DON'T YOU...

Why don't you – These hints suggest activities for you to try to help you practise and learn.

ACTIVITY

Activities – The activities help to test your understanding and learn from your colleagues' experiences.

SmartScreen B5 handout 8

SmartScreen – These icons refer to the City & Guilds SmartScreen resources and activities. Ask your tutor for your log-in details.

At the end of each unit are some 'Test your knowledge' questions. These questions are designed to test your knowledge of what you have learnt from that unit. This can help with identifying further training or revision needed.

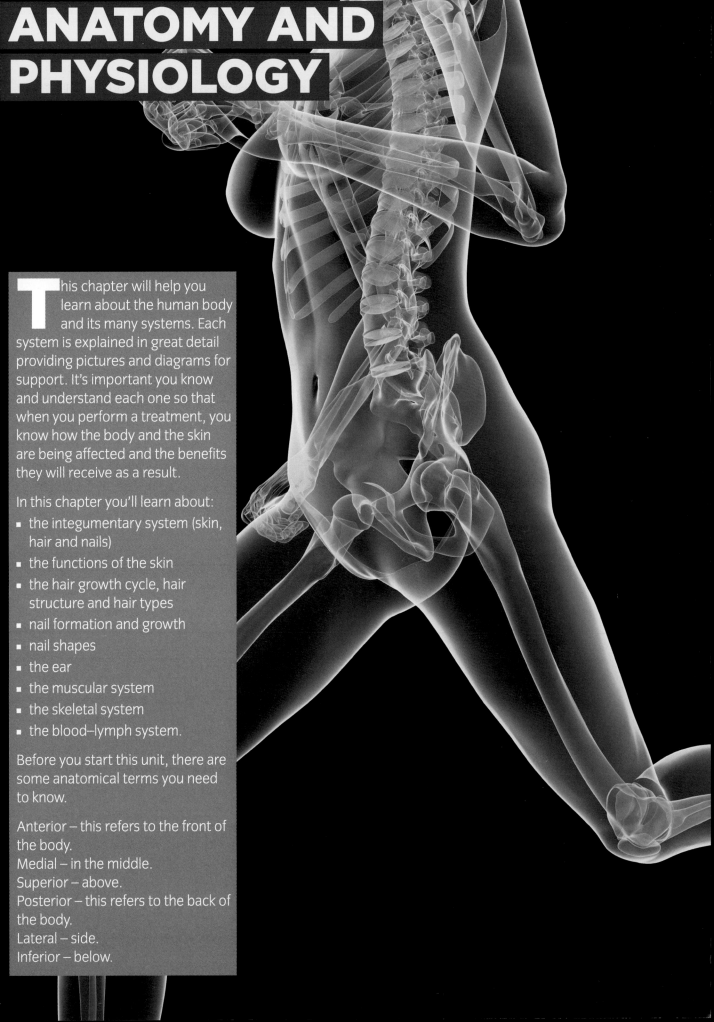

ANATOMY AND PHYSIOLOGY

This chapter will help you learn about the human body and its many systems. Each system is explained in great detail providing pictures and diagrams for support. It's important you know and understand each one so that when you perform a treatment, you know how the body and the skin are being affected and the benefits they will receive as a result.

In this chapter you'll learn about:

- the integumentary system (skin, hair and nails)
- the functions of the skin
- the hair growth cycle, hair structure and hair types
- nail formation and growth
- nail shapes
- the ear
- the muscular system
- the skeletal system
- the blood–lymph system.

Before you start this unit, there are some anatomical terms you need to know.

Anterior – this refers to the front of the body.
Medial – in the middle.
Superior – above.
Posterior – this refers to the back of the body.
Lateral – side.
Inferior – below.

THE INTEGUMENTARY SYSTEM (SKIN, HAIR AND NAILS)

The integumentary system includes the skin, the hair and the nails. They all have one thing in common: they're made of a protein called keratin.

THE SKIN STRUCTURE AND FUNCTIONS

The skin is the body's largest organ and is made up of three distinct layers: the epidermis, the dermis and the subcutaneous layer.

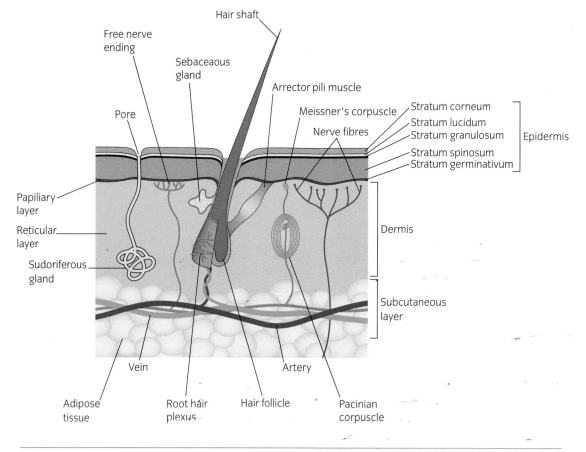

Cross-section of the skin

Keratinisation

The hardening of a cell caused by the production of a protein called keratin and the degeneration of its nucleus.

THE EPIDERMIS

The epidermis is above the dermis and contains five layers. The cells in these layers go through a process called **keratinisation** as they're pushed upwards and reach the skin's surface.

These five layers are called:
- the stratum corneum (horny layer)
- the stratum lucidum (transparent or clear layer)
- the stratum granulosum (granular layer)
- the stratum spinosum (prickle cell layer)
- the stratum germinativum (basal layer).

THE CITY & GUILDS TEXTBOOK

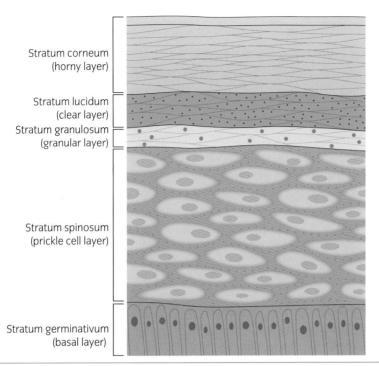

Layers of the epidermis

Stratum corneum/horny layer

The stratum corneum is the uppermost layer of the epidermis and is otherwise known as the horny layer because of the hard, flattened cells. These cells have completely keratinised, meaning they have no nucleus at all. There are approximately 25 layers of these dead cells in the stratum corneum that are constantly shedding. This process is called **desquamation**.

Desquamation
The skin's own natural exfoliation process.

Stratum lucidum/transparent or clear layer

This is the transparent layer, sometimes referred to as the clear layer, and is often only found on the palms of the hands and the soles of the feet where the skin is much thicker. It's made up of approximately 3–4 layers of cells that form a waterproof barrier, sometimes referred to as the barrier layer.

Stratum granulosum/granular layer

The stratum granulosum contains 2–3 layers of flat cells that are hard. It's otherwise known as the granular layer because keratinisation is almost complete and the nucleus has almost **degenerated**.

Degenerated
Fallen below normal amounts; deteriorated.

Stratum spinosum/prickle cell layer

This is also referred to as the prickle cell layer. The 8–10 layers of cells are more rounded in shape. They have 'fingers' that attach to other cells as they try to feed from each other at the start of the keratinisation process. Langerhan's cells are also found in this layer and help fight infection.

Cell mitosis
Cell division that is also referred to as cell metabolism and cellular renewal.

Stratum germinativum/basal layer

The basal layer is attached to the dermis via the basement membrane, which provides nourishment and allows **cell mitosis** to occur. There's only one layer of cube-like cells with **melanocytes** between them.

Melanocytes
Cells that produce melanin, the skin's own natural pigment.

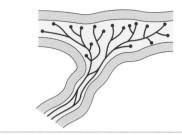

Ruffini corpuscle

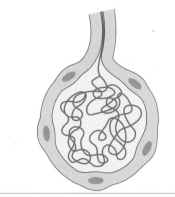

Krause corpuscle

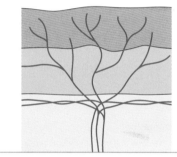

Free nerve endings

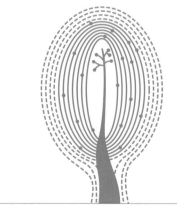

Pacinian corpuscle

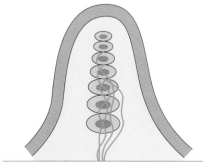

Meissner's corpuscle

THE DERMIS

The dermis is the layer of the skin that lies beneath the epidermis and is made up of two layers called the upper papillary region and the lower reticular region. Both contain various structures and components.

The upper papillary region

This is the thinnest of both regions and connective tissue keeps the skin elastic and forms various sensory nerve endings. It's this layer that is attached to the stratum germinativum via the basement membrane and provides nourishment to stimulate cell mitosis. There are also blood capillaries in the upper papillary region which supply blood and nutrients to the skin.

Sensory nerve endings

There are various nerve endings that help us experience and identify different sensations, such as heat, cold, pain, pressure and touch.

Ruffini corpuscles

These are nerve endings that respond to heat and are found deep in the papillary region.

Krause corpuscles

Krause corpuscles are nerve endings that respond to cold and are found midway in the papillary region.

Free nerve endings

Free nerve endings respond to pain and are found just beneath the basement membrane.

Pacinian corpuscles

Pacinian corpuscles are nerve endings that respond to pressure and are found deep in the reticular region.

Meissner's corpuscles

Meissner's corpuscles are nerve endings that respond to touch and are found high up in the papillary region.

The lower reticular region

This is the thickest of the two layers situated below the upper papillary region. It contains structures such as the hair follicle, sebaceous glands, arrector pili muscles, sweat glands and blood supply. This region also produces **collagen** and **elastin fibres** from cells called **fibroblasts**. Mast cells are stimulated to release histamine into the bloodstream when the skin is irritated by an allergen, while phagocytic cells fight harmful particles, such as bacteria.

The hair follicle and arrector pili muscle

The hair follicle is surrounded by the epidermis but its base is in the dermis. The dermis holds the hair shaft and supports its structure and growth until it's shed. There are hair follicles all over the body, except for the palms of the hands, the soles of the feet and the lips.

The arrector pili muscle is attached to the hair follicle and holds the follicle in position. When the muscle contracts, it makes the hair shaft in the follicle stand on end and produces goose bumps on the skin.

The hair shaft

This comes out from the follicle on the skin's surface. It's considered dead because it's been keratinised; the hair in the follicle that isn't visible on the surface is considered living. There are three layers that make up the hair shaft. These are discussed in more detail later in this unit.

Sebaceous glands

These apocrine glands are found all over the body and are attached to the hair follicle. They produce a substance called **sebum** that is **secreted** on to the skin's surface. The hair follicle and sebaceous gland together are often referred to as a pilosebaceous unit.

Sweat glands

Also known as sudoriferous glands, these are eccrine glands that lie deep in the dermis and produce sweat that is **excreted** on to the skin's surface. Sweat mixes with sebum to produce the **acid mantle**. See Unit B4 for information on pores.

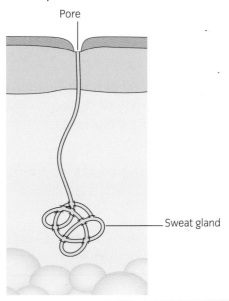

Pore

Sweat gland

Cross-section of a sweat gland

Blood supply

There are tiny blood vessels called capillaries supplying fresh oxygen and nutrients to the dermis, the hair follicle and the epidermis. This helps form structures in the dermis, hair growth and the production of new cells in the epidermis.

Collagen and elastin fibres

These are produced by cells called fibroblasts. Collagen fibres make the skin plump, whereas elastin fibres make it supple. Collagen and elastin fibres are produced in large amounts in babies and this is why their skin is so supple and plump. As they grow older, this production reduces and their skin becomes less supple.

THE SUBCUTANEOUS LAYER

This is the deepest layer of the skin and is also called the hypodermis because it's located beneath the dermis. The subcutaneous layer contains one structure called adipocytes, which literally means fat cells. This layer of fat provides protection for the bone structure and organs, and acts as an **insulator**.

Collagen
Keeps the skin plump.

Elastin fibres
Make the skin supple.

Fibroblasts
Cells that produce collagen and elastin fibres.

Sebum
Produced in the sebaceous gland and is the skin's own lubricant.

Secretion
The release of a substance from a cell or gland.

Excretion
The removal of waste, such as sweat from the skin.

Acid mantle
Made up of sebum and sweat on the surface of the skin, the acid mantle forms its own umbrella of protection against bacterial infection. Refer to page 95 for more information on the pH of the skin.

Insulator
A material that reduces heat loss.

THE FUNCTIONS OF THE SKIN

The skin performs various functions in the body. An easy way to remember these functions is through SHAPES:

Sensation: the skin feels touch, pressure, heat, cold and pain through the stimulation of sensory nerve endings.

Heat regulation: when a person is cold, vasoconstriction occurs which redirects blood to the vital organs to keep them warm. The arrector pili muscle contracts and makes the hair stand on end. This traps a warm layer of air just above the skin's surface. When a person is warm, vasodilation occurs which releases heat from the body and redirects blood to the skin's surface. The sudoriferous glands produce sweat that cools the skin.

Absorption: the skin absorbs nutrients, water and minerals into the body. However, only a small amount of absorption happens through the skin, such as topical medication and creams. This is only superficial absorption.

Protection: the skin protects itself by producing collagen fibres to heal wounds. Melanocytes provide natural protection against UV rays. Sweat and sebum mix together to form the acid mantle which provides protection against bacterial invasion.

Excretion: sweat contains waste products, such as salt, urea and water. They're removed from the sudoriferous glands and excreted on to the skin's surface.

Secretion: sebum is an oil that stops the skin drying out by keeping the epidermis supple. See Unit B4 for more information on how the sun can affect the skin.

SKIN CHARACTERISTICS

As well as understanding the skin and its structures you need to be aware of certain features that might be present in the skin. You will come across many of these in your working life as a therapist and you will need to be able to identify each of them.

Comedones

These are more commonly known as blackheads and are caused by trapped sebum in the pore which has oxidised and turned black. You can remove them manually or with a comedone extractor after steaming. Using incorrect methods to remove comedones can cause tissue damage and the spread of infection. Comedones are common along the T-zone but can be found all over the face, sometimes on the ears, and usually accompany an oily or combination skin type.

Milia

More commonly known as whiteheads, milia are caused by small deposits of fat in the pores that harden and become trapped. They're difficult to remove and can be annoying for your client. If your client picks at them, they can become red and sore. Milia can only be

Comedones

Milia

removed with a micro-lance (a tiny probe) after steaming. This pierces the skin but can sometimes leave a tiny scar. Milia are commonly found around the upper cheeks and eye areas and usually accompany a dry skin type.

Pustules

More commonly known as spots or zits, pustules have a head on them and contain pus. As there's pus present, we know there's also an infection and so they shouldn't be squeezed. But as everyone has been guilty of doing this at least once, it's important to know how to do it in the safest possible way to avoid spreading the infection. See manual comedone extraction for instructions on safe working methods. Pustules usually accompany an oily skin type.

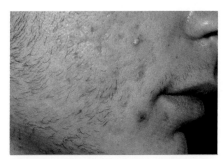
Pustules

Papules

These are similar to pustules but without a head, so they cannot be squeezed. They tend to be angry looking and can be quite sore and painful. Usually they appear and are gone in a matter of days but while they're around, they can cause your client irritation, pain and discomfort. Papules usually accompany an oily skin type.

Dilated capillaries

These are mostly present on dry, dehydrated or sensitive skins and can also be referred to as 'broken' capillaries. They are caused by ongoing environmental aggravation, which causes the vessel walls to weaken and eventually break down, leaving a small red line that appears on the skin's surface.

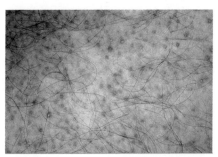
Papules

Relaxed pores

When the walls of a pore have relaxed this causes the pore to appear larger than it is – a relaxed pore. Relaxed pores are usually more common on an oilier skin due to the amount of sebum secreted.

Ingrown hairs

When a hair is removed from the follicle, it doesn't always grow back above the skin's surface. As the skin grows over it, the hair continues to grow but down into the skin. It's important this hair is removed safely to prevent further infection of the follicle.

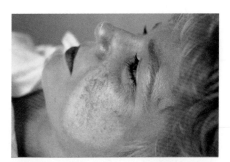
Dilated capillaries

Pseudo-follicultis

This is inflammation and erythema of the hair follicle caused by an ingrown hair and can affect any area of the body. When it occurs on the face it is referred to as *pseudo-folliculitis barbae*. In Caucasian skin, it's easy to identify, but in Afro-Caribbean skin it's not because when erythema is produced, the skin will go darker rather than red. Pseudo-follicultis barbae is more common in Afro-Caribbean skin as the hair is curly (because of curly hair follicles), which means that when the hair is cut during shaving, it might pierce and grow back into the skin as an ingrown hair.

Keloid scarring

This is the result of an injury where the skin produces more collagen to assist with the healing process but, in this instance, it produces too much collagen and continues to produce it so that the resulting scar is much larger than the original wound. Keloid scarring is more common in

Keloid scarring

Afro-Caribbean and Asian skin than Caucasian skin, and generally affects the head, neck and shoulders. It's not painful or damaging to the skin but can be annoying for your client. It's identified as raised areas of skin that can look shiny and feel rubbery in texture.

Dermatosis papulosa nigra

This is a small area of raised skin with hyper-pigmentation, the cause of which is unknown, although it is harmless. This condition only affects Afro-Caribbean skin.

Hyper-pigmentation

This is where the skin becomes darker in patches due to stimulation of the melanocytes, which produce melanin. This stimulation can be in the form of UV rays, medication or pregnancy. The following conditions come under the umbrella of hyper-pigmentation:

- chloasma
- ephilides
- solar keratoses
- lentigines.

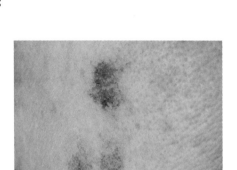

Hyper-pigmentation

Hypo-pigmentation

This is the opposite of hyper-pigmentation where the skin becomes lighter in patches. It can be caused by medication or illness, which causes the melanocytes to stop functioning or 'die'. The most common condition associated with hypo-pigmentation is vitiligo, which can be distressing; the cause is unknown.

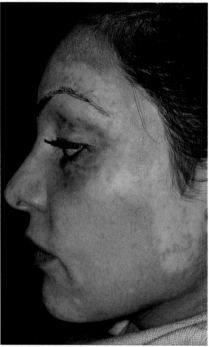

Hypo-pigmentation

ACTIVITY

Look at your own skin in the mirror to see if you can identify any of the characteristics identified above.

THE HAIR GROWTH CYCLE, HAIR STRUCTURE AND HAIR TYPES

Hair does not grow at the same rate all over the body. Each stage of hair growth lasts for a different length of time. There are three different stages of hair growth.

ANAGEN

Early anagen and anagen are often referred to as the active stages of hair growth. The follicle is either forming or fully formed and the cells are still attached to the base of the follicle. Cell mitosis occurs in this stage. New cells allow the hair to grow up towards the skin's surface, while the follicle grows down towards the dermis and forms the **dermal papilla**. This provides nourishment for the hair to grow.

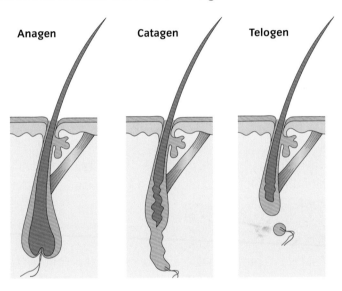

Anagen   Catagen   Telogen

CATAGEN

Catagen is also called the transitional stage because the hair begins to detach from the life-giving dermal papilla and causes the follicle to begin to shrink. The hair rises towards the skin's surface while it's still attached to the follicle wall.

TELOGEN

Telogen is the final stage of the hair growth cycle and is known as the resting stage because the hair is dead. The dermal papilla has completely withdrawn from the follicle and will only be stimulated again at the start of a new hair growth cycle. It's at this point that the hair is shed from the follicle and the cycle starts again.

The hair is made of three layers of keratinised cells:

- the medulla
- the cortex
- the cuticle.

HANDY HINTS

Hair on the scalp can grow for anything between two and seven years, with a resting stage of around four months. The hair of the eyebrows can take as little as two or three months to grow, with a resting stage of around three months. The eyelashes can take 3–6 weeks to grow, with a resting stage of around three months.

Dermal papilla

The base of the follicle is attached to the blood supply and provides oxygen and nutrients, stimulating hair growth throughout the anagen phase.

HANDY HINTS

The hair bulb is the base of the hair follicle that is present in hair that is removed by waxing or tweezing during the anagen phase of hair growth. It houses the dermal papilla and its lower part is called the **matrix**. The epithelial root sheath is made up of two parts: an outer area and an inner area. The outer area forms the wall of the hair follicle and doesn't grow upwards with the hair but instead remains in place. The inner area grows from the dermal papilla with the hair follicle until it becomes level with the sebaceous gland. It interlocks with the cuticle of the hair and anchors it in place.

Matrix

Where cell mitosis occurs to create the hair. Underneath the matrix there are dividing cells which form the hair.

HANDY HINTS

It's important not to attempt to treat abnormal hair growth, such as **hirsutism**, **hypertrichosis** and **superfluous** hair, as it is very often caused by a hormonal imbalance. Instead you could suggest other, more permanent, methods of hair removal, such as electrolysis.

Hirsutism

When a person's hair growth is abnormal for their gender, eg when a female has hair growth on the face that follows the male hair growth pattern.

Hypertrichosis

When hair growth is considered abnormal for a person's gender, age or race, and may be present at birth (congential) or appear later in life due to illness, medication or possibly linked to an eating disorder (acquired).

Superfluous

Excessive hair growth that occurs naturally in females at certain points of their lives. During puberty, females will begin to grow terminal hair in their pubic regions, but during pregnancy this hair growth might increase or stop. During the menopause, it usually increases permanently. The cause is a hormonal imbalance.

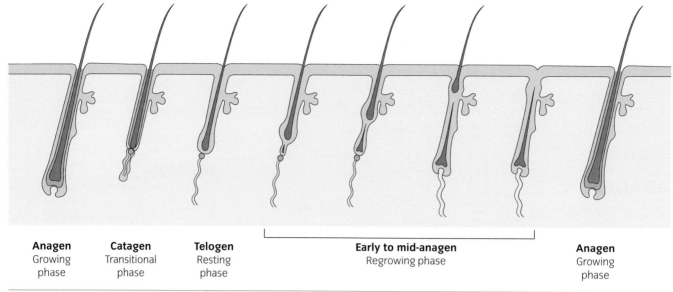

| **Anagen**
Growing
phase | **Catagen**
Transitional
phase | **Telogen**
Resting
phase | **Early to mid-anagen**
Regrowing phase | **Anagen**
Growing
phase |

The hair growth cycle

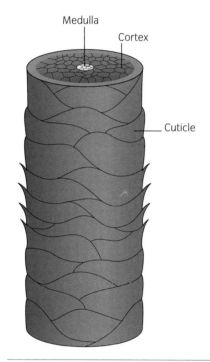

Keratinised cells of the hair

Pigment
A substance that produces colour.

MEDULLA

The medulla is the innermost layer of the follicle but isn't always found in vellus hair. It's formed of loosely connected, keratinised cells with air spaces in between. The medulla determines the sheen and colour tones of the hair by light reflection.

CORTEX

This middle layer forms the bulk of the hair. It contains melanin that gives hair its natural colour and elongated keratinised cells that are bound together.

CUTICLE

This outermost layer is made up of scale-like cells that point towards the tip of the hair and interlock with the cuticle of the hair follicle, anchoring it into place. There's no **pigment** in the cuticle and its job is to protect the cortex.

There are three types of hair found on the body, depending on the location:

- lanugo
- vellus
- terminal.

LANUGO HAIR

This is found on a foetus and is usually shed just before or just after birth.

VELLUS HAIR

This is found all over the body and is soft, fine and downy hair. It has shallow roots and contains hardly any pigment.

TERMINAL HAIR

At birth, terminal hair is found on the scalp, eyebrows and lashes. During puberty, it grows under the arms and in the groin areas. The hair is thick and coarse in texture, is deep rooted with a rich blood supply and contains a lot of pigment. Terminal hair has much more nerve supply than vellus hair so removal of terminal hair tends to feel more uncomfortable for the client.

NAIL FORMATION AND GROWTH

The main function of the nail is to provide protection for the nail bed (see page 12). The structure of the nail is similar to the structure of the skin because it's produced through the processes of mitosis and keratinisation. In the matrix of the nail, mitosis causes the nail cells to reproduce. As these cells grow out from the matrix they form the lunula and the nail plate where they become keratinised and harden until they reach the free edge. This growth is constantly guided by the nail walls and grooves to ensure the nail remains parallel. The following structures make up the nail:

- mantle
- matrix
- lunula
- eponychium
- cuticle
- nail bed
- nail plate
- free edge
- hyponychium
- nail wall
- nail groove.

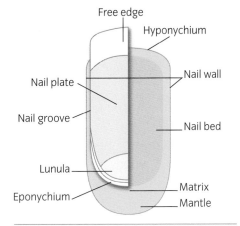

The structure of the nail

MANTLE
The mantle is the deep fold of skin in which the nail is embedded.

MATRIX
The matrix is where the new living cells are produced through cell mitosis. It's similar to the stratum germinativum because it's where cell mitosis occurs. These new cells are pushed forward to produce the nail plate.

LUNULA
The lunula is the only visible section of the matrix and forms a bridge between the living and dead cells. It's more commonly known as the half moon because of its opaque colour and shape. This structure is similar to the stratum spinosum because it's where the cells are keratinised. Not everyone has visible lunulas.

EPONYCHIUM
The eponychium protects the matrix which, in turn, prevents infection.

CUTICLE
The cuticle is the dead skin shed from under the eponychium and sticks to the nail plate.

HANDY HINTS

The nail curves in two directions, **transversally** and **longitudinally**.

Transversally
Across the nail, or along the width of the nail.

Longitudinally
Along the length of the nail.

NAIL BED

The nail bed is an extension of the matrix. It lies under the nail plate and gives the nail its natural colouring. Blood gives the nail enough nourishment to grow. As the nail plate grows over the nail bed, it follows its form exactly. This results in ridges.

NAIL PLATE

The nail plate lies above the nail bed and is made up of hundreds of layers. These are found in three sections of keratinised cells bound together by sulphur bonds, moisture and fat. The uppermost layer is the thickest and the innermost the thinnest. If there's not enough water or fat in the nail plate, the nails dry out, the bonds between the layers break easily and the nails start to peel. The thickness of the nail plate can determine its strength and flexibility. It takes about six months for the cells to push up from the matrix to the free edge and this growth can be affected by trauma and damage. The nail plate is similar to the stratum corneum/horny layer because the keratinisation process is complete.

FREE EDGE

The free edge is the portion of the nail plate that extends beyond the fingertip. It protects the hyponychium which lies at the edge of the nail bed.

HYPONYCHIUM

The hyponychium lies at the edge of the nail bed and just beneath the free edge. It has a seal that protects the nail bed from infection.

NAIL WALL

The nail wall is the fold of skin found at either side of the nail. It protects the nail plate and the nail bed.

NAIL GROOVE

The nail groove is also found at either side of the nail plate. It holds the nail plate in place and makes sure it grows in a parallel line.

NAIL SHAPES

There are three natually occurring nail shapes:

- spoon
- fan
- hook.

SPOON

A naturally occurring nail shape where the nail tends to curve up at the free edge causing it to look like a spoon.

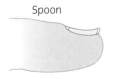
Spoon

FAN

A naturally occurring nail shape where the free edge appears to be much wider than the rest of the nail.

HOOK

A naturally occurring nail shape where the free edge is much thicker than the rest of the nail and curves over the tip of the finger causing it to look like a hook.

Fan

Hook

THE EAR

The ears are part of the auditory system and help a person hear sounds and keep their balance. The bulk of the ear is called the pinna. This is made up of cartilage and cartilaginous tissue so it can be moved around. The ear lobe contains a lot of blood and keeps the ears warm. The prominent rim of the ear is called the helix. This is made up of cartilage. The helix is not suitable for piercing as it doesn't heal well.

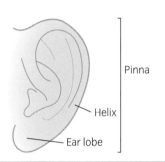

Parts of the ear

THE MUSCULAR SYSTEM

There are three types of muscle found in the body:
- voluntary: skeletal muscle, such as the orbicularis oris
- involuntary: smooth muscle, such as the oesophagus
- cardiac: heart muscles cause the heart to contract and relax, which pumps blood around the body.

Skeletal muscle is made up of 75 per cent water, 5 per cent inorganic substances and 20 per cent muscle-forming cells called **myoblasts**. These produce muscle fibres called **actin** and **myosin** filaments that are bundled together in **myofibrils**. When a muscle contracts, these fibres are pulled closer together.

HANDY HINTS

The part of the muscle that is attached to a bone and is immovable is called the origin. The part of the muscle that is attached to a bone and is moveable is called the insertion.

Myoblasts

When myoblasts fuse together, they form myotubes that eventually develop into skeletal muscle fibres.

Actin

A protein involved in the formation of filaments.

Myosin

The commonest protein in muscle cells, responsible for the muscle's elasticity.

Myofibrils

Function as cellular support, movement and intra-cellular transport and are found in muscle cells.

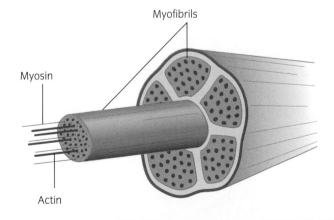

Myofibrils

Myosin

Actin

Cross-section of a muscle

The following tables identify the names, actions and positions of the muscles.

Facial muscle	Position	Action
Frontalis	Forehead	Raises the brows and forms horizontal frown lines or wrinkles across
Platysma	Extends from the chin to the chest	Pulls the jaw and lower lip downwards
Temporalis	Side of the head stretching to the mandible	Lifts the mandible during chewing
Masseter	Runs from the temples to the jaw	Works with the temporalis to close the mouth during chewing
Zygomaticus	Runs from the corners of the mouth to the temple	Lifts the sides of the mouth and cheeks to laugh
Risorius	Runs from the corners of the mouth	Lifts the corners of the mouth into a smile
Orbicularis oris	Surrounds the mouth	Brings the lips into a pout
Orbicularis oculi	Surrounds the eyes	Closes the eyelids
Sternocleidomastoid	Side of the neck extending from below the ear to the sternum	Pulls the head down towards the chest and moves it from side to side
Buccinator	Lies below the risorius	Squeezes the cheeks together during chewing
Depressor labii	Runs down the chin from the lower lip	Pulls the lower lip down
Mentalis	Under the lower lip in the centre of the chin	Raises the lower lip and lifts the chin
Corrugator	Between the eyebrows	Depresses the brows to frown
Levator labatis (levator labii)	Sides of the upper lip	Elevates the upper lip
Triangularis	Runs towards the neck from the corners of the mouth	Brings the mouth downwards to an inverted 'U' shape
Procerus	Between the brows, extending down to the nasal bone	Draws the eyebrows down in a frown

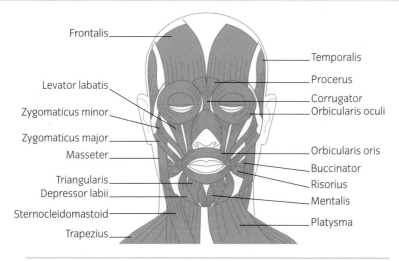

Muscles of the face and neck

Muscles in the arm and hand	Position	Action
Biceps	Anterior upper arm	**Flexes** the forearm
Triceps	Posterior upper arm	**Extends** and **adducts** the shoulder
Brachio radialis	Between the upper arm and forearm	Flexes the forearm
Flexor carpi radialis	Located above the radius bone	Flexes and **abducts** the wrist
Flexor carpi ulnaris	Located above the ulna bone	Flexes and adducts the wrist
Flexor digitorum	Lateral aspect of the forearm	Flexes the fingers
Extensor digitorum	Extends from the elbow to the carpals on the posterior aspect of the forearm	Extends the fingers
Extensor carpi radialis brevis and extensor carpi radialis longus	Medial aspect of the forearm	Extends and abducts the wrist
Extensor carpi ulnaris	Located to the right of the extensor digitorum muscle	Extends and adducts the wrist
Palmaris longus	Lies between the flexor carpi ulnaris and flexor carpi radialis	Flexes the wrist
Thenar eminence	Palm of the hand at the base of the thumb	Controls movement of the thumb
Hypothenar eminence	Palm of the hand lying opposite the thenar eminence	Controls movement of the little finger

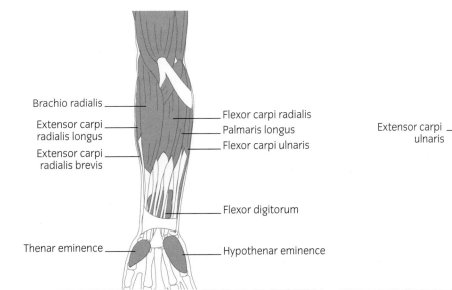

Muscles of the forearm (front view)

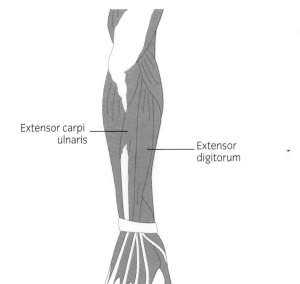

Muscles of the forearm (back view)

Extends
To bend backwards or to straighten and make the angle bigger between the joints.

Adducts
To bring towards the midline.

Abducts
To take away from the midline.

Flex
To bend forwards and make the angle smaller between the joints.

Muscles of the upper body	Position	Action
Trapezius	Extends from the occipital bone across the shoulders towards the deltoids and midway down the back, attaching at the spine	Rotates and elevates the scapula
Pectoralis	Extends over the chest, attaching at the top of the arm	Adducts and rotates the upper arm
Deltoid	Covers the shoulder	Assists with lifting the arm and moving it back and forwards

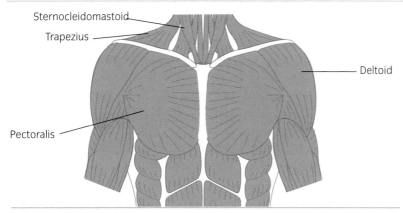

Muscles of the upper torso

Muscles of the lower leg	Position	Action
Gastrocnemius	More commonly known as the calf muscle	**Plantar flexion** of the foot to assist with walking. Plantar flexes the foot and flexes at the knee.
Soleus	Lies beneath the gastrocnemius and attaches to the Achilles tendon	Plantar flexion of the foot
Tibialis anterior	Extends from the lateral edge of the patella to the medial edge of the ankle	**Dorsi flexion** and **inversion** of the foot
Extensor digitorum longus	To the outer edge of and just behind the tibialis anterior, extending from the outer edge of the knee to the outside of the ankle	Flexes the foot downwards and allows the toes to grip

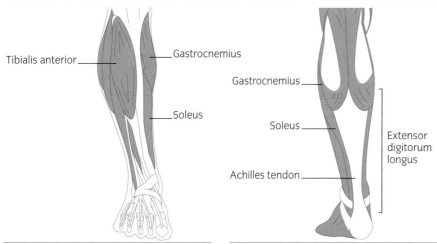

Plantar flexion
Increases the angle between the toes and the legs.

Dorsi flexion
Decreases the angle between the toes and the legs.

Inversion
To bring the foot inwards.

Muscles of the lower leg (front view)   Muscles of the lower leg (back view)

THE SKELETAL SYSTEM

The skeletal system is made up of connective tissue forming bones, joints, cartilage, tendons and ligaments. There are two types of connective tissue: cancellous, which is soft and spongy; and compact, which is hard and solid. Below and on the next pages are tables identifying the positions of the bones of the body.

Bones of the head	Position
Occipital	One bone forming the back of the skull
Frontal	One bone forming the forehead
Parietal	Two bones forming the crown of the skull
Temporal	Two bones forming the sides of the skull behind the ears
Sphenoid	One bone forming the back of the eye sockets
Ethmoid	One bone between the eye sockets forming part of the nasal cavities

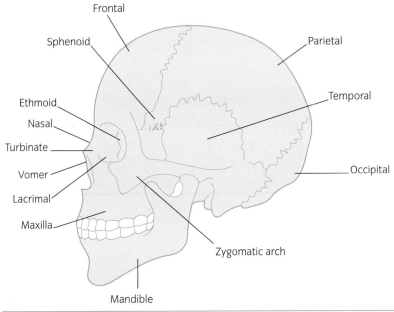

Bones of the skull

HANDY HINTS

The average human skeleton is made up of 206 bones. Bones give us our shape.

Bones of the face	Position
Zygomatic arch	Two bones forming the cheekbones
Mandible	One bone forming the lower jaw and the only moveable joint in the skull
Maxillae	Two bones forming the upper jaw
Nasal	Two bones forming the bridge of the nose
Vomer	One bone forming the nasal septum
Turbinate	Two bones forming the outside of the nose
Lacrimal	Two bones forming the inner walls of the eye socket
Palatine	Two bones forming the floor of the nose and the roof of the mouth

Bones of the chest, neck and shoulders	Position
Hyoid	A 'U'-shaped bone at the base of the neck between the clavicle bones
Cervical vertebrae	Seven discs forming the top part of the spine. The first, the 'atlas', supports the skull, the second, the 'axis', rotates the skull.
Clavicle	More commonly known as the collarbone, it forms a joint with the scapulae and sternum
Scapulae	More commonly known as the shoulder blades
Humerus	The bone of the upper arm, which is more commonly known as the funny bone
Sternum	More commonly known as the breastbone

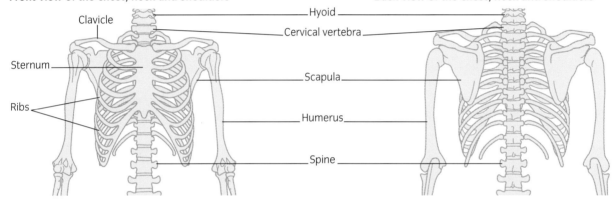

Front view of the chest, neck and shoulders

Back view of the chest, neck and shoulders

Bones of the arm and hand	Position
Ulna	Located on the lateral aspect of the forearm
Radius	Located on the medial aspect of the forearm
Carpals	Form the wrist and are made up of eight small bones
Metacarpals	Five bones form the length of the hand
Phalanges	Fourteen individual bones make up the fingers and toes

HANDY HINTS

There are a total of 27 bones in the hand.

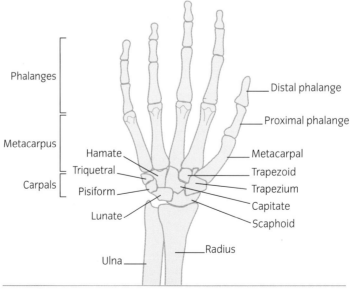

Bones of the arm and hand

Bones of the foot and leg	Position
Femur	Thigh bone (longest bone in the body)
Patella	More commonly known as the knee cap
Tibia	More commonly known as the shin bone
Fibula	Located just behind the tibia
Tarsals	Form the ankle and are made up of seven bones
Metatarsals	Form the length of the foot and are made up of five bones, the cuboid, two cuneiforms, the talus and navicular
Phalanges	Form the toes and are made up of fourteen bones
Calcaneus	Heel bone

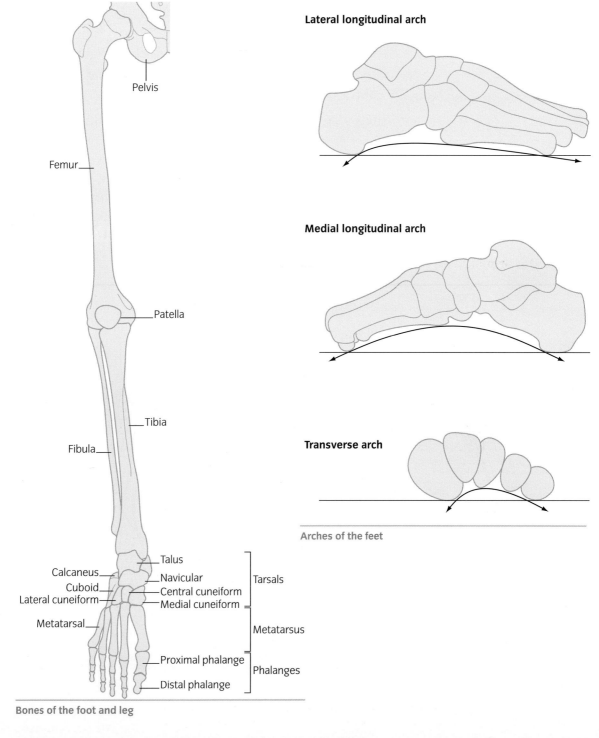

Lateral longitudinal arch

Medial longitudinal arch

Transverse arch

Arches of the feet

Bones of the foot and leg

THE BLOOD–LYMPH SYSTEM

The lymphatic and circulatory systems work closely together to transport oxygen and nutrients around the body and eliminate waste products. Both systems complement each other and work hard as a defence mechanism to protect the body from bacterial invasion and viruses.

BLOOD

Blood is a two-way transportation network. It delivers fresh oxygen from the lungs to the body via the heart and carbon dioxide back to the lungs. It also carries nutrients from food via the digestive system. There are three different types of blood cell in the blood:

- erythrocytes: red blood cells responsible for the transportation of oxygen and carbon dioxide
- leucocytes: white blood cells responsible for fighting infection
- thrombocytes: platelets responsible for forming blood clots when the skin is damaged.

These cells are suspended in a liquid called plasma, which contains 90 per cent water and 10 per cent proteins. Plasma makes up 55 per cent of our blood, while the remaining 45 per cent is made up of blood cells. Blood is transported throughout the body via vessels called arteries and veins. Arteries take oxygenated blood away from the heart to the rest of the body and veins bring de-oxygenated blood back to the heart. Veins have valves to prevent the backflow of de-oxygenated blood. Capillaries are the smallest of the blood vessels.

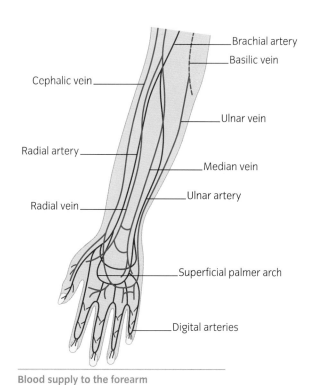

Blood supply to the forearm

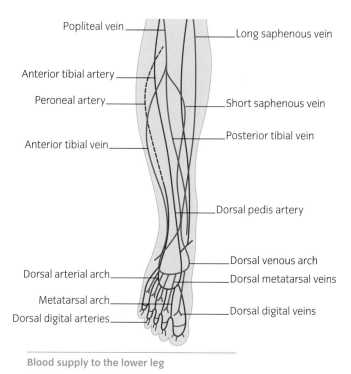

Blood supply to the lower leg

Above are two diagrams highlighting blood supply to the forearm, hand, lower leg and foot. All veins are shown in blue to depict de-oxygenated blood, and all arteries are shown in red to depict oxygenated blood.

LYMPH

Lymphatic fluid is straw-like in colour and has a similar consistency to plasma. The main difference between lymph and blood is that the heart doesn't pump lymph around the body. Instead, it moves around the body by muscle contractions and bodily movements.

The lymphatic system disposes of waste products taken from the blood via filtering stations called lymph nodes or lymph glands. The lymph nodes drain the lymph back into the blood via the thoracic or right lymphatic ducts. The following tables identify the names and positions of the various lymph nodes.

Lymph nodes of the body	Position of nodes
Axillary	At the underarms
Supra-trochlear	Just in the crease of the elbow
Popliteal	At the back of the knee
Right lymphatic duct	At the base of the neck on the right. Drains waste from the right side of the head, the right arm and the right side of the torso.
Thoracic duct	Beneath the body of the sternum. Drains waste from the left side of the head, the left arm and the rest of the body.

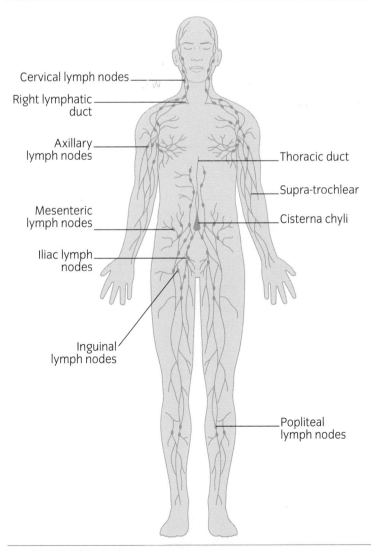

Lymph nodes of the body

Lymph nodes of the head	Position
Supra-clavicular	Above the clavicle just above the sternum
Superficial and deep cervical	Back of the neck
Sub-mental	Under the chin
Sub-mandibular	Under the mandible
Buccal	Either side of the mouth
Parotid	Just in front of the ear
Pre-auricular	In front of the top of the ear
Post-auricular (retro-auricular)	Behind the top of the ear
Occipital	Base of the skull at the back of the head

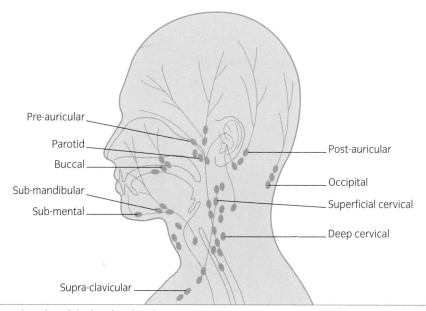

Lymph nodes of the head and neck

CHAPTER SUMMARY

Now you've reached the end of the unit, check the following list to see if you feel confident in all areas covered. If there are still any areas you're unsure of, go back over them in the book and ask your tutor for additional support:

- the integumentary system (skin, hair and nails)
- the functions of the skin
- the hair growth cycle, hair structure and hair types
- nail formation and growth
- nail shapes
- the ear
- the muscular system
- the skeletal system
- the blood–lymph system.

TEST YOUR KNOWLEDGE

Now that you're aware of, and have an understanding for, the different systems of the body, let's see how much you can remember. These questions will help you to revise what you've learnt in this chapter.

Turn to pages 395–396 for the answers.

1 How many layers make up the epidermis and what are their names?

2 What does mitosis mean?

3 Explain the term keratinisation.

4 How many layers make up the nail plate?

5 What is the function of the matrix?

6 Describe the hair growth cycle.

7 What is the bulk of the ear called?

8 What fibres are found in muscles?

9 What is skeletal muscle made up of?

10 What are the action and location of the frontalis muscle?

11 What are the action and location of the sternocleidomastoid muscle?

12 What are the action and location of the thenar eminence muscle?

13 What are the action and location of the soleus muscle?

14 What is the difference between cancellous and compact bone tissue?

15 Where are the carpals and what are their individual names?

16 How many discs make up the cervical vertebrae?

17 Is blood a two-way or one-way network?

18 What are erythrocytes?

19 Where would you find the parotid lymph nodes?

20 What is the function of the lymphatic system?

G20
ENSURE RESPONSIBILITY FOR ACTIONS TO REDUCE RISKS TO HEALTH AND SAFETY

As a beauty therapist or nail technician, your first and foremost concern will be the welfare of your clients, your colleagues and yourself. Health and safety is relevant to all industries and must be acknowledged and followed to provide and maintain the correct working conditions. This unit is about understanding the health and safety legislation that affects all beauty therapists and nail technicians and identifying the hazards in the workplace and the risks they present. This will ensure you maintain a safe and harmonious working environment for yourself, your colleagues and your clientele.

In this chapter you'll learn how to:

- identify the hazards and evaluate the risks in your workplace
- reduce the risks to health and safety in your workplace.

This unit will be used in conjunction with all other units to ensure the wellbeing of yourself and those around you.

IDENTIFY THE HAZARDS AND EVALUATE THE RISKS IN YOUR WORKPLACE

The Health and Safety at Work Act (HASAWA) 1974 is an umbrella for all other legislation relating to health and safety in the workplace. Under this Act, your **employer** must provide a safe working environment; as the **employee**, it's your responsibility to do your job according to the legislation and the product manufacturers' instructions.

The Health and Safety Executive (HSE) enforces this law and defines the following concepts:

- hazard: something with the potential to cause harm
- risk: the likelihood of that hazard's potential being realised
- control: the means by which the risks identified are eliminated or reduced to acceptable levels.

To identify and control hazards, a business must complete an initial risk assessment before it can open to the public. This risk assessment should be kept up to date each time a new hazard is identified. Therefore, it's important that you, as the employee, remain alert to the potential hazards around you at all times, so that if you notice anything untoward, you can deal with it accordingly.

As an employee, you'll be given a copy of your job description, which will outline your responsibilities for maintaining health and safety in the workplace. You must read and fully understand these responsibilities so that if you do come across any hazards or risks, you'll know how to deal with them. For example, you can deal with a low-level risk, such as a trailing wire, quite easily; however, frayed or exposed electrical wires present a high risk and so you need to pass this on to the **responsible person** to deal with.

Employer

A person who owns a business and employs people to work for them.

Employee

A person who is employed by a business to do work for them.

Responsible person

A person allocated with the responsibility of dealing with hazards and risks as they arise. This can be the salon owner, manager, a senior therapist, or a designated health and safety manager.

WHY DON'T YOU...
Read through SmartScreen handout 1 for further information on HASAWA.

SmartScreen G20 handout 1

ACTIVITY

List the potential hazards presented with each individual treatment you perform, making suggestions for their control and identifying who should deal with them.

The legislation covered by HASAWA are:

- the Control of Substances Hazardous to Health (COSHH) Regulations
- the Personal Protective Equipment (PPE) at Work Regulations
- the Reporting of Injuries, Diseases and Dangerous Occurrences Regulations (RIDDOR)
- the Electricity at Work Regulations (EAWR)
- the Workplace (Health, Safety and Welfare) Regulations
- the Manual Handling Operations Regulations
- the Provision and Use of Work Equipment Regulations (PUWER)
- the Fire Precautions Act.

Additional legislation you need to be aware of are:

- the Disability Discrimination Act (DDA)
- the Data Protection Act (DPA).

HANDY HINTS

Always make sure you know what to do about risks you're unable to deal with, and where and when to get additional health and safety assistance.

Fire retardant
A chemical used to slow down the spread of fire.

Incinerate
To burn something to ashes.

A therapist following PPE and COSHH legislation

THE CONTROL OF SUBSTANCES HAZARDOUS TO HEALTH (COSHH) REGULATIONS

There are various chemicals we come across in our lives that are seen as hazardous, such as cleaning substances and bleach. A hazardous substance in the workplace can put a person's health at risk and cause disease or injury, such as asthma, dermatitis or a burn. Under this Act you must ensure that any hazardous substances are stored, handled, used and disposed of correctly and safely. The best way to remember this is by following SHUD:

- **S**torage: in a locked cupboard at room temperature when not in use; ideally, this cupboard should also be **fire retardant**.
- **H**andling: wear appropriate personal protective equipment (PPE), such as gloves, masks and aprons.
- **U**sage: according to the manufacturer's instructions or workplace guidelines.
- **D**isposal: ensure you dispose of all hazardous waste in a hazardous waste bag; the local authority or a private company will collect the waste and **incinerate** it. This usually consists of tissues, cotton wool and wax strips that have been in contact with bodily fluids, eg blood.

ACTIVITY

Check your salon's store cupboard and see how the following hazardous substances should be stored, handled, used and disposed of correctly. Record your findings in the table below. Is your salon doing everything correctly?

Substance	Storage	Handling	Usage	Disposal
Acetone				
Hydrogen peroxide				
Tint colour				
Barbicide				

HAZARD SYMBOLS

Hazard symbols allow the user of a hazardous substance to identify how hazardous it is and in what way. Without these symbols, a person could become injured, disfigured or even die if they're exposed to certain substances. The following symbols are some that you might come across not only in the salon but in everyday life:

Irritant
This symbol means a substance is hazardous and could be dangerous if you don't use it correctly. Ensure you wear PPE when you're using such substances as they can be an irritant. They're not necessarily corrosive but could cause an immune response in the body that can result in itching, burning, redness and swelling.

Flammable
This symbol means a substance can catch fire quite easily if it's exposed to high temperatures. Keep it stored in a cool, dry cupboard away from direct sunlight.

Explosive

This symbol means a substance has the potential to be explosive if it's exposed to shock, pressure or high temperature. It should be stored in a dry cupboard at normal room temperature and away from direct sunlight.

Oxidising

This symbol means that the substance itself might not be **combustible** but can cause other materials to combust by providing them with oxygen. Store these types of chemical separately from other chemicals to make sure there's no reaction between them.

Toxic

These types of substance could be potentially lethal if they enter the body. The ways in which a substance can enter the body are through inhalation, absorption and ingestion. Ensure you wear gloves, an apron and a mask at all times when you're dealing with these chemicals.

Corrosive

This substance is extremely dangerous and will attack living tissue, including the skin and eyes. Ensure you wear gloves, an apron and a mask when you're dealing with these chemicals.

THE PERSONAL PROTECTIVE EQUIPMENT (PPE) AT WORK REGULATIONS

Under this Act, it's your employer's responsibility to check you're provided with the necessary protection to carry out your work as there might be an element of risk involved. Your employer should also provide training on how and when you should wear PPE. It's your responsibility as an employee to wear this protective equipment to reduce the risks of skin sensitivity and developing skin conditions caused by **overexposure** to different chemicals. PPE can cover all types of equipment from the uniform you wear to the gloves you need for a bikini wax. If your employer requires you to wear a uniform, it's their duty to provide you with one. However, it's your responsibility to wear PPE if it's required.

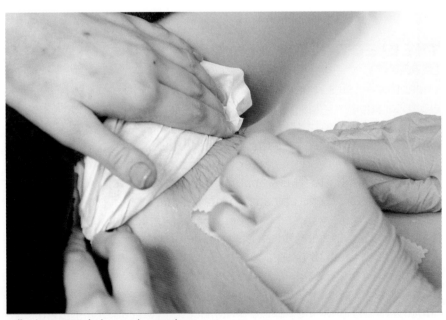

Adhering to PPE during waxing services

Combustible

The tendency of something to react with oxygen and catch fire.

WHY DON'T YOU...
Read through SmartScreen handout 6 for further information on COSHH.

 SmartScreen G20 handout 6

Overexposure

Being regularly exposed to a product or chemical. You might not be allergic to the substance at first, but the body's immune system could develop sensitivity to it over time.

WHY DON'T YOU...
Look at each practical unit and identify the PPE you need as a beauty therapist to perform your job safely and effectively.

THE REPORTING OF INJURIES, DISEASES AND DANGEROUS OCCURRENCES REGULATIONS (RIDDOR)

It's the duty of an employee or an employer to report a major injury, an injury resulting in a person taking more than three days off work, work-related disease and a dangerous occurrence (near miss) to the HSE by calling the local Incident Contact Centre (ICC). All occurences should also be recorded in an accident report book. It's then up to the HSE to work with the employer to reduce the risk of such occurrences happening again.

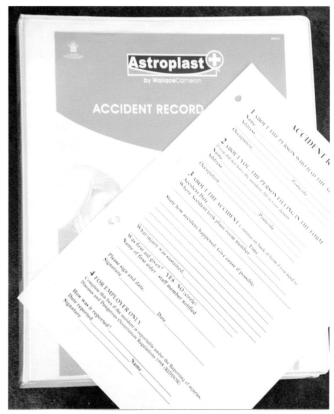

Make sure you know where the salon's accident report book is.

THE ELECTRICITY AT WORK REGULATIONS (EAWR)

Under this Act, it's your employer's responsibility to make sure all electrical equipment is portable appliance tested (PAT) annually by a qualified electrician. It's your responsibility to use it safely and correctly, and to make sure that it's safe for use. If you find there's an electrical fault, tell your manager immediately. Do not, under any circumstances, try to fix the equipment yourself as you're not qualified to do so and could end up causing more damage and, more importantly, injure yourself or others. For example, if you have a piece of electrical equipment, such as a steamer and the wiring is frayed, you must not touch this equipment or try to deal with it yourself as it's considered a high risk. Inform a responsible person who will take it out of use until it's been fixed by a qualified electrician. However, if you notice a jar of Barbicide next to a wax heater, you can deal with this yourself because it's considered a low risk; just move the Barbicide jar to the shelf underneath.

Never try to fix electrical equipment yourself.

THE DATA PROTECTION ACT (DPA)

Under this Act, it's both the employer's and employee's responsibility to keep personal information secure. The key factors relating to this Act are:

- Data should be used only for the specific purposes for which it was collected.
- Data must not be disclosed to other parties without the consent of the individual, unless there's legislation or other overriding legitimate reasons to share the information (for example, the prevention or detection of crime). It's an offence for other parties to obtain this personal data without authorisation.
- Individuals have a right of access to the information held about them, subject to certain exceptions (for example, information held for the prevention or detection of crime).
- Personal information shouldn't be kept for longer than is necessary and must be kept up to date.
- Personal information shouldn't be sent outside the European Economic Area unless the individual has consented or adequate protection is in place.
- Businesses holding personal information are required to have adequate security measures in place. These include technical measures (such as firewalls) and organisational measures (such as staff training).
- Individuals have the right to have factually incorrect information corrected (note: this doesn't extend to matters of opinion).

WHY DON'T YOU...
Identify who the responsible person for health and safety is in your salon.

ACTIVITY

Find out how your salon records and stores its **clients**' personal information. Are there adequate security measures in place? How long should this information be kept for if a client stops coming to the salon?

Client
A person who comes into the salon to receive a treatment.

THE WORKPLACE (HEALTH, SAFETY AND WELFARE) REGULATIONS

An employer is required to ensure the workplace meets the health and safety welfare needs of their employees, clients, **customers** and **contractors**, including people with disabilities. For example, entrances and floors must be accessible to all people by making sure doors are wide enough, and that there are washing facilities, ramps and lifts for wheelchair users.

Customer
A person who isn't necessarily a client but has come into the salon to enquire about the services offered or to buy a product.

Contractor
A person who isn't directly employed by a business but does have a contract with them to complete work by a set deadline. For example, a builder.

ACTIVITY

Does your salon meet the health and safety welfare needs of all its potential customers and clientele? Are there any improvements that could be made? If so, why not suggest them to the responsible person?

THE MANUAL HANDLING OPERATIONS REGULATIONS

Under this Act, you must make sure you lift and carry goods properly to avoid injury. For example, if there's been a delivery to the salon and there are a lot of boxes, don't try to lift and move them all by yourself; ask someone to help you instead. If you can lift a box on your own, lift it using your legs and not your back. If you don't bend your legs, you could damage your spine. The picture below left demonstrates the correct lifting technique.

WHY DON'T YOU...
Watch how a small child picks their toys up and notice how they bend at the knees. This is the body's natural way of protecting the spine. However, as we age we become lazy and use shortcuts, which can often lead to injury.

 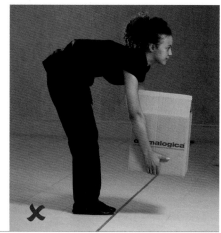

The picture on the left shows the correct lifting technique; the lifting technique on the right is incorrect. This technique will put pressure on the spine and could lead to injury.

THE PROVISION AND USE OF WORK EQUIPMENT REGULATIONS (PUWER)

This Act requires that all equipment is suitable for its intended use and is maintained in a safe condition. Your employer must make sure you've received adequate training in the use of such equipment; as an employee, it's your responsibility to follow this training so you're using the equipment safely and correctly. If you notice a difference between the manufacturer's instructions and your workplace instructions, inform the responsible person who will deal with it accordingly.

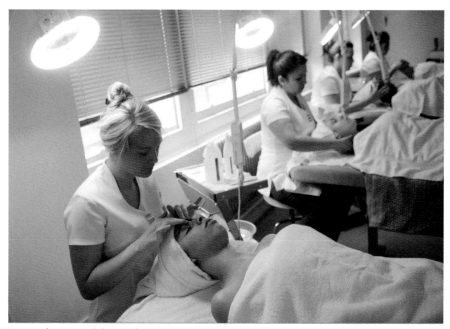

Beauty therapy training environment

ACTIVITY

Write a checklist of all the equipment in your salon that you'll be using. When you've been fully trained in its use, you can tick it off the list.

THE FIRE PRECAUTIONS ACT

This Act states that all staff must be trained in fire and emergency evacuation procedures. If there are more than 20 employees, it's compulsory for a fire certificate to be displayed. An evacuation route is the safest route available by which staff and visitors can escape a building; these must be clearly identified and kept free from obstruction. This Act also requires employers to carry out **risk assessments** for the premises in the event of an emergency or fire. Employers should also fit smoke alarms and test them regularly to check they work and there should be a warning method where either an automatic alarm sounds or a responsible person raises the alarm. Adequate fire-fighting equipment must also be available for use by trained persons only. There are different extinguishers for different fires so the correct extinguisher must be used on a fire to avoid making it worse.

Risk assessment

An assessment of all the possible hazards in a business including their location and whether they are a high or low risk. The assessment also includes suggestions on how these risks can be controlled, managed or eliminated.

Type of extinguisher		Identified by?	Used for?
Water extinguisher		Red label and a thin hose	Class A fires involving paper, hair and textiles
CO₂ extinguisher		Black label and wide nozzle	Class C fires (electrical type)
Foam extinguisher		Cream label and a thin hose	Class B fires involving liquids except cooking oils
Dry powder extinguisher		Blue label and a thin hose	Class C fires (electrical type)

FIRE BLANKETS

These should be used on small fires, such as waste paper fires, chip pan fires or to wrap up a person whose clothes are on fire.

THE DISABILITY DISCRIMINATION ACT (DDA)

This Act aims to ensure that all people with a disability or illness are not discriminated against. It requires businesses to promote equal opportunities for disabled people.

ACTIVITY

Work with some of your classmates to discuss and record the different working practices and aspects of your workplace that can cause harm to you and others. Place these findings in order starting with the highest risk to the lowest risk and suggest how they should be dealt with and whose responsibility they are. You should base this information on what you've learnt about health and safety legislation. Discuss your findings with your tutor and identify what the workplace policy is for managing risks you shouldn't deal with.

ACTIVITY

Think about how you would like to feel if you were to enjoy a beauty treatment. What could your therapist do to help you relax during the treatment? Discuss your responses with a peer and see if you come up with the same ideas. Do any of them included the following factors:

- heating
- lighting
- ventilation
- general comfort?

CREATING THE RIGHT ENVIRONMENT

HEATING

The ideal working temperature of any salon is 16–18°C as this ensures comfort for both the client and therapist. However, remember that your clients might need to undress for certain treatments, such as facials and waxing, so check the temperature is no less than 16°C otherwise your clients might not be able to relax as much as they'd hoped.

LIGHTING

As your client will be lying **supine** for most treatments, check the lights don't glare in their eyes. Ideally, the salon will have dimmer switches to add to the relaxing atmosphere; this way you can keep the lighting low enough to help your client relax but not too low that you also begin to relax! If the salon doesn't have a dimmer switch, you can turn the lights off and use a magnifying lamp (provided it's turned away from your client) and candles to create a calm atmosphere.

Natural daylight can also enhance the atmosphere but not all salons or treatment rooms have this luxury. You also need to remember your own requirements; you need to see what you're doing, so don't have the lighting too low.

Supine
Lying face up.

VENTILATION

Ideally, you'll be able to open a window if the room gets too hot and stuffy. If your salon has a busy road nearby or is in a larger building, this might not be an option. Alternatively, you might have access to air conditioning to keep the work area cool and fresh.

GENERAL COMFORT

When your client is on the treatment couch, make sure you maintain their modesty for the whole treatment. Ask if they're comfortable and if they would like a pillow under their knees or lower back to support their spine. Check they're covered appropriately with towels and a blanket, and ask them to tell you if they get too cold or too hot at any point during the treatment. Use a bolster or a rolled-up pillow for neck support, and bring the head of the couch up at an angle if necessary. Remember to tuck the end of the towels and blanket under your client's feet; this also prevents any tripping hazards for you. Make sure you maintain client comfort at all times to minimise the risk of injury or fatigue.

WHY DON'T YOU...
Think about how the ideal environment for a facial treatment would be different from that for a hair removal service.

Creating a calming environment

HANDY HINT
After you've finished your treatment, set up the work area for the next treatment. This shows good organisational skills and team work. It also prevents clients from being kept waiting and promotes good working relationships.

PREPARING THE THERAPIST

It's important you display a high standard of personal presentation to your clients as they will notice how much pride you take in your appearance. Whether we like it or not, our clients judge us on our appearance; they look to us for guidance on how to look after themselves. If they sense that we don't care about our appearance, they won't take our advice and recommendations seriously. This can have a negative impact on your confidence and on the success of the business. The following questions give you an idea of whether or not you're maintaining good personal presentation:

☐ Have you showered this morning and washed your hair?

☐ Is your breath fresh?

☐ Have you applied deodorant?

☐ Have you cleaned your teeth?

☐ Are you wearing light make-up?

☐ Is your hair tied back and off your face?

☐ Are you wearing a clean and pressed uniform?

☐ Are your shoes clean, flat and closed-toe?

☐ If you're a smoker, have you used breath freshener before starting work?

☐ Have you washed your hands before starting the treatment?

☐ Are you wearing the appropriate PPE for this treatment?

☐ Are your nails short, free of polish and well manicured?

☐ Are you wearing only a minimum of jewellery?

If you've answered no to more than one of these questions, have a think about what your first impression would be if you were the client. Would you feel comfortable with a therapist who didn't seem to care about their personal appearance? Would that make you confident in their care? Remember, first impressions count and are everything!

HANDY HINT

A pair of stud earrings and a wedding band are acceptable for a therapist or nail technician to wear in the salon.

WHY DON'T YOU...

Have a go at SmartScreen worksheet 3 to test your knowledge on suitable salon dress code.

SmartScreen G20 worksheet 3

Correct personal presentation

Incorrect personal presentation

PREPARING YOUR CLIENT

It's important you give your client clear instructions on how you want them to prepare themselves for the treatment. Even if they're a regular client and know the routine, it shows consistency and eliminates any risk of embarrassment.

Many clients feel more comfortable when they're less restricted during a treatment and will prefer to remove all clothing down to their underwear, which is perfectly acceptable. Others might be more nervous and will prefer to remove only their top and shoes. Below is a good example of how to check that your client is properly prepared for a facial treatment. This example can be applied to any treatment with a few minor adaptions:

> **"***I'm going to leave the room to let you undress and lie on the couch. I need you to remove your top and shoes. You can also remove your bra but this is optional. If you want to keep it on, I will lower the straps from your shoulders to avoid getting any product on them. You can lie face upwards on the couch with your head at this end (indicate which end here). I will just be on the other side of the door and will knock before coming back in and, if you need any assistance, just shout.***"**

Here the client has been given clear instructions and hasn't been made to feel uncomfortable. You've reassured them by saying you're just outside and will knock before entering. This tells them they can take as long as they want without anyone walking in unannounced.

ELDERLY OR DISABLED CLIENTS

If you have an elderly or disabled client, you might need to help them into a comfortable position. Try to use an electric or hydraulic couch so you can adjust the height; if not, use a step to help your client get onto the couch. Remember to ask them if they need any help or support from you before you leave the room to let them change.

When your client is on the couch, make sure you maintain their modesty at all times to prevent any embarrassment. Most treatments require some amount of undressing; some clients might be quite nervous and others will be open and relaxed. Make sure you're prepared for both with plenty of towels, pillows and blankets just in case.

A therapist assisting a client onto the treatment couch

TREATING MINORS

Remember that there are restrictions when you're working on minors (persons under 16 years old). Check that you've obtained informed signed parental or guardian consent and make sure that a parent or guardian is present for the duration of the treatment as well.

REDUCE THE RISKS TO HEALTH AND SAFETY IN YOUR WORKPLACE

Now you know the difference between a hazard and a risk, you need to identify potential hazards and risks in the salon. Refer to the list you created earlier with your peers and see if there are any similarities between your findings and the examples below.

A trailing wire is an obvious hazard. If it's trailing across an area where people walk, it's a high risk as someone might trip over it. Your job is to suggest it's covered or ask if it can be moved. However, if the wire is trailing along a wall, the risk is significantly reduced.

Hazardous substances are also obvious hazards but, if the salon follows the COSHH guidelines, the risks are greatly reduced.

Running in the salon is poor behaviour and hazardous as you could fall and injure yourself. By walking and watching where you're going, the risk is reduced.

AVOIDING WASTE

When you're working in the salon and providing beauty treatments, you must make sure you're not wasting resources. Ask yourself the following questions:

- ❑ Do you leave electrical equipment switched on even after you've finished using it?
- ❑ Do you find you have lots of products left over at the end of the treatment?
- ❑ After a facial, do you find you have prepared too many cotton pads?
- ❑ Do you use more than 6–8 wax strips during a leg wax?
- ❑ Do you forget to put the lids back on bottles?
- ❑ Have you forgotten to switch off lights at the end of the day when the salon is closing?
- ❑ Do you take out product from tubs with your fingers?
- ❑ Do you find yourself putting towels in the laundry that weren't actually used?
- ❑ Do you leave the steamer on after you've finished with it?
- ❑ Do you forget to put all hazardous waste in the appropriate hazardous waste bin?
- ❑ Do you forget to use recycling bins to reduce the salon's waste?

If you answer yes to two or more of these questions, you're negatively affecting your salon's profit margins and the environment. Ask yourself this question: if the salon was your own and you were responsible for buying the products, equipment and materials, would you be as wasteful? Look at the following guidelines to check that you're being resourceful with your materials and consumables and you're minimising your waste:

- ❐ Always switch off electrical equipment when it's not in use.
- ❐ Only take what you need from a product tub or tube as you cannot replace it due to the risk of **cross-infection**. You can always take more, you cannot put it back.
- ❐ Count out how many cotton pads you think you'll need for a facial, or take half the amount and split them in half.
- ❐ An experienced therapist will only need four wax strips for each leg wax. Make it your goal to use no more than double that amount.
- ❐ Always replace lids on product bottles. If you leave the lid off, bacteria can enter the product, reducing its shelf life and its effectiveness.
- ❐ Always remove product from a tub with a spatula to prevent the risk of cross-infection. No matter how clean you think your hands are, they will still carry bacteria.
- ❐ Check all electrical equipment is switched off before closing the salon at the end of the day.
- ❐ Make sure you only put used towels in the laundry after each use.
- ❐ Always switch off a steamer after use. Distilled/purified water is not cheap and if you leave the steamer on, you're wasting it.
- ❐ Always place hazardous waste into a hazardous waste bin. Anything contaminated with blood or bodily fluids is considered to be hazardous waste and should NEVER be put into a normal waste bin.
- ❐ If there's recycling available, make sure you use it appropriately.

POSTURE AND POSITIONING

It's vital to maintain good posture at all times; when you're providing treatments, either sitting down or standing up, and when you're lifting and moving equipment. For treatments where you'll be seated, check the chair has adequate back support and allows you to keep a straight back with your shoulders relaxed so you don't hunch over your client. If the chair doesn't have any back support, pay special attention to your posture for the duration of the treatment. When you're sitting, make sure the treatment couch is at the correct height so you're not stretching or hunching to do your job. Check the trolley is close enough so you don't have to stretch to reach anything.

If you're standing for a treatment, make sure your legs are shoulder width apart and slightly bent at the knee. Again, keep your back straight at all times with your shoulders relaxed and, if you need to bend, do so at the knees. This keeps your centre of gravity low and helps to maintain your balance. Poor posture can lead to all kinds of problems and injuries.

Cross infection
The spread of infection from one person to another or from an object to a person. This is caused by poor hygiene practices.

Always use a spatula to decant products

For all treatments, you must maintain safe working practices to avoid injury to yourself and your client. Posture and positioning play an important role in this, as do the following:

- health and safety legislation affecting that treatment
- the manufacturer's or workplace instructions for performing that treatment correctly and safely
- maintaining a safe and appropriate working environment
- remaining alert to potential hazards and the risks they present
- dealing with low risks in your control and reporting high risks that are not your responsibility
- maintaining client modesty
- maintaining high standards of professionalism and behaviour
- maintaining high standards of personal presentation and following the necessary PPE regulations for your salon
- adhering to local by-laws.

MAINTAINING SALON HYGIENE AND STERILISATION PROCEDURES

To prevent the risk of illness or disease to yourself and your clients, you need to be aware of and follow hygiene procedures for your salon to avoid cross-infection. What is cross-infection? It's when a disease or disorder is passed from one person to another, either:

- directly, from person to person
- indirectly, from person to object to person
- through airborne particles and spores entering the body via the respiratory system.

Can cross-infection be stopped completely? Not really, no, because bacteria is everywhere, both good and bad, but it can be prevented by following some simple measures. Sterilisation and **disinfection** are the two most important things for any beauty therapist. You must make sure that all your implements, materials, tools and work surfaces are as clean as possible to maintain hygiene levels and reduce the risk of cross-infection. There are two types of bacteria that you can come into contact with:

- pathogenic
- non-pathogenic.

Disinfection
The destruction of some (but not all) micro-organisms.

PATHOGENIC BACTERIA

Pathogenic bacteria are the bacteria which cause infection. They can enter the body through an open wound or when the immune system is low.

NON-PATHOGENIC BACTERIA

Most bacteria are considered harmless by the body and the immune system so they present no risk of infection or disease. These are called non-pathogenic bacteria.

STERILISATION

Sterilisation is the complete destruction of all micro-organisms and their spores. When a tool has been sterilised, it's completely clean until it comes into contact with a person or another object or surface. There are two methods of sterilisation:

- in an autoclave
- in a glass bead steriliser.

AUTOCLAVES

An autoclave is the most effective method of sterilisation. It exposes metal implements to extremely high-pressured steam at temperatures of around 121°C for approximately 30 minutes. Remove the implements from the autoclave with forceps and place them in Barbicide immediately to maintain the effects.

GLASS BEAD STERILISERS

This method of sterilisation uses dry heat and works by heating tiny glass beads in a metal jar to temperatures of around 210–300°C. This steriliser is ideal for smaller metal implements, such as tweezers and cuticle nippers. Put them in for 30–60 seconds, remove with forceps and place in Barbicide to maintain the effects.

DISINFECTION

Disinfection can destroy some micro-organisms and inhibit the growth of others. When an implement or surface has been disinfected, it's clean to use but it's not sterile. There are two methods of disinfection available to beauty therapists:

- a UV cabinet
- Barbicide.

UV CABINET

A UV cabinet uses UV rays to destroy micro-organisms and is safe to use on disposable or non-metal materials, such as sponges, spatulas, mask brushes and nail files. They should be left in the cabinet for 20 minutes and turned over half-way through. The problem with this method is that you cannot guarantee every area of the implement has been exposed to the UV rays. However, if an implement has been sterilised using another method, it's a good idea to store it in the UV cabinet to maintain the sterile effects.

BARBICIDE

This is a blue translucent liquid that is used by hairdressers, beauty therapists and hospitals as a means of disinfection. It's an effective fungicide, virucide and bactericide that can kill the hepatitis B, C and HIV-1 viruses. Mix with water according to the manufacturer's instructions and use to store metal and plastic implements that have already been sterilised and disinfected.

An autoclave

A glass bead steriliser

WHY DON'T YOU…
Have a go at SmartScreen worksheets 7 and 8 to test your knowledge on sterilisation and hygiene methods.

SmartScreen G20 worksheets 7 and 8

A UV cabinet

Tools soaking in barbicide

ANTISEPTICS

An antiseptic is a substance that can be applied to the skin to reduce infection, and can also act as a bactericide. Surgical spirit is an effective antiseptic used in many hospitals and salons to clean surfaces. Dettol is another antiseptic that can be used to clean surfaces and reduce infection. Remember that both substances can be hazardous and must be used according to the manufacturer's instructions.

To prevent the risk of cross-infection, you must wash your hands before, during and after every treatment. Think about all the things you do with your hands and all the surfaces you touch – that's a lot of bacteria your hands can carry. Think of it this way: you're on the treatment couch waiting for a facial and your therapist doesn't wash their hands before beginning the treatment. For all you know, they could have just been to the toilet, and even if they washed their hands afterwards, they've touched at least two door handles between the wash room and the treatment room. Not very hygienic, is it?

If you touch the bin or pick something up off the floor during the treatment, you must wash your hands before continuing as you might be picking up pathogenic bacteria. Wash your hands again when you've finished the treatment to remove any product and avoid getting it on the door handle. Below is a guideline to washing your hands.

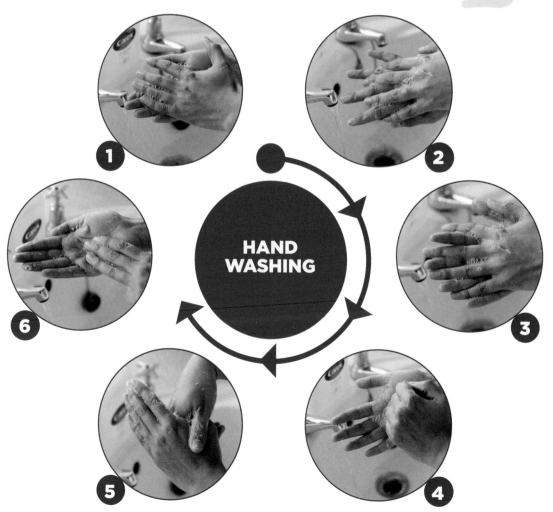

HAND WASHING

1 · 2 · 3 · 4 · 5 · 6

CONTRA-INDICATIONS

It's important that you're aware of the various contra-indications to beauty treatments to prevent the risk of cross-infection. Some contra-indications are **contagious** and must NEVER be worked on; others aren't contagious but working on them could result in further problems for your client. You'll need to refer your client to their GP for some contra-indications; other problems won't necessarily stop the treatment but will restrict it, so you'll need to modify your treatment plan to avoid the area affected. If and when you come across a contra-indication, you must NEVER name it; you're not a doctor so you're not qualified to do this and you could be wrong. This could cause a lot of distress for your client. Explain to your client that you've identified a contra-indication that prevents the treatment and advise them to see their GP for a full and clear diagnosis.

Contagious
A contra-indication that can be passed on to another person.

WHAT IS A CONTRA-INDICATION?

This is when a treatment cannot go ahead or needs to be adapted in some way because your client suffers from a medical or non-medical condition. If a contra-indication prevents a treatment, it cannot be performed because it's contagious or could be made worse. If a contra-indication restricts a treatment, it means the treatment needs to be adapted in some way to avoid or work around the condition.

If a beauty therapist or nail technician carries out a treatment without finding out if there are any contra-indications, they could face unhappy clients, complaints or, in worse cases, legal action. There are contra-indications that will apply to all treatments you perform, and there will be more specific ones that will only affect certain treatments. In that case, you could offer a completely different treatment that would not be contra-indicated.

Some contra-indications, such as diabetes, require medical approval before your client can receive a treatment. This helps the beauty therapist or nail technician make sure they're providing a safe treatment with written approval, and there's no risk of causing harm or injury to your client.

SKIN DISEASES

Skin conditions might or might not be contagious but they do affect the cells of the skin and the way they work. Common skin diseases, such as herpes simplex, can be improved with topical or oral medication from a GP. However, some skin diseases, such as basal cell carcinoma, need to be diagnosed as early as possible to prevent them from spreading. It's these types of skin diseases that, if left, could be life threatening. The medical term for a skin disease is dermatosis and the plural is dermatoses.

Fungal infections (ringworm)

These are microscopic organisms that require warmth, moisture and darkness to thrive. They can reproduce through tiny spores in the air, making them most likely to affect the skin or lungs. You can identify fungal infections of the skin as red circles with yellow centres. The skin is likely to be raised, itchy and inflamed. This condition heals from the centre outwards. Fungal infections can affect any area of the body, and all will prevent beauty treatments:

Tinea Corporis

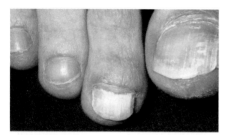

Tinea Unguium

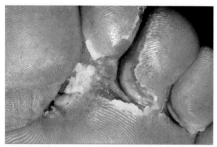

Tinea Pedis

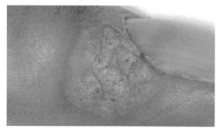

A wart

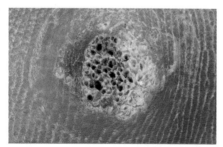

A verruca

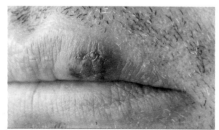

A cold sore

- tinea capitis – affects the scalp
- tinea facei – affects the face
- tinea corporis/ringworm – affects the body
- tinea manuum – affect the hands
- tinea unguium/onychomicosis – affects the nails
- tinea pedis/athlete's foot – affects the feet
- tinea cruris/jock itch – affects the groin area.

Viral infections

A virus is a micro-organism that cannot live without a host. The virus can enter the body through inhalation or the skin and can infect healthy cells where they multiply until the cell walls break down. This releases more of the virus to attack other healthy cells, and so the virus spreads quickly. This causes an immune response, which results in a disease that cannot be treated with antibiotics and needs antiviral medication from a GP.

Warts

Warts are areas of raised, rough skin on the hands and fingers caused by the human papilloma virus (HPV). They're contagious and can be passed through direct or indirect contact. They require medical referral.

Verrucae

Verrucae (singular verruca) are warts found on the soles of the feet. As our feet carry our weight, the wart grows inwards. The area will feel similar to a wart but will also present black speckles near the centre. Verrucae require medical referral.

Conjunctivitis

Also known as 'pink-eye', the eye area appears red and inflamed and the eye is bloodshot. There's unlikely to be any pus when it's a viral infection, but it can be painful for your client. Conjunctivitis is often associated with respiratory tract infections, such as the common cold or a sore throat. It can also be a bacterial infection. Both cases require medical referral.

Herpes simplex

The common cold sore which, once someone is infected, remains in the body for life. It's incurable but treatable with topical and oral medication. The sores normally start with irritation, and then blistering. When the blisters 'pop', they release a fluid, which causes the skin to crust. Cold sores are usually found around the mouth and the following factors can be triggers:

- exposure to sunlight and heat
- stress
- being run-down
- ill health
- lowered immunity
- dehydration.

This condition is only contra-indicated during a flare-up as it's not contagious when the virus is inactive. Active infection will prevent facial treatments.

Bacterial infections

There are two types of bacteria: pathogenic (infectious) and non-pathogenic (non-infectious). Bacterial infections are caused by pathogenic organisms entering living tissue through broken skin. Generally, pus is present as the body responds by trying to get rid of the infection. This is often accompanied by irritation and inflammation.

Impetigo

Impetigo is caused when bacteria enters broken skin and forms blisters. The infection spreads when the irritation is scratched. These blisters are filled with a fluid that crusts when the blisters burst. Impetigo is highly contagious and can be caught through direct and indirect contact. The condition will affect all facial beauty treatments as it normally flares up on the face, neck, ears, nose and mouth. If a client's legs are infected, this would prevent a leg wax, and so on.

Conjunctivitis

This is similar to the viral infection but pus can be present and cause the eyelids to stick together. This pus can become quite gritty and cause irritation and discomfort. It's important not to share eye products with a person suffering from conjunctivitis as it's highly contagious and prevents all facial beauty treatments.

Blepharitis

This is a chronic infection of the eyelids causing them to appear inflamed and swollen, plus irritated, sore and tender. Although this is a bacterial infection, it's not contagious, but does require medical referral.

Hordeolum

This is more commonly known as a stye and is a result of bacteria entering the hair follicle of the eyelashes. It causes a small raised lump along the lashline that is inflamed and red. It can be uncomfortable and irritating for your client and is a contagious condition that prevents all facial treatments.

Folliculitis

This is an infection of the hair follicle, most likely more than one at a time. A small papule forms over the mouth of the follicle, resulting in redness, irritation and inflammation. It's not contagious but, depending on the area affected, it can prevent or restrict beauty treatments. For example, if the legs are affected, it would prevent leg waxing and pedicures because of the risk of spreading the infection.

Furuncles

More commonly known as a boil, a furuncle is an infection of the hair follicle or sebaceous gland. It will appear red initially, then turn yellow due to pus collecting under the skin. Furuncles can be quite painful and feel solid and are mainly found on the face, neck, underarms and buttocks, although can occur anywhere on the body. Scarring can occur even after the furuncle has gone. A group of furuncles is referred to as carbuncles where several follicles or sebaceous glands are affected. This condition is not contagious but will restrict beauty treatments; carbuncles will also prevent treatments as there's a risk of developing a secondary infection.

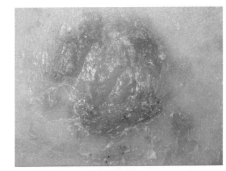
Impetigo (bacterial infection)

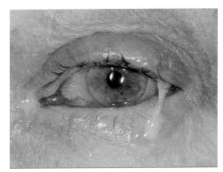
Conjunctivitis (bacterial infection)

Blepharitis (eye infection)

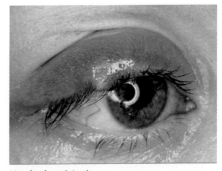
Hordeolum (stye)

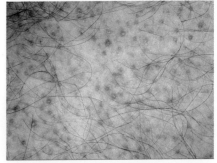
Folliculitis (infected hair follicles)

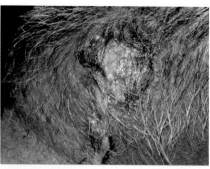
Furuncles (boil)

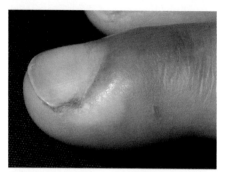
Paronychia (infection of cuticle)

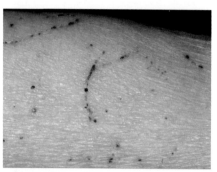
Scabies

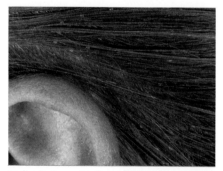
Pediculosis capitis (head lice)

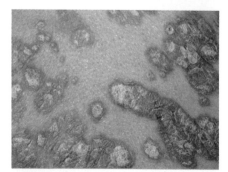
Psoriasis

Paronychia

This is an infection of the cuticle caused by bacteria entering skin tissue through a cut. The skin becomes red and inflamed, and there's usually pus present. It's important not to mistake paronychia for whitlow, which is an infection of the tip of the finger. Paronychia is not contagious but will prevent beauty treatments affecting the hands and feet; it would be too painful and is likely to become inflamed.

Parasitic infestations

This is when a living animal enters the body and survives by feeding off blood and living tissue. These parasites are tiny compared with their host but can cause lots of problems. Even though they require a host to thrive, they can survive for up to 14 days without one.

Scabies

Scabies affects the body and limbs, but rarely affects the face. The mite is microscopic and unidentifiable to the naked eye but, under magnification, you can see a 'burrow'. This causes irritation and scratching, leading to further burrowing and further infection. Sometimes the mite is identified as a tiny dark spot. This is contagious and will prevent all beauty treatments.

Pediculosis

Another small mite that can affect various parts of the body that causes the sufferer to scratch the skin. However, this mite doesn't burrow, but stays on the skin's surface. If the infection is on the head, the eggs are attached to the hair; when the infection is on the body, the eggs are laid in the seams of clothing. Pediculosis is a contagious condition and will prevent all beauty treatments. It can take the following forms:

- pediculosis capitis – more commonly known as head lice
- pediculosis corporis – affects the body
- pediculosis pubis – affects the pubic region and is also known as crabs.

SKIN DISORDERS

These are conditions that aren't contagious and might not be completely cured, but can be treated to reduce the symptoms.

Psoriasis

This is a chronic auto-immune disease that manifests itself in the skin, making cell renewal occur much more quickly than it should. This results in the cells of the stratum spinosum reaching the skin's surface before they've **keratinised** (see anatomy and physiology chapter for more information). It's not known what causes psoriasis and there's no known cure. Research shows that stress and some dairy products can make the condition worse. If the skin isn't open or weeping, it will only restrict a treatment if you make the appropriate adaptations.

Eczema/dermatitis

Eczema and dermatitis are one and the same. There are several types of eczema but essentially it's a dry skin condition that affects people in

Keratinised
The hardening of the cells as the nucleus degenerates and keratin is produced.

varying degrees. Mild eczema is identified by dry, scaly skin that feels rough to touch and can be itchy for your client; in which case, this will only restrict beauty treatments. Severe eczema will also display these conditions as well as open skin, weeping, blisters, dryness, cracking and crusting; in which case, this will prevent all beauty treatments. Eczema is common in young children who tend to grow out of it as they get older. There's also a link between eczema, asthma and hay fever, although the reasons for this link aren't yet known. The following are the different types of eczema you're likely to come across as a beauty therapist:

- atopic eczema: the most common form of eczema that affects young children and some adults. It can be triggered by the following irritants:
  - pollen
  - cat and/or dog hair
  - house dust/dust mites and their droppings
- contact dermatitis: caused by **irritants** or **allergens** that a person is exposed to.

Acne vulgaris

This is a common condition that affects most teenagers to some degree as they go through puberty but also affects many adults. It's identified by the presence of comedones, pustules and papules, although milia can also be present. In severe cases, the condition is inflammatory and can become infectious (not to other people but your client can become reinfected through poor hygiene practices). The spots are caused by overproduction of sebum and sweat together. Sebum and sweat mix to produce the acid mantle, which acts as a protective barrier against bacterial invasion. As more sebum and sweat are produced, the skin's pH levels can be affected. Acne can affect a person's confidence as they might be very self-conscious. Treatment for it tends to be topical creams and/or oral medication depending on its severity. Acne vulgaris normally affects the face and neck, but also the **décolleté** and back in severe cases. Comedones, milia, pustules and papules are all discussed in more depth in the anatomy and physiology chapter. It's important to take great care when you're providing treatments to acne sufferers, as a facial treatment could exacerbate the condition. Also, if your client is treating the acne with medication such as tretinoin (a cream or gel) or Roaccutane (an oral medicine), skin sensitivity might be increased due to thinning of the skin.

Acne rosacea

This isn't a type of acne, but severe **erythema** of the skin that mostly affects the nose and cheeks and is identified as a butterfly pattern. It can affect the forehead and chin and it's a harmless condition unless it affects the eyes. The skin will appear erythemic and possibly with papules, which is why it can be called acne rosacea rather than just rosacea. The skin feels rough in texture and can be triggered by the following:

- exposure to extreme environmental conditions
- alcohol consumption
- exposure to allergens, such as dairy, spicy foods and citrus fruits.

Treatment for acne rosacea usually includes topical creams aimed at reducing the erythema.

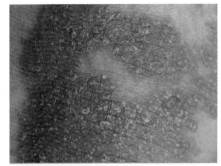
Eczema

Irritant
A substance, product or chemical that damages the skin and makes it inflamed.

Allergen
A substance that causes your immune system to react abnormally.

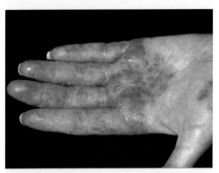
Contact dermatitis

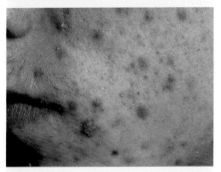
Acne vulgaris

Décolleté
The area between the neck and bust where the skin is much thinner and almost always exposed to the environment.

Erythema
Redness of the skin due to increased blood supply to the affected area.

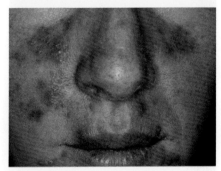
Acne rosacea

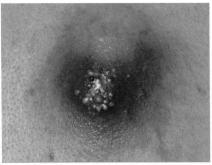

Sebaceous cyst

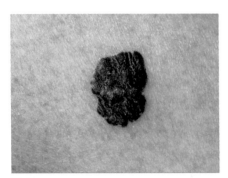

Melanoma

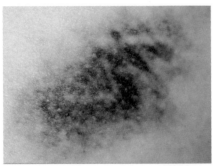

Bruising

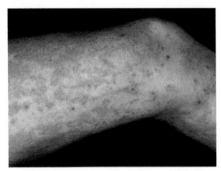

Urticaria (hives)

Sunburn

Sebaceous cyst

This is a small sac in the hair follicle or beneath the sebaceous gland that contains sebum. The sac is hard and can be tender and inflamed. It's important not to touch or squeeze out the pus in a sebaceous cyst as secondary infection might occur. If there is only one present, simply avoid the area during a treatment. If there are several, the treatment might be contra-indicated completely.

Melanoma

This is the most dangerous type of skin cancer but is not the most common. It affects the melanocytes in the epidermis, which produce melanin and give the skin its natural colour. Melanoma can appear black, dark brown, red, pink, purple or even white and, if detected in the earlier stages, can be 100 per cent curable. If left untreated, the cancer can spread to other areas of the body including the organs and as such can be life threatening. All treatments are completely contra-indicated.

Bruising

A bruise occurs when there has been a blow to the skin causing trauma to the blood vessels. These vessels burst and blood is released into the tissues, causing a purplish pink appearance on the skin's surface. As the bruise begins to fade and the tissue heals, the skin changes to a bluish colour and finally a yellowish green colour. If there is severe bruising, the treatment might be contra-indicated. If it's a small area, you might be able to work around it.

Heat rash

This occurs when the body is not able to cool itself down. When a person is hot, the body sweats to release excess heat but sometimes this isn't enough and small red pimples form on the skin, usually around the décolleté, neck, elbow crease and groin areas. This condition would prevent a treatment due to the increased sensitivity and heat in the skin's tissues.

Urticaria

Also known as hives or nettle rash, this is caused by exposure to an allergen, such as animal hair, food or latex. It's identified as an itchy rash with white bumps or weals that are surrounded by inflamed skin. This would prevent a treatment as it might be aggravated.

Sunburn

This is caused by overexposure to UVB rays which stimulates melanocytes in the epidermis to produce melanin, its own natural pigment. However, if the skin is exposed to too much sun, it appears inflamed, swollen, and will feel warm, tender and sore. In severe cases, blisters can occur, which are painful to touch. Increased sun exposure can lead to melanoma. Sunburn would prevent a treatment as the skin might be damaged. However, you might be able to offer a treatment where the area wouldn't be affected.

Skin tags

Generally caused by friction, skin tags are merely excessive small areas of flesh that grow out from the skin on a stalk. They're harmless and in rare cases fall off without a person even noticing. However, it's not advisable to try and remove them as they can bleed quite excessively. It is possible to work around skin tags.

Scar tissue

Scar tissue occurs at the site of an injury and is the body's way of protecting an injured area of tissue from further damage. It's identified as swelling, or oedema (which is described later on). If it surrounds an injured joint, it can become quite solid because of a lack of **circulation**. If scar tissue is major, it cannot be worked over for 12 months. If it's minor, it needs to be avoided for six months.

Hyper-keratosis

Excessive keratin production in the upper layers of the epidermis causes the skin to appear rough and uneven in texture. Hyper-keratosis is common on the elbows, knees, heels and palms. This wouldn't restrict or prevent any treatment. In fact, you should recommend your client exfoliates and moisturises.

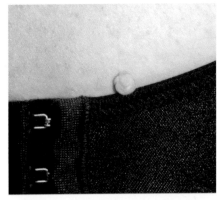

A skin tag

Scar tissue

Hyper-keratosis

Circulation
Nutrients moving around the body.

SYSTEMIC CONDITIONS

These are conditions that affect a system of the body, either circulatory or nervous. It's not contagious but could be affected by beauty treatments and cause pain and possibly injury. Systemic conditions are generally treated by oral medication.

Epilepsy

This is a complex chronic neurological condition which affects the brain and causes the recipient to have recurrent seizures. There are various factors that can trigger a seizure, which is why it's vital you obtain written GP approval prior to treating anyone with epilepsy. These factors can include:

- stress
- panic
- nervousness
- trauma.

If a client does book a beauty treatment and has GP approval, it's important you do everything you can to keep them calm and relaxed throughout the treatment.

Diabetes mellitus

This is a chronic condition whereby a person's blood sugar levels are affected because their body doesn't produce enough insulin. There are two types of diabetes:

- Type 1: caused by genetic and environmental factors meaning a person cannot produce enough insulin. As a result, insulin needs to be injected to keep levels as close to normal as possible.
- Type 2: mostly caused by a person's lifestyle and genetics. Smoking, obesity, lack of regular exercise, an unhealthy diet, high cholesterol and high blood pressure can all lead to this type of diabetes. Control of this

condition is through changing poor lifestyle habits and replacing them with healthier ones. It can also be treated with oral medication.

Diabetes is likely to prevent treatments.

High/low blood pressure

High blood pressure, or hypertension, is when arterial blood pressure is raised. It's believed to be exacerbated or triggered by smoking, poor diet, high alcohol consumption, and can be controlled by changing to a healthier lifestyle and taking oral medication. If left untreated, it can lead to a stroke, heart attack and possibly heart failure, which is why it's important that steps are taken to reduce these risks.

Low blood pressure is also referred to as hypotension. A person with low blood pressure can be prone to fainting, dizziness, an irregular heart beat and shortness of breath. Low blood pressure can be caused by hormonal changes and a widening of the blood vessels, and can be treated with medication.

Varicose veins

As blood travels through the veins towards the heart, there are tiny valves that prevent backflow. However, if these valves become damaged, they stop working properly and cause blood to collect in the veins. When this happens, the veins appear to bulge from the skin and look blue or purple in colour. In severe cases, the veins can also appear twisted and lumpy. If severe, varicose veins will prevent treatments on the legs. Otherwise, it will only restrict them.

Oedema

This usually occurs as a result of poor circulation. It's common around the ankles and lower legs where the tissue fills with lymphatic fluid and becomes swollen and puffy. Oedema can also be caused by weight gain/loss and hypotension, and can result in fatigued limbs and stiffness in the joints. It's advisable to obtain GP permission before working on an area affected by oedema.

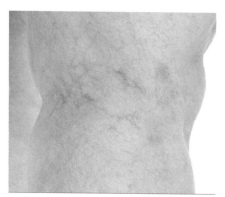

Varicose veins

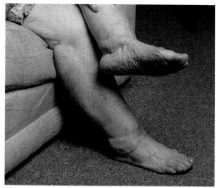

Oedema (swelling)

NAIL CONDITIONS

The table below displays various nail disorders that can prevent or restrict manicure and pedicure treatments:

Condition	Infectious?	Description
Onychia	Bacterial infection	Affects the nail folds, resulting in weeping and pus around the nail
Onychocryptosis	Non-infectious	More commonly known as an ingrown toenail. The nail grows into the side wall, piercing the skin and causing pain, weeping and bleeding. As the skin is damaged, it's open to infection.
Onychogryphosis	Non-infectious	More commonly known as a hook nail. This is where the nail thickens and curves over the fingertip like a horn.
Onycholysis	Non-infectious	Separation of the nail plate from the nail bed
Onychomadesis	Non-infectious	Severe separation of the nail plate from the nail bed, resulting in the nail falling off completely
Onychomicosis	Fungal infection	Also referred to as tinea unguium. The nail appears thick and chalky.
Onychoptosis	Non-infectious	Periodic shedding of part of, or the whole, nail

Condition	Infectious?	Description
Paronychia	Bacterial infection	Affects the eponychium, resulting in weeping and pus
Koilonychia	Non-infectious	More commonly known as a spoon-shaped nail. This is where the nail curves upwards like a spoon.
Leuconychia	Non-infectious	Commonly mistaken to be a calcium deficiency when it's simply a trauma to the nail. It causes air bubbles between the keratin layers, and is identified as white spots on the nail plate.
Hang nail	Non-infectious	More annoying than a cause for concern, and also referred to as a rag nail. The skin at the nail groove detaches from the nail itself and can become sore.
Beau's lines	Non-infectious	Transverse ridges that lie across the nail. This is often a sign of previous illness.
Psoriasis	Non-infectious	Identified as pitting of the nail with some discolouration as well. This can be identified as small circular dents in the nail plate.
Eczema	Non-infectious	The nail plate can appear shiny with some flaking
Eggshell nails	Non-infectious	The nails are thin and fragile with the free edge growing over the tip of the finger

END OF UNIT SUMMARY

Now you've reached the end of the unit, and before you test your knowledge with the end of unit assessment, check the following list to see if you feel confident in all areas covered. If there are still any areas you're unsure of, go back over them in the book and ask your tutor for additional support:

- identify the hazards and evaluate the risks in your workplace
- reduce the risks to health and safety in your workplace.

TEST YOUR KNOWLEDGE G20

Now that you're aware of, and have an understanding of, the different health and safety regulations that will affect you throughout your working life, let's see how much you can remember. These questions will help you revise what you've learnt in this chapter.

Turn to pages 396–397 for the answers.

1 Identify what is meant by the terms hazard, risk and control.

2 Give **one** example of a low-risk hazard.

3 Give **one** example of a high-risk hazard.

4 State your obligations under HASAWA 1974.

5 What is the purpose of a risk assessment?

6 What are your obligations under COSHH 2002?

7 What does SHUD stand for?

8 List the hazard symbols and state what they mean.

9 List the types of PPE your employer should provide and when you should wear them.

10 How often should a PAT test be performed and who should do it?

11 List **five** key factors to follow under the DPA.

12 What type of fire extinguisher would you use on a computer fire?

13 When would you use a fire blanket?

14 What are the **four** key factors to consider when you're creating the ideal salon environment?

15 What is the correct working temperature for a salon?

16 What is considered to be good personal presentation?

17 What is the difference between pathogenic and non-pathogenic bacteria?

18 Explain how an autoclave sterilises metal implements.

19 How long should you leave small metal implements in the glass bead steriliser?

20 What is the difference between sterilisation and disinfection?

WHY DON'T YOU...
Test your knowledge further by logging into SmartScreen and completing the revision activities before attempting the sample GOLA revision questions.

G18
PROMOTE ADDITIONAL SERVICES OR PRODUCTS TO CLIENTS

Recommending products and additional services to your clients is something many therapists avoid because they don't want to be pushy. A beauty therapist or nail technician should never make a 'hard sell' – instead, they should make recommendations with their client's best interests in mind. It's your duty to highlight any products and services you think might suit your client's needs. Any therapist who doesn't do this isn't doing their best to help their client.

First of all, you need to believe in what you're recommending otherwise your clients will see right through you. Talk about how the product or service works in a way that makes your client feel like you've used it. Your employer could use commission schemes to encourage you to recommend products by adding to your wages and improving profits.

In this chapter you'll learn how to:

- identify additional services or products that are available
- inform clients about additional services or products
- gain client commitment to using additional services or products.

This unit will be used in conjunction with all other units to ensure your clients and customers are given the opportunity to experience the very best you and your salon have to offer them.

HANDY HINTS

If you're finding it difficult to recommend services or products to your clients, your employer might ask you to perform role plays with a senior therapist to highlight how your confidence and skills can be improved.

WHY DON'T YOU...

Think about the training you've received so far. How has this impacted on the way you recommend treatment plans and additional products and services to your clients?

Planting the seed

Telling your client about the benefits of a product when you're discussing a treatment plan so that they'll be thinking about it throughout the treatment.

HANDY HINTS

Refer to Unit G4 to remind yourself of the consultation process.

WHY DON'T YOU...

Read through SmartScreen handout 2 for further details on how to make recommendations.

 SmartScreen G18 handout 2

IDENTIFY ADDITIONAL SERVICES OR PRODUCTS THAT ARE AVAILABLE

When you start a new job as a beauty therapist, your employer should organise various training courses to make sure you're familiar with the product ranges and the services the salon offers. These courses will help you build treatment plans, offer specific home care and product recommendations, and suggest various promotions that will generate extra business for the salon. When you've completed the training, you'll need to put into practice what you've learnt. More experienced therapists will be able to help you develop the new skills.

PLANTING THE SEED

When you've worked out your client's needs and requirements, start thinking about which treatment and products you should recommend. If you discuss your ideas with your client, you're already **planting the seed** about what products or treatments you can offer. As the treatment progresses, remind your client about the benefits each product can offer as you go along. When the treatment is finished, show your client the product(s) you originally planted in their mind. Remind them how much it will enhance their current regime and invite them to try the product(s) for themselves. Let them hold and smell the product before indicating for them to hand it back.

Remember to 'plant the seed' during a consultation!

LINK-SELLING

You've just told your client about the product(s) you've used during the treatment three times. By letting them hold it, smell it and try it, you're activating three senses: touch, smell and sight. Hopefully, they're now thinking about using it at home as part of their daily routine. When you take the product back from them, this should make them want it even more. This is not **hard selling** but just a normal, clever recommendation technique used by every therapist in the industry. This is called **link-selling**.

This same approach can be used when you recognise an opportunity to recommend an additional service that you think will improve your client's salon experience. For example, your client has booked a facial and, during the consultation, they tell you how stressed they've been at work and how tight their neck and shoulders are. Tell your client that you'll adapt your facial massage to relieve the stress and make sure you recommend a back, neck and shoulder massage as their next appointment.

During the facial, remind your client that you'll be working a little deeper than usual around the neck and shoulders and ask them to tell you if the pressure is too hard or too light. This is a reminder of the seed you planted during the consultation when you suggested the change.

When the treatment is over, ask your client how they feel and whether their neck and shoulders feel a little looser; and remember to watch their body language! Explain that although the massage has had some benefits, a 30-minute back, neck and shoulder massage would really help to get rid of all that tension. This is your client's second reminder of how a different treatment would enhance their salon experience.

Hard selling

Putting a client under pressure to buy what you're recommending when they don't really want it or feel like they need it.

Link-selling

The recommendation of products and services to meet a client's needs and enhance their experience.

ACTIVITY

Think about the different treatments you could recommend that complement one another and design a poster to promote them.

Remember when you're providing recommendations that you should never make a hard sell but you do have a job to do and money to earn like everybody else. Extra sales are important because not only do they benefit the salon but they can also help you reach **commission** incentive targets and boost your monthly wage.

Commission

An incentive from your employer to encourage you to make recommendations and boost your monthly wage, as well as the salon's profits.

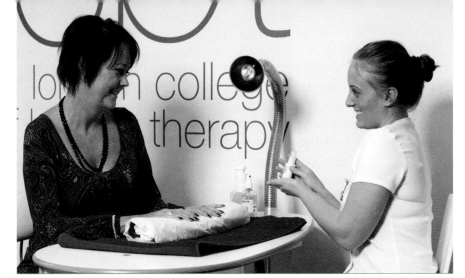

A therapist recommending products after a manicure

Up-selling

Recommending a product or service that isn't directly linked to a client's needs and expectations but will enhance their salon or home experience.

WHY DON'T YOU...
Have a go at SmartScreen worksheet 4 to enhance your knowledge of the different beauty treatments.

 SmartScreen G18 worksheet 4

UP-SELLING

During a treatment, you might identify an opportunity to **up-sell** a product or treatment that isn't directly linked to that treatmant but you believe will enhance your client's experience. For example, your client has come in for an underarm wax and you notice she has long blonde eyelashes and blue eyes. Explain to her how much an eyelash tint would enhance and define her eye area. If she's interested, suggest performing a skin sensitivity test and book her in before she leaves. This means you've just recommended a treatment that your client might never have thought of. Another example is if a client comes into the salon to buy her usual anti-ageing facial moisturiser but it doesn't have a sun protection factor (SPF). Your salon offers an SPF that she can apply on top of her daily moisturiser, so you make the recommendation and possibly sell two products instead of one.

INFORM CLIENTS ABOUT ADDITIONAL SERVICES OR PRODUCTS

When you're recommending services and products, it's important you choose the right time to approach your client. For example, if you're half way through a facial massage and you find there's a lot of tension but your client is almost asleep, they will be annoyed if you wake them up to tell them how tense they are; they already know this. Instead, make a mental note of how tense they are and talk to them at the end of the treatment.

COMMUNICATION

You also need to think about your communication and how you approach clients when you're recommending a service or product. For example, during a facial, try to lower your tone of voice as most clients want to switch off and go to sleep. If you do find your client is tense, explain gently that the massage will be deeper than usual but ask them to tell you if your pressure is too hard or too light.

 CHAMPNEYS

Customers looking at products in a salon reception area

WHY DON'T YOU...
Read through SmartScreen handout 1 for further details on good and bad selling techniques.

SmartScreen G18 handout 1

SPECIAL OFFERS

It's common for salons to offer a special introductory price to generate interest in a new service they're offering. They might offer an additional treatment half price or free when the new service is paid for in full. For example, a 30-minute back, neck and shoulder massage could be offered free with a new facial as the only extra cost to the salon is the medium used for the massage.

LEAFLETS AND POSTERS

Another method of communication for promoting additional services or products is the use of leaflets and posters. Promotional leaflets can include plenty of information in a small space to capture your client's interest. If you've recommended a treatment to a client but they want time to think about it before making the appointment, you can give them a leaflet that will remind them of the salon when they're at home.

naturasun™
pure natural spray tanning

Posters are useful for advertising products or treatments that are new to the salon.

Place your promotional leaflets in a key place on the reception desk.

ACTIVITY

Design a poster promoting a service you've just learnt. What will your special offer be?

HANDY HINTS

Be discreet when you're making recommendations in public areas. If your client thinks people are listening, they might feel pressured to buy what you're recommending even though they might not be interested.

TAKING NO FOR AN ANSWER

Although it's a big part of your job as a beauty therapist to make recommendations, it's important you don't lie to your clients to make a sale. Never make false promises about a product or service because your client will lose their trust and confidence in you. Always make sure your advice is accurate and to the point, otherwise your client will think you need this sale more than they need the product; also, they will get bored if you talk for too long. It's all about getting the right balance; making your client feel like they need the product or service without making them feel uncomfortable or pressured. A client should never feel like they can't say 'No thanks'.

ANSWERING HONESTLY

When you've made your recommendations, invite your client to ask any questions so you can clarify everything for them. If they ask a question you can't answer, don't make something up; your client will appreciate your honesty when you say 'I'm not sure, let me double check that for you'. Ask a colleague or refer to your training manual as this will show you're not simply telling them anything just to make a sale.

A therapist pointing out products in a brochure

FACTORS INFLUENCING A CLIENT'S DECISION

When you make recommendations, there are several factors that can influence a client's decision:

- cost
- time
- your experiences
- smell
- sight
- texture
- visualisation.

COST

The one thing any client will ask themself is 'Can I afford this?' If they can't, no matter how good the product or treatment is, nothing will change their mind.

TIME

Another major obstacle that stands in your way is time. If your client doesn't have the time to have the treatment you're recommending, they won't make the appointment.

HANDY HINTS

How can you overcome the time obstacle? Some clients can be gently persuaded if they can see the benefits the treatment will give them. Others might not be as interested as you'd hoped, so you'll just have to let it be.

A client making an appointment

WHY DON'T YOU...

Ask your manager or senior therapist if you can try out a product at home or if you can experience a new treatment for yourself.

YOUR EXPERIENCES

When you learn a new skill or the salon introduces a new product range, it's important you're given the opportunity to experience the effects and benefits. Many salons will allow you to take products home to use overnight or allow you and your colleagues to give each other treatments during quieter periods. This way you'll come to believe in the products and services you're offering, which is an invaluable part of recommendation. Without that belief, you won't convince your client that you like the product or treatment you're recommending.

WHY DON'T YOU...

Try smelling some of the products in your salon or in your bathroom and see if they bring back any memories, then think about how these smells make you feel.

SMELL

When you're recommending products, let your client smell them so they can get a sense of the ingredients. So much of what a person feels is through smell and certain smells can bring back memories. The way a product smells can help your client decide whether or not to buy it.

A client smelling a product that's been recommended

SIGHT

Always have a tester with you so your client can see what the product looks like. If the packaging doesn't appeal to them, they might not buy into it; if they like the packaging, they might want to know more about its benefits.

HANDY HINTS

Look at the Dermalogica products above (if you're not familiar with this range, search for them online). Perhaps they're not the most colourful products you could have on your bathroom shelf but that's because they pride themselves on products that work. The company believes their packaging doesn't sell their products, the benefits and effects produced on the skin do. Also, because of their white and grey packaging, they cater to both men and women.

TEXTURE

When your client has seen and smelt the product, let them have a try so they can feel the consistency, see how easy it is to apply and how much they would need for one application. If a product glides on to the skin and leaves it feeling softer and smoother, your client will see the benefits to their skin and hopefully buy the product.

VISUALISATION

Now your client has tested and smelt the product and seen its packaging, they'll begin to visualise it on their bathroom shelf amongst the rest of their products. They'll begin to see themselves using it as part of their daily or weekly routine. So subconsciously they've already bought into the product and will want to take it home. Now all you need to do is close the sale.

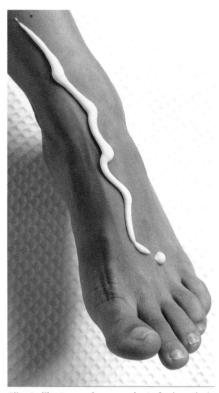

Clients like to see how products feel on their skin

WHY DON'T YOU...
Have a go at SmartScreen worksheet 2 to assist you in identifying opportunities to make recommendations.

 SmartScreen G18 worksheet 2

GAIN CLIENT COMMITMENT TO USING ADDITIONAL SERVICES OR PRODUCTS

If a client tells you they're not interested, don't worry; just tell them that if they change their mind, they know where you are. This way the discussion is closed, your client doesn't feel pressured to buy anything, and doesn't feel bad about turning down your recommendation. It's always better to have a client say 'No thanks' and come back for more treatments, than have a client book a treatment but never actually show up.

A client declining a product recommendation

If your client is interested and wants to know more, discuss the product or treatment further by expanding on the benefits. For a product, talk about two key ingredients and their benefits before asking 'Shall I pop this in a bag for you?' This way you've asked them a closed question rather than an open one and means all your client has to say is yes or no. If your client is interested, they're likely to respond positively.

CLOSING THE SALE

When you've established that your client wants to buy the product or book in for the service you've recommended, make sure you provide any final information they will need. For products, ask them about how they will incorporate them into their daily or weekly regime so you're certain they know how to use them properly. For a treatment, agree on a date and time before writing it down on an appointment card. If this is the receptionist's duty, take your client through to reception and invite them to take a seat while the receptionist organises their product(s) or treatment. Remember to tell the receptionist whether your client wants to buy a specific product or needs to make an appointment.

WHY DON'T YOU...
Have a go at recommending an additional product or service to your next client.

HANDY HINTS
See Unit G8 for information on target setting.

A receptionist placing purchases in a bag for the client

WHY DON'T YOU...
Have a go at SmartScreen worksheet 3 to see what recommendations you would make.

 SmartScreen G18 worksheet 3

WHY DON'T YOU...
Look at the products and treatments your salon offers; for each product find out the two key ingredients and their benefits; for each treatment find out the four main effects.

A client receiving her purchases

If your client wants to know more about a product or service that you're not trained in, tell them what you do know before explaining that you need to find a colleague who knows more about that particular product or service. This shows you're honest and trustworthy.

WHY DON'T YOU...
Look at the treatments you're not yet trained in and ask a colleague about their effects and benefits. Then if a client asks you about it, you can give them a more informed opinion.

HANDY HINTS

Remember, failing to provide product recommendations could lose you a loyal client. No one likes to be pressured into buying something they're not interested in but all clients want to know how they can improve or maintain their appearance, and they especially want to know how the products and treatments you're offering can help them achieve this.

END OF UNIT SUMMARY

Now you've reached the end of the unit, and before you test your knowledge with the end of unit assessment, check the following list to see if you feel confident in all areas covered. If there are still any areas you're unsure of, go back over them and ask your tutor for additional support:

- identify additional services or products that are available
- inform clients about additional services or products
- gain client commitment to using additional services or products.

Now that you have an understanding as to why it's important to recommend additional services and products, let's see how much you can remember. These questions will help you revise what you've learnt in this chapter.

Turn to pages 397–398 for the answers.

1 Why is it important to make sure your knowledge of the services and products your salon offers is always up to date?

2 What can you do if you're unsure about a new service or product?

3 Explain the term 'planting the seed'.

4 How can you identify opportunities to recommend additional services or products?

5 What is meant by the term 'link-selling'?

6 Give **one** example of link-selling.

7 How should you adapt your communication methods when you're providing recommendations?

8 Explain why it's important to provide accurate information when you're recommending services and products.

9 Why is it important to encourage your client to ask questions regarding the recommendations you've made?

10 What is meant by the term 'up-selling'?

11 Explain the difference between a hard sell and a recommendation.

12 What action should you take when your client shows no interest in the recommendations you're making?

13 If your client is interested, how can you move the situation forward to close the sale?

14 If it's not your responsibility to close sales, how can you make sure this happens?

15 Why is it important to refer your client to other therapists when your knowledge of a particular service or product is limited?

16 Explain how a client's use of additional services or products will benefit the salon.

17 What **seven** factors influence a client's decision to buy into a service or product?

18 Why is it important to check the information you give is balanced and to the point?

19 How can you overcome any nervousness when you're recommending additional services or products?

20 Why is it important for you always to provide recommendations to your clients?

WHY DON'T YOU...
Test your knowledge further by logging into SmartScreen and completing the revision activities before attempting the sample GOLA revision questions.

G8
DEVELOP AND MAINTAIN YOUR EFFECTIVENESS AT WORK

Team work is an essential part of any business; without it, a company can't grow and progress. Although it's unrealistic to think that you'll be best friends with all your colleagues, it is realistic to expect you to be professional and work together as a team to ensure the smooth running of the business. Another area you need to understand is target setting and appraisals. These will help you identify your strengths and weaknesses and make sure you contribute effectively to the success of the business.

In this chapter you'll learn how to:
- improve your personal performance at work
- work effectively as part of a team.

This unit will be used in conjunction with all other units to make sure you develop and maintain your effectiveness at work. It will also help you understand your role in the team and how you can be part of a successful salon.

IMPROVE YOUR PERSONAL PERFORMANCE AT WORK

To help you improve your personal performance, you need to identify your strengths and weaknesses. Your manager or employer can help you with this on a bi-annual (every six months), quarterly or monthly basis. When you've identified these areas, your employer will give you a development plan or **targets** to reach in a certain time. Your employer might also give you **incentives** and **objectives** to help you reach your targets.

Before this can be done, you need to be aware of your role in the team and the role of those around you. If you're unsure, ask your manager or look in your handbook as this will summarise everyone's roles and responsibilities so you know who to approach and when with certain issues and questions.

Targets

Goals to reach in a certain time to help you develop your skills.

Incentives

Rewards that you get when you've reached your target, which will give you the motivation to work towards them.

Objectives

Your line manager will set you objectives that you need to achieve in a year. You should discuss short-term steps to help you achieve them.

HANDY HINTS

Remember not to worry if you don't reach your targets first time around. Your colleagues and superiors will always be on hand to give you support and advice so don't be afraid to ask for their help.

WHY DON'T YOU...

Read through SmartScreen handout 1 to familiarise yourself with the information that should be included in a contract of employment. Then have a go at SmartScreen worksheets 1 and 2 to identify your salon's organisational chart, and your colleagues' roles and responsibilities.

SmartScreen G8 handout 1 and worksheets 1 and 2

IDENTIFYING STRENGTHS AND WEAKNESSES

When you apply for any salon or spa position, you'll have to attend an interview and also perform what's called a trade test. This is where the interviewer will ask you to perform various treatments on an existing employee or model so they can see your strengths and weaknesses, and whether you're suitable for the position. These treatments are usually the most popular ones in that salon. If you apply for a position in a spa, for example, you might have to perform a facial or a massage. If you apply for a city salon position, you might have to perform a wax, a tint or a file and polish. This shows the interviewer how they can use your skills

Training and development plan

A plan based on a therapist's weaknesses to help them build their confidence and skills.

Appraisal

A meeting between an employee and line manager to discuss the progress, effectiveness and development of the employee through target setting and incentive schemes.

Job description

What your responsibilities are in your job and who you report to.

Person specification

Your role in the team and how you contribute to the team's effectiveness.

to build a client base. It also highlights any areas that need developing and helps them put a **training and development plan** in place for you.

Senior therapist organising training with newly employed therapists

THE PROBATIONARY PERIOD

When you're offered a position, you'll be given a probationary period, usually of three months. This is the time you have to prove yourself to your employer, and your employer will watch you closely to see how you interact with customers, clients and the existing team. Although it's rare, sometimes the position doesn't work out and the therapist is asked to leave at the end of the probationary period. In most cases, the therapist will get on well with the team and prove to be a success with clients. At the end of the probationary period, you'll be given a contract and attend your first **appraisal**. This contract will include a **job description** and **person specification**, both of which outline what your employer expects of you and your role in the team.

A therapist attending an appraisal

APPRAISALS

In an appraisal, both parties discuss how the probationary period went and identify the therapist's strengths and weaknesses. You'll study the appointments you had over the probationary period to see how busy you were and how many clients came back. This indicates client loyalty to both you as a therapist and the business. At the end of the appraisal, you'll be given various targets to reach and various incentives to motivate you.

WHY DON'T YOU...
Refer to Unit G4 to remind yourself of the questioning and listening skills you need to find out information. This will help if you need your line manager to clarify points raised during your appraisal.

TARGET SETTING

The table below shows what types of targets you can expect and is called a performance assessment review:

	Monthly target	Week 1	Week 2	Week 3	Week 4	Week 5	Variance against target (comparison)	Target for next month
Total no. of clients	16 per week	14	16	19	15	16	3/5	20 per week
No. of new clients	10 per week	7	5	8	5	6	0/5	8 per week
No. of return clients	6 per week	5	7	6	6	6	4/5	8 per week
No. of rebookings	***	2	4	5	4	4	***	5 per week
No. of clients sold retail	6 per week	4	5	3	4	4	0/5	6 per week
Total value of treatments	***	£305	£350	£402	£372.50	£359.80	***	£358 per week
Total value of retail sales	***	£130	£156	£105	£240	£210	***	£169 per week

Here, the therapist has been given targets to help them build their client base and improve their retail sales. The therapist reached the target for the total number of clients twice throughout the month and exceeded it once so the new target for next month has been increased to 20 per week. The therapist didn't reach the target for the number of **new clients** so this has been reduced for next month to make it more achievable. The therapist met the target number of **return clients** three times and exceeded it once; this shows that the therapist is building up their client base, so this target has been increased to eight per week next month. The manager chose not to set a target for **rebookings** to see how many clients the therapist could encourage to return. During three of the five weeks, four clients rebooked and, in one week, five rebooked, so the target for next month is five.

New clients

Clients that are new to the salon and the therapist.

Return clients

Clients that have returned to the same therapist and remain loyal to them.

Rebookings

Clients who remain loyal to the salon but are happy to see any therapist.

HANDY HINTS

Remember: taking care of your clients is the most important thing about your job. Treat them with respect, whether they're a new or returning client.

A receptionist confirming an appointment with the client by handing her an appointment card

WHY DON'T YOU...
Look at your own strengths and weaknesses by completing SmartScreen worksheet 7. Identify the need for feedback and personal development plans by completing SmartScreen worksheet 8.

SmartScreen G8 worksheets 7 and 8

The therapist was also given retail targets to see how comfortable they are selling products or if it's an area that needs developing. The target was to sell something to six clients and, although the therapist came close, they didn't quite reach it, so the target has stayed the same for next month. The employer could give the therapist additional incentives or support to help them reach this target the following month. The reason why retail sales and treatment sales are recorded is so the therapist can see how they're contributing to the financial effectiveness of the business.

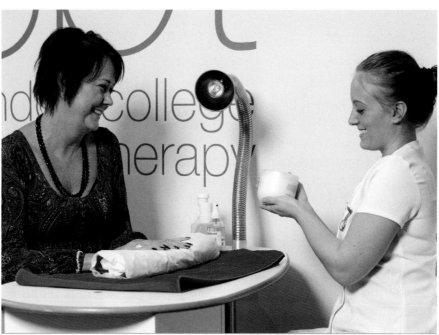

A therapist making recommendations to a client as part of her incentive scheme

This is an in-depth performance review which lets the manager see exactly where the therapist's strengths lie and helps them agree on realistic and achievable targets for the following month. This therapist's strengths lie in link-selling and making sure their appointment sheet is busy rather than empty. However, their weaknesses lie in retail and bringing in new clients so the manager must assist the therapist in building on and improving these skills. The best method is observation and shadowing a more experienced therapist who is comfortable encouraging new clientele and recommending products to clients. It's important targets are not only set and agreed but also used effectively and updated when necessary. For example, the therapist in this situation knows how to use this performance review now that their targets have been discussed and agreed. In a month's time when they meet with their manager again, they will review and discuss these targets before updating them and arranging any additional training.

Beauty therapy students researching information to assist with studies

Following this performance assessment review, the therapist and manager will agree on a personal development plan to help the therapist or nail technician improve their weaknesses by attending external and in-house training courses. The manager will also update this plan when the therapist reaches their targets and weaknesses become strengths, and identify the need for further training.

INCENTIVE SCHEMES

One of the most popular methods of helping therapists reach their targets is by offering incentives as a reward, not only for their hard work but to give them something to work towards. The best way to do this is by offering commission schemes based mainly on retail sales rather than treatment sales. This is when a therapist can earn more money on top of their wages by reaching set targets. Below is an example of a

WHY DON'T YOU...
Refer to Unit G18 to remind yourself what up-selling and link-selling mean.

monthly commission scheme which will allow the therapist to earn more money and work towards buying their own products. This lets them experience the products themselves and helps them improve their recommendation skills:

Target (retail sales per month)	Incentive
£250	£5 added to wages
	£10 gift voucher to be used towards products
£350	£10 added to wages
	£15 gift voucher to be used towards products
£500	£15 added to wages
	£20 gift voucher to be used towards products
£650	£20 added to wages
	£30 gift voucher to be used towards products
£800	£25 added to wages
	£50 gift voucher to be used towards products
£1,000	£40 added to wages
	£60 gift voucher to be used towards products
£1,000+	£50 added to wages
	£75 gift voucher to be used towards products

WHY DON'T YOU...
Read through SmartScreen handout 7 for further information on appraisals and personal development plans.

 SmartScreen G8 handout 7

Normally, salons will review each therapist's performance on a monthly basis and hold an appraisal approximately every six months. This is because it takes around three months to build a client base and a further three months for a therapist to feel confident in that client base and their own skills and abilities. Employers design incentive schemes, set targets and perform appraisals to make sure everyone knows where they stand, what their roles are and how they contribute to the success of the team and the business.

OBJECTIVES

These are short-term steps to help therapists achieve their targets. An objective is defined as being SMART:

Specific: Relating directly to the intended goals

Measurable: Measured over a set period of time to ensure success

Achievable: With the right promotion and skills the target can be achieved

Realistic: Objectives are achieveable

Time bound: The timescale in which to achieve the objective.

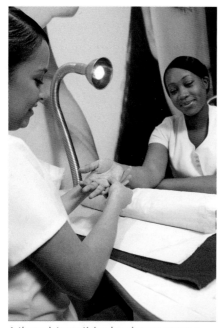

A therapist practising hand massage on a colleague, as part of her self-development targets

KEEPING UP TO DATE WITH INDUSTRY TRENDS

Therapists can easily stay up to date with current and emerging trends by attending training courses, staff development days, reading trade journals and visiting exhibitions. It's common for businesses to pay for training, although some businesses ask therapists to pay for their own travel and expenses and reimburse them later. After a training course, therapists are encouraged to practise in their own time and on their colleagues so that the other therapists can experience the treatments and promote them to their clients. This will help boost return clients and the success of the business.

WHY DON'T YOU...
Refer to Unit G4 to remind yourself of the industry accepted times for treatments.

HANDY HINTS
Where training is particularly expensive, many businesses ask their therapists to sign a disclaimer agreeing to pay back the cost of the course if they leave within a year of attending the course.

CONTINUING PROFESSIONAL DEVELOPMENT (CPD)

It's vital to continue your own professional development so you never get left behind. The beauty industry is growing fast and, if you don't update your training and develop your skills, you'll get left behind by others who are more passionate about their jobs. Make sure you check the **National Occupational Standards** (NOS) set by **Habia** for any updates and changes in the way treatments are delivered. These standards will show you if you need any additional training and help you build on your skills. This will give you more experience and help you apply for a promotion at work.

National Occupational Standards (NOS)

Standards set by Habia for the hairdressing, nail, spa and beauty industries to check all therapists are working to the same set of guidelines.

Habia

The Hair and Beauty Industry Authority.

WHY DON'T YOU...
Read through SmartScreen handout 6 to familiarise yourself with the NOS for beauty therapy and check out **www.habia.org** for the latest NOS before completing SmartScreen worksheet 9.

SmartScreen G8 handout 6 and worksheet 9

Beauty therapy students practising make-up techniques

WHY DON'T YOU...
Work in groups of five and nominate a salon manager, senior therapist, receptionist, therapist and junior, and record the role and responsibilities of each member of the team. Compare the differences and discuss how they relate to one another.

It's important for all therapists to understand not only their own roles and responsibilities, but also everyone else's and how they relate to one another. This will help the team contribute effectively to the success of the business. When you begin working at a salon, you might be given a handbook that highlights this information, or you can discuss it with your line manager.

If your manager gives you targets, they will discuss what objectives will help you achieve them. For example, your manager might look back at your performance review and suggest you offer promotions in the treatments you're particularly good at. This will have a knock-on effect as it will help you encourage repeat custom and create opportunities for you to reach your targets. It will also help you earn more money and improve your confidence when you're recommending products.

If you're still unsure of how to reach these targets and you're concerned you might fail, it's your responsibility to approach your manager again and ask for additional support. You could also speak to a senior therapist to get some advice and assistance. If you don't ask for help and ignore the problem, you could find yourself in more trouble because your manager will want to know why you haven't met your targets.

HANDY HINTS
Always ask for help the minute you feel you need it. Don't ignore the problem thinking it will go away because it won't.

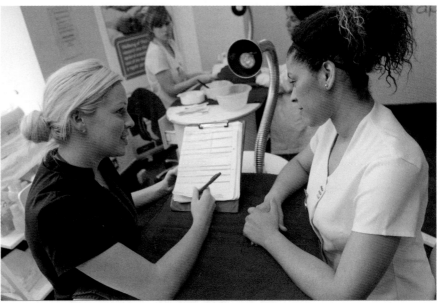
Senior therapist and therapist agreeing targets

ANTICIPATING THE NEEDS OF OTHERS
As you get more confident and gain more experience, you might be approached by a colleague for help. Try to remember how you felt when you were lacking in confidence and always try to help if you can. You'll also learn to anticipate the needs of those around you and this will help you offer assistance. For example, a senior therapist has just completed a full body massage but as their client was late, they've run over time and are late for their next client. Explain the situation to the waiting client and offer them refreshments while they wait. When the senior

therapist brings their client to the reception area, start preparing the treatment area for the next client. This means you're using your free time to help those around you.

WHY DON'T YOU...
Read through SmartScreen handout 4 to familiarise yourself with the qualities that make an effective team player.

 SmartScreen G8 handout 4

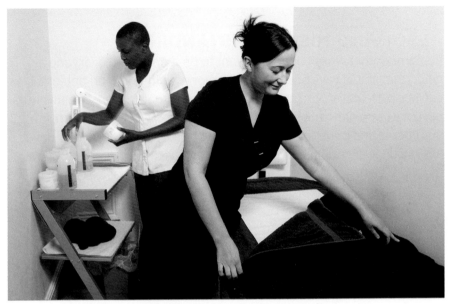

Junior therapist assisting a senior therapist in setting up their work area.

USING AND MANAGING YOUR TIME EFFECTIVELY

It's important to use your free time effectively when you're at work. The best way to do this is to make sure you're always prepared for your next client and check the salon and adjoining treatment and public areas are clean and well maintained. You could also suggest a new promotion that the salon could provide or offer to hand out leaflets to passers-by outside.

When you're performing treatments, you must manage your time effectively to make sure clients receive the best treatment you can offer and you don't run late and keep other clients waiting. For example, you might find that during a facial, you need to use the steamer for ten minutes because your client has oily skin. This will make you run over the allocated 60 minutes. You can manage this time effectively by reducing your massage by five minutes and leaving the mask on for less time than normal.

PROBLEMS THAT CAN AFFECT SALON SERVICES

As well as remaining alert to the needs of your colleagues, you also need to remain alert to any problems that can affect salon services, such as stock shortages, therapists running late and urgent messages that require therapists to leave work early. You must report these problems to the responsible person at an appropriate time. For example, if there's a stock shortage and you need something that day, you must tell the responsible person immediately so they can buy the product from the local supplier. Or, if a therapist is in the middle of a treatment and receives an urgent message, pass the message to a senior therapist who has the authority to interrupt the treatment without causing alarm and upsetting the client.

A therapist offering leaflets to passers-by to promote the salon

ACTIVITY

Identify the responsible people to report stock shortages to, urgent messages regarding other therapists and clients running late. List the consequences of not working within your own responsibilities.

RESOLVING MISUNDERSTANDINGS

Remember that while you might want to be friends with everyone at work, this isn't always possible as everyone is different and personalities can clash. However, you must also remember that to work effectively as part of a team, you must put aside these differences to avoid tension, arguments and unhappiness amongst your colleagues. If you do have any misunderstandings, try to resolve them as quickly as possible. You must NEVER argue or shout at a colleague at work, especially in public areas. This is highly unprofessional and could lead to disciplinary procedures. It will certainly put clients off returning and could affect the success of the business.

ACTIVITY

Make a list of what you consider to be appropriate and inappropriate behaviour when you're in the salon. Now imagine you're a client observing this behaviour, and write down how you would feel and react.

Therapist shouting at a colleague

Therapists resolving their issues with the help of a mediator

Problems can be resolved by approaching the person and explaining to them how you feel. You might find they're also feeling the same and that a simple apology is enough to clear the air. If this doesn't work, you might need another person to **mediate** and help both parties to resolve the issue.

If you feel you're being bullied in any way, you need to tell the responsible person so that appropriate action can be taken to stop it. When you start a new job, try to familiarise yourself with the company's grievance and appeal procedures so you know how to deal with issues accordingly. Identify the person you need to approach so they can help you deal with any difficulties when you're working with others.

A therapist listening to a colleague

Mediate
Trying to help resolve an issue between two people or groups.

A therapist reading her salon's policy guidelines

WHY DON'T YOU...
Read through SmartScreen handout 3 to identify the ways in which you should communicate with your colleagues.

 SmartScreen G8 handout 3

SmartScreen G8 handout 2

HANDY HINTS
To create a happy work environment, make sure you're friendly, helpful, approachable and respectful to your colleagues regardless of how you feel about them on a personal level. This shows a high standard of professionalism and helps you work well as a team.

HANDY HINTS
According to a survey compiled in 2008, beauty therapists are the happiest people in their jobs, so enjoy every day because you're providing an invaluable service!

END OF UNIT SUMMARY

Now you're at the end of the unit and before you test your knowledge with the end of unit assessment, check the following list to see if you feel confident in all areas covered. If there are still any areas you're unsure of, go back over them in the book and ask your tutor for additional support:

- improve your personal performance at work
- work effectively as part of a team.

A happy working team

TEST YOUR KNOWLEDGE G8

Now that you have an understanding of how to manage your effectiveness at work and work as part of a team, let's see how much you can remember. These questions will help you revise what you've learnt in this chapter.

Turn to pages 399–400 for the answers.

1 Why is it important to understand your contract?

2 Why is it important to understand the roles and responsibilities of your colleagues as well as your own?

3 Explain why it's important to understand your own strengths and weaknesses.

4 Why is it important to agree to the targets your manager has set?

5 Why is it important to ask for additional support if you feel your targets aren't achievable or you're worried about not reaching them?

6 What does CPD mean and why is it important?

7 What does NOS mean and where can you find out more about them?

8 Why is it important to understand NOS?

9 What is Habia?

10 What steps can you take to ensure you're up to date with current and emerging trends?

11 What is a target?

12 What is an objective and how is it identified?

13 How long do probationary periods tend to last for beauty therapists and why?

14 Why should incentives be put in place when you're agreeing targets?

15 What is an appraisal?

16 What is a personal development plan?

17 Why is it important to put personal differences to one side when you're at work?

18 Why is it important to resolve issues right away with the appropriate person?

19 Explain why you need to be aware of and understand your salon's appeal and grievance procedures.

20 How can you ensure you're an effective team player?

WHY DON'T YOU...
Test your knowledge further by logging into SmartScreen and completing the revision activities before attempting the sample GOLA revision questions.

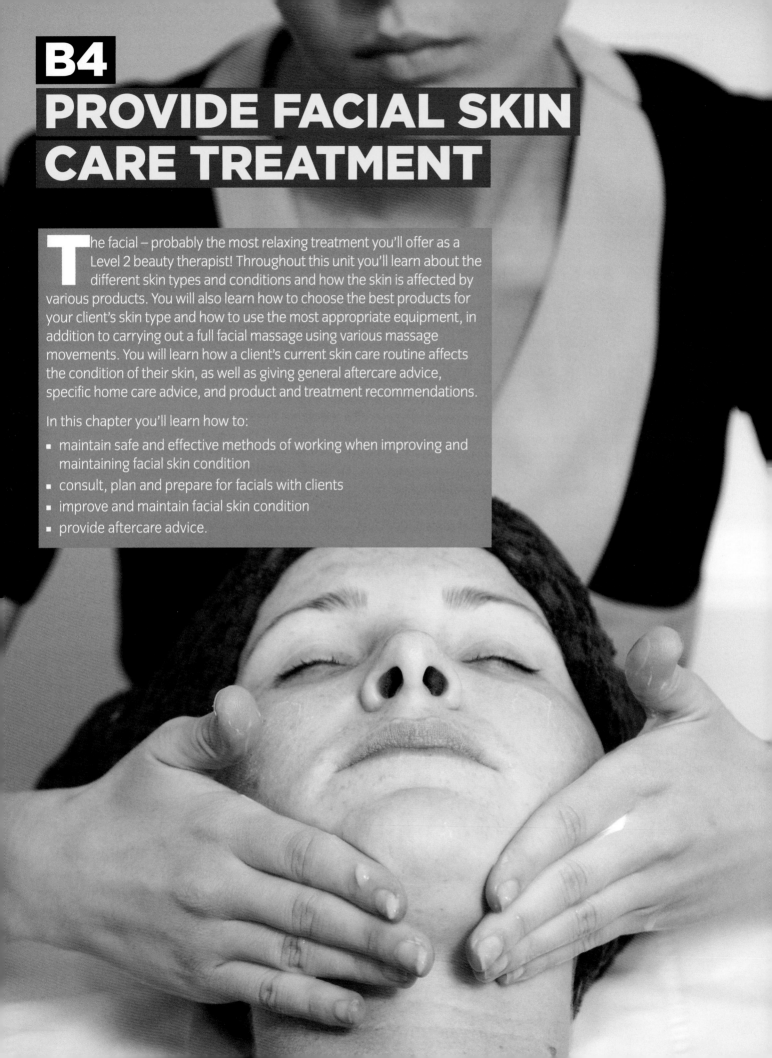

B4
PROVIDE FACIAL SKIN CARE TREATMENT

The facial – probably the most relaxing treatment you'll offer as a Level 2 beauty therapist! Throughout this unit you'll learn about the different skin types and conditions and how the skin is affected by various products. You will also learn how to choose the best products for your client's skin type and how to use the most appropriate equipment, in addition to carrying out a full facial massage using various massage movements. You will learn how a client's current skin care routine affects the condition of their skin, as well as giving general aftercare advice, specific home care advice, and product and treatment recommendations.

In this chapter you'll learn how to:

- maintain safe and effective methods of working when improving and maintaining facial skin condition
- consult, plan and prepare for facials with clients
- improve and maintain facial skin condition
- provide aftercare advice.

MAINTAIN SAFE AND EFFECTIVE METHODS OF WORKING WHEN IMPROVING AND MAINTAINING FACIAL SKIN CONDITION

As with all beauty treatments, it's important you understand and adhere to the relevant health and safety legislation throughout to ensure you perform a safe and enjoyable treatment for your client. The main legislation affecting facial treatments is:

- Data Protection Act (DPA)
- Disability Discrimination Act (DDA)
- Control of Substances Hazardous to Health (COSHH) Regulations
- Electricity at Work Regulations (EAWR)
- Provision and Use of Work Equipment Regulations (PUWER).

Each of these Acts is described fully in Unit G20 along with all other health and safety legislation.

SALON ENVIRONMENT

Before beginning a treatment, it's important that you've set up your work area properly. To reduce the risk of cross-infection, sterilise all metal implements and disinfect all non-metal implements and work surfaces; check Unit G20 for further assistance with this. Starting with the trolley, disinfect the surfaces with an appropriate product and protect the trolley with couch roll before placing the following items on the top shelf:

- a selection of cleansers
- a selection of toners
- a selection of exfoliators
- a selection of massage mediums
- a selection of masks
- a selection of moisturisers
- a small bowl for damp and dry cotton pads and cotton swabs
- a mask brush
- disposable spatulas
- tissues.

On the second shelf you'll need the following:

- a jar containing Barbicide
- a **comedone extractor** (optional)
- a large bowl for warm water
- disposable sponges and/or cotton wool/mitts/facial pads
- a small towel
- a headband
- a mirror
- disposable gloves.

HANDY HINTS

When you're providing a facial treatment, it's important to use the skills you've learnt in the following units:

Unit G20   Ensure responsibility for actions to reduce risks to health and safety

Unit G18   Promote additional services or products to clients

Unit G8   Develop and maintain your effectiveness at work

Unit G4   Fulfil salon reception duties.

WHY DON'T YOU...
Log into SmartScreen and familiarise yourself with other legislation about facial treatments by reading through handout 4, and then answer the review questions to see if you understand the information.

 SmartScreen B4 handout 4

HANDY HINTS
You may have been taught to set up your trolley/work area in a different way.

Comedone extractor
A metal implement used to release comedones (also known as blackheads).

A steamer

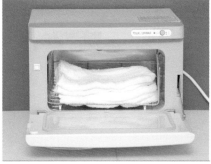

A hot towel cabbie

On the bottom shelf you should have the client record card and any aftercare advice leaflets to give to your client before they leave. Check you have a lined pedal bin next to the treatment couch for any waste.

Additional equipment you might need:

- a steamer
- a magnifying lamp
- a hot towel cabbie.

Before you use any equipment, make sure it has been disinfected and is in safe working order by checking it has passed a PAT test in the last 12 months.

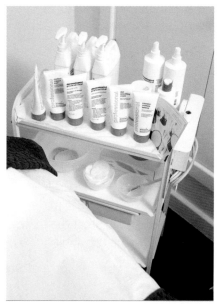

Products ready for treatment

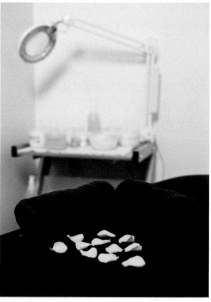

A magnifying lamp and treatment couch

PREPARING THE TREATMENT AREA

Make sure the treatment couch is covered with a protective sheet. Lay a large sheet or blanket over the couch, cover this with couch roll and, if required, use a pillow or neck roll for extra support. Place a small towel at the head of the couch to protect your client's hair and fold a large towel at the centre of the couch for your client to cover themselves with. When your client is on the couch with the towel covering them, bring up the length of the sheet on both sides to wrap your client up and tuck it in at the feet. How you set up your couch is up to you but you should always have enough blankets or towels to hand in case your client gets cold.

When you're happy with the trolley and treatment couch, adjust your chair so it supports your back, and make it the right height so you can reach everything you need without having to stretch. You might want to stand throughout the treatment, especially if your client prefers to lie in a semi-reclined position. Be careful to maintain the correct posture at all times as you could be there for over an hour, depending on the type of facial your client has booked, and you want to minimise the risk of fatigue and injury.

It's equally important to check that the environment you create is both relaxing and welcoming so your client feels at ease the minute they enter the treatment area. Refer to Unit G20 for details on creating the right environment, and make sure you focus on lighting and temperature. The room needs to be relaxing and the best way to do this is to keep the lighting as low as possible – but remember that you need to see what you're doing. Candles can enhance the relaxing ambience, as will oil burners, but be aware of the fire risk and always make sure they're put out at the end of the treatment. Check the room temperature is no lower than 18°C – you want your client to feel cosy and warm at all times because they will be lying down for at least 30 minutes, depending on the type of facial they choose, and they could get cold quickly.

Before starting the consultation, make sure you're aware of the industry accepted times for facial treatments. These times exclude consultation.

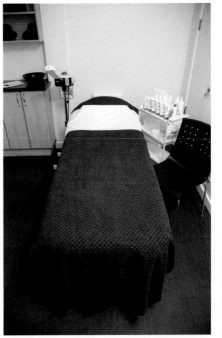

Treatment	Times
Basic facial	45 minutes
Facial	60 minutes
Specialised facial	75–90 minutes

The overall time for a facial can be broken down into sections. Use the guidelines below to make sure you follow the correct times for a standard facial. Please note that these times are only a suggestion and don't have to be followed exhaustively.

- eye and lip cleanse: three minutes
- superficial cleanse: three minutes
- skin analysis: three minutes
- deep cleanse: five minutes
- exfoliation: two minutes
- steam: 3–10 minutes depending on skin type and condition (apply exfoliation with steam for effective time management)
- comedone extraction: three minutes
- facial massage: 15–20 minutes
- face mask: 5–15 minutes depending on the manufacturer's instructions
- tone and moisturise: three minutes.

CONSULT, PLAN AND PREPARE FOR FACIALS WITH CLIENTS

It's always important to carry out a consultation and obtain your client's signature before beginning any treatment to safeguard yourself and the salon. However, with a facial treatment you'll need to gather a lot of additional information so that you can decide on a suitable treatment plan that will improve or maintain your client's current skin condition. The information you'll need for this includes:

- daily skin care routine
- weekly skin care routine

- products used, how they're used and how often
- your client's opinion of their skin type and condition
- family life
- work and home life balance
- environmental factors
- internal factors.

ENVIRONMENTAL FACTORS AFFECTING SKIN CONDITION

These are quite important considerations as your client's environment will greatly affect their skin condition and could explain certain conditions and characteristics. The factors to consider include:

- pollution
- UV exposure
- climate.

POLLUTION

Our skin's pH is affected by our environment as we are exposed to car fumes and waste gases. This can make the skin's protective barrier less tolerant and could promote or exacerbate certain skin conditions, such as eczema and psoriasis.

UV EXPOSURE

UV rays come from the sun and can have both positive and negative effects on the skin. There are three types of UV rays:

- UVA, which causes ageing of the skin and invisible skin damage that can lead to malignant melanoma
- UVB, which burns the skin and can also lead to malignant melanoma
- UVC, which is extremely dangerous but does not penetrate the ozone layer.

It's dangerous to stay in the sun for too long

CLIMATE

The climate a person lives in will have an immediate effect on their skin. For example, in a cold climate, vasoconstriction occurs as the blood is redirected to the centre of the body to keep the vital organs warm. The body produces less sebum which affects the skin's pH balance and reduces the protective barrier. In a warm climate, vasodilation occurs as the blood is directed to the skin's surface to allow the body to cool. Repeated exposure to extremes of temperature and climate can cause conditions such as rosacea, premature ageing, sun/wind burn and breakouts.

INTERNAL FACTORS AFFECTING SKIN CONDITION

As well as external influences, there are also internal influences that can affect a person's skin condition. The main factors to consider include:

- general health
- fluid intake
- diet
- stress levels
- smoking
- sleep patterns.

GENERAL HEALTH

A person's overall health affects the condition of their skin and, if they've been ill, it will show, especially if they've needed medication. This can lead to dehydration, puffiness, breakouts and hyper-pigmentation. Medication must be discussed during the consultation and taken into account in your treatment plan.

FLUID INTAKE

The body is made up of 70 per cent water and we need to replenish this water daily to maintain hydration levels. The recommended daily water intake is two litres, and this is vital in assisting with kidney, liver and bladder function.

Alcohol intake is also an important factor as it can dehydrate the skin. Excessive amounts of alcohol can lead to liver disease and cause vasodilation.

Caffeine is a popular ingredient found in tea, coffee and fizzy drinks and, in excess, can be addictive. Common signs of excessive caffeine intake include migraines, dehydration and a **lacklustre** complexion.

Drinking water helps your body function

Lacklustre
Drab or dull.

DIET/HEALTHY EATING

For a person to have a well-balanced diet, they need to have a moderate intake of all food groups to ensure they're not deficient in any nutrients. This means a balanced intake of vitamins and minerals, carbohydrates, fibre/roughage, protein and fats. For example, the recommended daily fruit and vegetable intake is five per day, which is easy when you consider people generally have three meals a day, and a glass of natural orange juice counts as one portion. Everyone needs vitamins:

- vitamin A aids tissue repair and prevents premature ageing
- vitamin B improves blood circulation and cellular renewal
- vitamin C is needed for collagen production
- vitamin E is a powerful anti-oxidant that fights free-radical damage.

STRESS LEVELS

Stress affects the majority of the population in one way or another and is defined by a person's ability or inability to cope with the tasks they're given, either professional or personal. Low to moderate levels of stress can actually be quite beneficial and make a person more productive as they feel challenged and able to cope. However, if these challenges are overpowering, stress levels rise and that is when the problems begin. A person can look drawn and tired as their skin becomes dehydrated and shows signs of ageing. If someone has irregular sleep patterns and isn't eating regularly, this can lead to other health problems.

SMOKING

Tobacco contains toxins, such as nicotine, which inhibit the production of collagen fibres in the skin. This results in premature ageing as the skin gets dehydrated and loses its plumpness. More seriously, the lungs become lined with tar and the respiratory system is affected, which can lead to lung cancer.

WHY DON'T YOU...
Consider the environmental and internal factors discussed above and examine your own skin to see if you can identify whether it has been affected in any way.

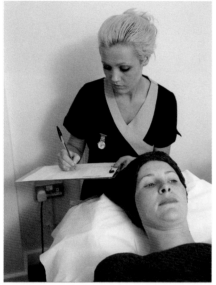

A therapist making notes on a consultation card

WHY DON'T YOU...
Draw up a list of open questions that will enable you to obtain the information you need before performing a facial and describe the types of body language you should use. Refer to SmartScreen handout 11 for more detailed information on the consultation procedure.

 SmartScreen B4 handout 11

SLEEP PATTERNS

A person's sleep patterns can be affected by all manner of things, from stress to diet to general health. The body needs a minimum of seven hours sleep each night, but the ideal amount is around eight hours to allow the body to repair the cells. If a person gets less than this, not only is their skin affected but also their daily lives as it can slow down reaction times and cause mood swings. On the other hand, too much sleep can also cause problems and lead to fatigue.

TREATMENT PLANNING

You need to obtain detailed information from your client to draw up a treatment plan. Think about the types of questions you should ask your client and the techniques you should use. Include a variety of open questioning techniques along with positive body language to encourage your client to open up and provide the information you need.

CONTRA-INDICATIONS

As part of the consultation, you need to identify whether or not your client has any contra-indications that will prevent or restrict the facial. However, you might not become aware of this until you perform the visual consultation as part of the superficial cleanse and skin analysis. The following list indicates which contra-indications require medical referral and, as a result, prevent facials:

- bacterial infections, such as impetigo, conjunctivitis and boils: risk of cross-infection and further skin damage
- viral infections, such as herpes simplex and warts: risk of cross-infection
- fungal infections, such as ringworm: risk of cross-infection
- parasitic infections, such as scabies and pediculosis: risk of cross-infection
- systemic medical conditions: risk of injury and skin damage
- severe skin conditions, such as inflamed psoriasis: the condition could worsen or result in a reaction
- acne: risk of cross-infection for your client and risk of a skin reaction
- eye infections: risk of cross-infection.

If you identify one of the above contra-indications, explain to your client that the treatment cannot go ahead but do not name the condition in case you're wrong. Instead, tell your client you've identified a contra-indication and that performing the facial could make it worse; then advise them to see their GP for a proper diagnosis.

The following list indicates the contra-indications that restrict a facial and require the treatment to be modified:

- Recent scar tissue: the skin is fragile and tender to touch, so work around the area.
- Eczema: if the skin is open and weeping, the treatment shouldn't go ahead; if it's not open and weeping, proceed with the treatment but use gentle products and regularly check the skin for any signs of a reaction.

HANDY HINTS
See the anatomy and physiology chapter for more information on contra-indications affecting the skin.

- Psoriasis: treat this in the same way you would eczema to prevent aggravating the condition and focus your attention on hydration.
- Hyper-keratosis: focus your attention on exfoliation and skin smoothing to even the rough texture of the skin.
- Skin allergies: communicate with your client and check the skin for any signs of reaction throughout the treatment. If your client is allergic to any of the products' ingredients, avoid using them and replace with an alternative.
- Cuts/abrasions: work around the area to avoid the risk of infection.
- Bruising: the skin will be tender to touch. Work around the area to avoid further tissue damage.
- Styes: if there are several styes, advise your client to see their GP and offer them another treatment. However, if there's only one and it isn't too painful, simply work around it.

PREPARING YOUR CLIENT

When you've completed the consultation and identified your client's skin care routine and any contra-indications, you need to agree a treatment plan with your client based on the information you've obtained. Think about the products you plan to use and ask yourself how they will benefit the skin; also think about what equipment you'll need to enhance these effects.

You should have a proposed treatment plan in mind and will need to discuss this with your client so they know what to expect. Encourage them to ask any questions so they're clear you understand their needs and are confident in the treatment you've suggested. It's important that your client fully agrees with your recommendation to make sure they'll be happy with the results.

When the consultation is complete and you've agreed an appropriate treatment plan, you need to tell your client how to prepare themself for the treatment. Remember you'll meet clients from different cultural backgrounds and also with different levels of ability so it's important you give the right instructions without causing offence or alarm and without discrimination. Advise your client that although some undressing is required (of their shoes and top only), you'll maintain their modesty throughout the treatment to ensure their comfort and wellbeing. You will also meet clients who feel more comfortable the less restricted they are, and will happily remove the majority of their outer clothing and their bra. This is fine as long as you maintain their modesty at all times. By discussing this with your client, you're reducing the risk of them feeling uncomfortable and nervous and gaining their confidence by making yourself appear approachable and in control of the situation.

When your client is on the couch, ensure they're warm and comfortable by supplying additional blankets and pillows if needed. Protect their hair by wrapping it in a small towel and tucking two tissues in at the hairline. You are now ready to begin the facial treatment.

WHY DON'T YOU...
Refer to Unit G20 for full descriptions of skin diseases, disorders and conditions that can contra-indicate various beauty treatments.

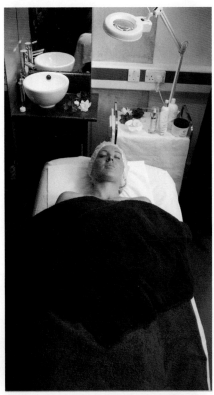

Maintain your client's modesty at all times.

HANDY HINTS
Remember to ask your client to remove their jewellery and place it in their bag so it's safe. Do not offer to look after it for them in case it goes missing. You could ask your client to place jewellery into their shoe as they're bound to find it at the end of the treatment!

WHY DON'T YOU...
Refer to Unit G20 for more details on how to prepare your client for a treatment.

SUPERFICIAL SKIN CLEANSING

Although no two facials should ever be the same, they will begin in the same way until you've identified your client's skin type and condition. Begin with an eye and lip cleanse followed by a superficial cleanse of the face, neck and décolleté.

EYE AND LIP CLEANSE

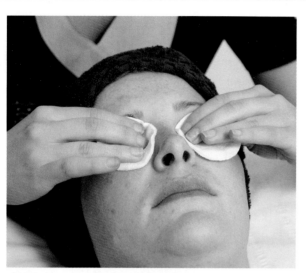

STEP 1 – First, apply make-up remover – or rehydrating cleanser – to two damp cotton pads, then gently place over the eyes and leave.

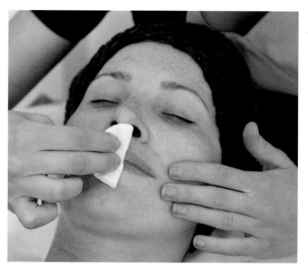

STEP 2 – Apply make-up remover to another damp cotton pad and use this to gently cleanse the lip area, wiping any excess product away with a dry cotton pad.

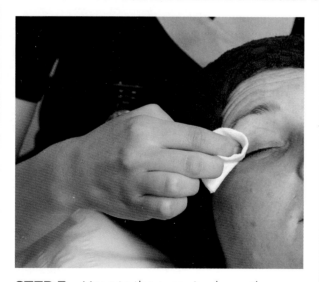

STEP 3 – Move to the eyes. Apply gentle pressure with your fingers and rotate to encourage the breakdown of any stubborn make-up. Gently stroke down and outwards across the eye towards the temple to avoid getting any product in the eye.

When the eyes are cleansed, move on to the superficial cleanse of the face, neck and décolleté.

SUPERFICIAL CLEANSE

Before you begin the superfical cleanse, apply an almond-sized amount of pre-cleansing solution – or a cleanser for sensitive skin – to the palm of your hand and gently rub it into your hands to warm it.

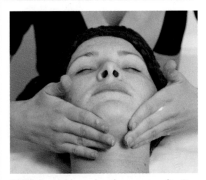

STEP 1 – Hold your hands over your client's face and gently distribute the cleanser over the entire face. Spread it down on to the neck and décolleté using gentle stroking movements.

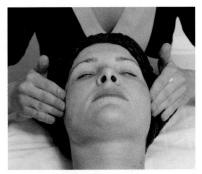

STEP 2 – Work back up the neck and face towards the forehead, bring the hands into a prayer-like position and stroke towards the temples. Repeat these steps three times.

precleanse

dermalogica®

5.1 FL OZ / 150 mL ℮

STEP 3 – Take two damp, disposable sponges or cotton pads and remove the cleanser by stroking up the décolleté and neck with alternate hands before stroking across the jawline towards the ears.

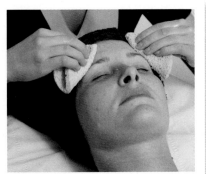

STEP 4 – Turn over the disposable sponges or cotton pads and remove the cleanser from the chin and cheeks using the same motions as before, coming up on to the forehead and stroking out towards the temples.

HANDY HINTS

Using sponges again and again is unhygienic. If you are using sponges, make sure they are disposable.

After you've removed the cleanser, apply toner to two new disposable sponges or cotton pads. Tone the face using the same motion used to remove the cleanser. Finish the superficial cleanse by taking a small tissue and making a hole in the centre for your client's nose. Place the tissue over your client's face and apply gentle pressure with your hands to absorb any excess toner and skin moisture. Remove the tissue, fold it in half and use it to blot the neck and décolleté.

HANDY HINTS

Toner is also available as a spray which is ideal for male clients as it eliminates the risk of getting cotton wool caught in facial hair. It is also more cost effective to use toner in a spray form.

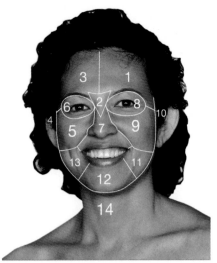

Dermalogica has developed its own unique method of skin analysis called 'face mapping', which draws on the age-old traditions of Chinese philosophy to identify underlying problems that could be causing the skin to display certain characteristics. For example, dark circles under the eyes could represent poor water intake as the eyes are said to be linked to the kidneys.

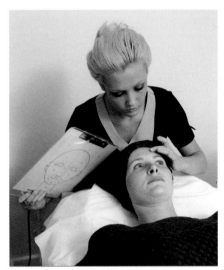

A therapist performing a skin analysis

SKIN ANALYSIS

Explain to your client that you'll now perform a skin analysis. If you're using a magnifying lamp, place damp cotton pads over the eyes. Carry out a consultation by touching and looking at the skin to determine its type and condition, remembering to look at all areas including the décolleté, neck and eyes.

When you're performing the skin analysis, you'll need to identify the skin type initially, and then the skin condition. There are various characteristics you might come across which will help you to determine your client's skin type and condition.

ACTIVITY

Research how internal problems might manifest themselves through the skin and create your own method of 'skin mapping'. Remember, never diagnose a condition you think your client might have – you could be wrong.

SKIN TYPES AND CONDITIONS

There is a distinct difference between skin types and skin conditions; skin types are not always controllable whereas skin conditions are. There are three skin types that your client might have:

- dry
- oily
- combination.

Skin types

Dry skin

Dry skin is caused by a lack of moisture or sebum in the skin due to an underactive sebaceous gland. It's important not to confuse dry skin with a dehydrated condition as they're different. Dry skin displays the following characteristics:

- small, refined pores
- tightness
- possible irritation
- coarse, tight texture
- possibly milia around the eyes
- thin epidermis.

The main disadvantage of having a dry skin type is that it's often the first to age; fine lines and wrinkles become more apparent because of the lack of moisture.

Oily skin

Think of this as the opposite to a dry skin type; it's caused by an overactive sebaceous gland producing too much sebum. This clogs pores and hair follicles with sebum and dead skin cells, resulting in pustules, papules and comedones. Some people suffer more severely than others and turn to their GP for guidance, who might recommend topical solutions or even oral medication to improve the condition. Oily skin displays the following characteristics:

- enlarged, relaxed pores
- coarse texture
- pustules, papules and comedones
- thick epidermis
- shiny appearance
- sallow, uneven pigmentation.

An advantage of oily skin is that it's often the last to age because the high moisture content maintains the skin's suppleness. However, scarring might be apparent depending on its severity.

Combination skin

This is the most common of all skin types and is when two or more skin types or conditions are present. Generally, skin appears both dry and oily in certain areas, which can be frustrating for your client. The oiliness tends to occur along the forehead, down on to the nose and chin, otherwise called the 'T-zone', with the dryness occurring across the cheeks and neck. Sometimes, however, a client might present an upside down T-zone, which usually indicates an underlying medical condition that they might not be aware of. An upside-down T-zone is when there's oiliness across the jawline and up the nose, with the forehead, cheeks and lower part of the neck remaining dry.

When you've identified your client's skin type, you need to see if there's an accompanying skin condition, and it's important you know how to distinguish the differences between them. Skin conditions are:

- dehydrated
- mature
- sensitive.

Skin conditions

Dehydrated skin

Dehydration is caused by a lack of water in the skin and can be controlled by using the correct day and night moisturiser, and by drinking approximately two litres of water per day. Dehydrated skin can accompany any skin type, including an oily type as your client could be using harsh products that are stripping away the natural oils. Dehydrated skin displays the following characteristics:

- superficial flaking
- some shiny areas
- obvious horizontal lines or an 'orange peel' effect
- tightness and some possible irritation
- dilated capillaries.

Mature skin

When a person reaches 25, their skin is classed as mature because it's around this time that our skin begins to age; collagen and elastin fibres aren't produced in as large quantities as before, the skin loses its tone and jowls form underneath the jawline. Muscle tone is also reduced and the underlying bone structure becomes more prominent. Sebum production also decreases and causes dryness. Mature skin displays the following characteristics:

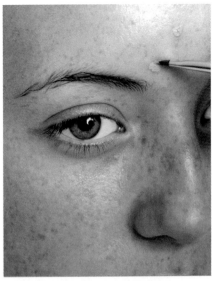

Covering up blemishes on oily skin

HANDY HINTS

A normal skin type is almost impossible to come across these days because of the environments we live in. A normal skin type is flawless and displays no additional conditions. Can you think of anyone you know who fits into this category?

- more prominent bone structure due to poor muscle tone
- lack of collagen and elastin production causing poor skin tone
- thinner and sometimes transparent epidermis
- uneven pigmentation
- dull and lacklustre complexion
- dryness and/or dehydration
- expression lines become a permanent feature.

Sensitive skin

Sensitivity can accompany any of the other skin types and conditions, so you need to be aware of any sensitivity or allergies your client might have so that you can use more gentle products. Sensitive skin can fall into three categories:

- touch sensitive
- product sensitive
- environmentally sensitive.

It will be immediately obvious if a client is touch sensitive; as you perform your superficial cleanse, the skin will produce more erythema than normal and will also feel warm to touch. This might not be a problem for your client but it's important that you keep an eye on how the skin responds to your pressure during the facial treatment, and especially the massage.

A client might not be aware they're product sensitive until after you've applied a product. Generally, a client will complain of irritation, warmth and a tingling sensation that quickly becomes more of a stinging sensation. Product sensitivity can occur almost immediately or over a period of time and is caused by exposure to a specific ingredient in a product or products.

Environmentally sensitive skin is caused by exposure to extreme weather conditions and pollution, for example a skin that is sun sensitive has a low tolerance to UV rays and will burn quickly if it's not adequately protected. Going quickly from a very warm to a very cold environment (or vice versa) can also result in sensitivity, for example leaving a heated house, where the skin is exposed to central heating, to a cold, wintery day outside. This causes the blood to rush from the skin's surface to our core to keep our vital organs warm, and dilated capillaries can form as the vessel walls start to weaken and eventually break down. Sensitive skin generally displays the following characteristics:

- warmth
- erythema
- hyperaemia
- tightness
- dilated capillaries
- thinner and sometimes transparent epidermis
- flakiness.

SKIN COLOUR/TONE

Everyone's skin is a different colour, and a person's skin colour will also affect the types of conditions and characteristics they're prone to, and what they can tolerate. The skin colours are described in more detail below.

Caucasian

Caucasian skin can display different colourings very easily. For example, in the sun it might go red or brown depending on how tolerant the skin is to UV rays; when damaged it will bruise; and when embarrassed or nervous it might go red around the décolleté and cheeks. Caucasian skin is the thinnest of all skin as the epidermis produces fewer cells, meaning it's usually the first to show signs of ageing. Dilated capillaries are often present and can easily be seen.

Caucasian skin

Afro-Caribbean

It's much harder to see changes in colour due to the darkness of the skin. For example, erythema and UV damage are seen as darker patches rather than redness, and it's also prone to keloid scarring. As there are more sebaceous glands than any other skin colour, it's more supple, explaining why it doesn't age as early as Caucasian skin. It's also more prone to pseudo-folliculitis, and is the only skin colour to suffer from dermatosis papulosa nigra (see description on page 8 in the anatomy and physiology chapter), the cause of which is unknown.

Afro-Caribbean skin

Asian

Asian skin tends to be more sensitive and prone to scarring and hyper-pigmentation because of very active melanocytes. Hyper-pigmentation tends to occur as a direct result of injury. For example, acne can cause scarring in any skin colour but for Asian skin it can also cause uneven pigmentation. Asian skin is also prone to solar lentigines due to sun damage and seborrhoeic keratoses, so it doesn't age well compared with Afro-Caribbean skin. However, Asian skin doesn't show the signs of wrinkles and fine lines as early as Caucasian skin.

Asian skin

Oriental

Oriental skin tends to be quite oily and so might have more blemishes. It also has high melanin production and is more prone to hyper-pigmentation and scarring. Therefore, blemishes should be treated with care to avoid this.

SKIN CHARACTERISTICS

To correctly determine your client's skin type and condition, you need to identify the various characteristics that might be present in their skin. See pages 6–8 in the anatomy and physiology chapter for a list of the skin characteristics you need to be aware of.

Oriental skin

IMPROVE AND MAINTAIN FACIAL SKIN CONDITION

Now that you've performed the skin analysis and determined your client's skin type and condition, you need to choose the right products to perform the facial so that you obtain the best results.

CLEANSING THE SKIN

Start with a deep cleanse to remove the build-up of dirt and grime on the skin, along with any left-over make-up. You will loosen dead skin cells and blocked pores in the process and prepare the skin for further treatment. Therefore, it's important you choose the right cleanser to complement your client's skin.

There are various cleansers you can use and each will suit a different skin type and condition. Available cleansers are:

- eye make-up remover
- cleansing milk
- cleansing cream
- cleansing lotion
- foaming cleanser
- cleansing balm
- cleansing bar.

Emulsion
A mixture of two or more liquids that don't mix well together naturally.

ACTIVITY

Familiarise yourself with the products available for a facial and look at which ones will suit each skin type and condition. Think about the effects they might produce and the benefits they might have.

EYE MAKE-UP REMOVER

These are often oil based and are designed to remove stubborn eye make-up and waterproof mascara. They are gentle enough to use without causing irritation to the delicate eye area. The biggest problem with oil-based eye make-up remover is that the oil can make the delicate and thin skin around the eye area puffy.

CLEANSING MILK

These cleansers are often made from oil-in-water **emulsions**, making them light in texture and gentle on the skin. They are ideal for use on the following skin types and conditions:

- dehydrated skin
- sensitive skin.

CLEANSING CREAM

These are similar to cleansing milks but have a higher oil-to-water content. The emulsion is thicker in consistency and, as a result, more effective at removing oil-based make-up and surface grease. Because of their higher oil content, cleansing creams are more suitable for the following skin types and conditions:

- dry skin
- mature skin
- dehydrated skin.

CLEANSING LOTION

This type of cleanser has a detergent-in-water consistency and contains little, if any, oil. As a result, they're quite good for removing make-up and are much lighter in texture than a cream or milk, thus making them ideal for the following skin types and conditions:

- oily skin
- combination skin.

FOAMING CLEANSER

These are becoming increasingly popular because they're easy to use and save time. Foaming cleansers often consist of a gel base with a mild detergent that foams when mixed with warm water, making them ideal for all skin types. This cleanser is popular with people who like that 'squeaky clean' feeling they get with soap and water or those with an oily or congested skin.

CLEANSING BALM

These are quite a new addition to the vast range of cleansers you can buy and have a lightweight consistency. The solid balm forms into a fluid when it's warmed. They have a moisturising and cleansing effect on the skin, making them ideal for the following skin types and conditions:

- dry skin
- sensitive skin
- mature skin
- dehydrated skin.

CLEANSING BAR

More product ranges are introducing these bars into their cleansing lines as there are still many people who prefer to use soap and water. Cleansing bars are popular with people with problem skin and men who like the time-saving aspect and the fact that it's not necessarily seen as a 'skin care product'. While they're not always ideal because they encourage the formation of bacteria, which can lead to cross-infection, they're a good method to use if you need to 'wean' your client off soap.

THE DEEP CLEANSE PROCEDURE

Now that you've looked at your client's skin and determined what skin type and condition they have, you can move on to the deep cleanse routine. Repeat each movement twice unless otherwise instructed. Please note this is just one cleansing procedure – you may have been taught a different one.

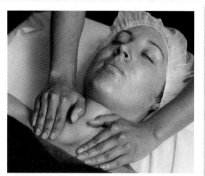

STEP 1 – Begin as you did with the superficial cleanse using stroking movements to distribute the cleanser across the face, neck and décolleté. Repeat this three times.

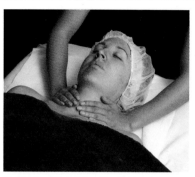

STEP 2 – Start at the décolleté and use effleurage movements (see page 100) down towards the sternum and move out across the décolleté towards the shoulders.

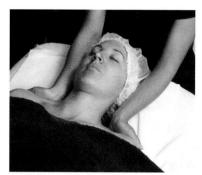

STEP 3 – Come back to the base of the neck and use circular motions with your fingers to loosen dead skin cells and built-up sebum, following the same direction as before.

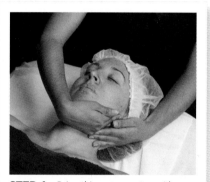

STEP 4 – Bring this movement up either side of the neck and stroke out across the jawline towards the ears.

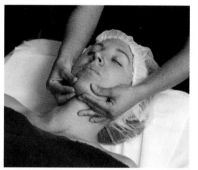

STEP 5 – Use the thumb and forefinger to grasp the jaw and knead with deep movements.

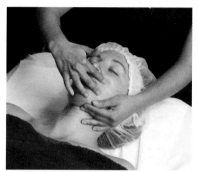

STEP 6 – Stroke up the cheeks towards the eyes with alternate hands beginning at the left cheek and moving over to the right, then back again.

STEP 7 – With deep movements, start at the jaw in front of the ear and apply finger kneading in circles covering the whole cheek area, finishing at the temples.

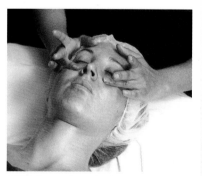

STEP 8 – Stroke under the eyes and come up to the centre of the forehead, stroking out towards the temples.

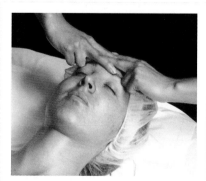

STEP 9 – Use your middle and index fingers and apply scissor movements across the forehead before coming down to the nose.

STEP 10 – With your middle fingers crossed over, apply small, gentle circular movements to either side of the nose.

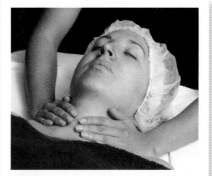

STEP 11 – Stroke back up to the forehead, down to the base of the neck and along the décolleté before using your full palm to stroke over the whole face to the hairline.

Finally, remove the cleanser with warm, damp sponges or heated mitts before toning and blotting.

TONING THE SKIN

When you've chosen an appropriate cleanser for your client's skin type and condition, follow up with a suitable toning method. Some people are afraid to use toners as they believe they're too harsh on the skin and contain high amounts of alcohol. In fact, toners have come a long way since they were first produced and are now designed to restore the skin's natural pH balance after it's been cleansed and remove any excess cleanser. There are different types of toners available, which will produce different effects on the skin:

- skin tonics
- bracers/fresheners
- astringents.

SKIN TONICS

These generally contain a small amount of alcohol, or an astringent, such as orange flower water, which produces a slightly tightening effect on the skin, making them ideal for normal or combination skin types.

BRACERS/FRESHENERS

These contain the least amount of alcohol and are usually made using purified water, making them the gentler option. They often contain rose water and are ideal for a dry skin type, or mature, dehydrated and sensitive conditions.

ASTRINGENTS

These contain much higher concentrations of alcohol or astringents, such as witch hazel, which is an antiseptic, to produce a more drying effect on the skin. Astringents are beneficial for oily skin types and congested conditions provided the skin isn't sensitive, otherwise they might cause irritation.

EXFOLIATING THE SKIN

An exfoliator is designed to **desquamate** the outer layers of the stratum corneum and encourage newer cells to the surface so the skin appears

HANDY HINTS

The skin's pH balance is between 4.5 and 6.2, making it slightly acidic and why it's more commonly referred to as 'the acid mantle'. Sebum and sweat mix on the skin's surface to provide protection against bacterial invasion.

HANDY HINTS

When you've applied an appropriate toning lotion, it's important to blot the skin afterwards as this will soak up any excess moisture on the skin.

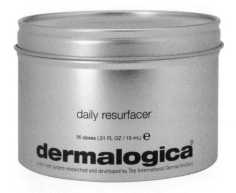

Desquamate
Natural shedding of the skin.

Exfoliate

To remove dead skin cells by product application.

Enzymes

Proteins found in fruit that speed up chemical reactions.

AHAs

Mainly derived from sugar cane and citrus fruit, the most common type is glycolic acid.

BHAs

Specifically describes salicylic acid, which is derived from plants.

Sloughing

Casting off dead tissue.

brighter and even in texture. The skin naturally desquamates all the time as it constantly sheds dead skin cells, but this technique speeds the process along and can be vital in improving or maintaining your client's skin condition. To apply the exfoliator, take an almond-sized amount and warm in your hands before distributing over the face, neck and décolleté in the same way as you would apply your cleanser. Take care to avoid the eye area and use circular motions with your fingers to help remove blockages from the skin. Remove the exfoliator with warm, damp sponges or heated mitts before toning.

There are various exfoliators available that will suit different skin types and conditions and it's important you use the right one for your client's skin as you might find their skin reacts if it's too abrasive. If it's too gentle, it might not produce enough of a difference in the skin so always check your pressure with your client to minimise discomfort. Here we will look at the different types of exfoliators in more detail.

PORE GRAINS

These usually contain crushed up stones derived from fruit and nuts, the most popular being olives or almonds. They are more commonly known as scrubs, which describes their action. They are inexpensive to make and the most popular on the market. However, the stones can be rough around the edges, making them abrasive and sometimes too harsh for more delicate skin types and conditions. They are only recommended for use up to three times a week, and are more beneficial for oily and combination skin types.

DAILY EXFOLIANTS

These are similar to pore grains in how they're applied but they're not as harsh on the skin. They are often made with synthetic grains or 'spheres', which **exfoliate** without being too harsh on the skin. They are gentle enough for daily use, and ideal for dry skin types and sensitive, dehydrated and mature conditions.

PEELS AND ENZYMATIC EXFOLIANTS

These types of exfoliators contain no grains at all; instead, they contain either fruit **enzymes**, alpha-hydroxy acids (**AHAs**) or beta-hydroxy acids (**BHAs**). They are applied like a mask and left to work, gently **sloughing** away the dead skin cells. Remove with warm sponges or, in the case of a peel, roll off the skin. They are gentle enough for use on any skin type, provided your client has no known allergies to the active ingredients, but they're not recommended for daily use as this can cause sensitisation. Peels are not ideal for a mature condition as they can cause dragging of the skin.

ACTIVITY

Look at the exfoliators and decide which one you think would best suit your skin type and condition. In the following table, state which exfoliator you would recommend for each skin type and condition.

Skin type/condition	Recommended exfoliator
Oily	
Dry	
Combination	
Mature	
Dehydrated	
Sensitive	

WARMING THE SKIN

There are two methods of skin warming, manual and mechanical. Your client's skin type and condition will determine the method you choose. Skin warming:

- hydrates the stratum corneum
- relaxes the pores
- warms the skin, preparing it for further treatment
- stimulates local blood supply, bringing fresh oxygen and nutrients to the area
- stimulates lymphatic circulation, encouraging the removal of waste products
- aids desquamation
- improves skin tone.

MANUAL SKIN WARMING

Rinse a compress or small towel under warm water before placing it in a hot towel cabbie where it will be heated and kept warm until you use it. It's important to do this before your client arrives so it's warm enough to produce the desired effect. Manual skin warming is not as stimulating on the skin as mechanical steam, making this treatment ideal for the following skin types and conditions:

- dry skin
- dehydrated skin
- mature skin
- sensitive skin.

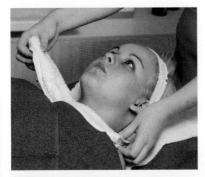

STEP 1 – Place the compress on your client's shoulder and ask them if the temperature is acceptable.

STEP 2 – Unravel the compress and fold in half lengthways. Begin at the base of the neck on the left side, laying across the neck and up the right cheek.

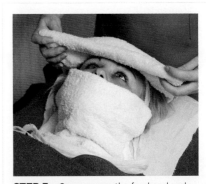

STEP 3 – Come across the forehead and down the left cheek so the two ends meet.

STEP 4 – Ensure the nose isn't covered but the chin and mouth are.

STEP 5 – Place your hands over the cheeks and hold in place until the compress has cooled.

Repeat the above process several times to produce a heating effect on the skin

MECHANICAL SKIN WARMING

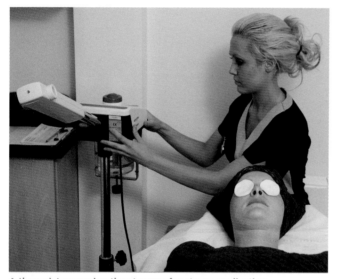

A therapist preparing the steamer for steam application

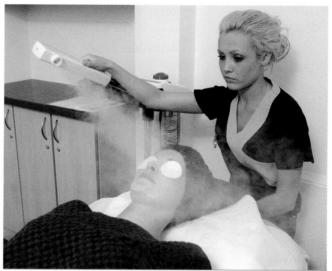

Application of steam to the face

Ozone

An antibacterial gas that is safe to use in small amounts. It is ideal for problem/oily skin.

HANDY HINTS

Ozone is created by passing steam over a high-intensity quartz mercury arc tube. Exposure to high levels of ozone can cause respiratory problems and so take care with clients who suffer with asthma and other respiratory disorders. Ensure there's sufficient ventilation to counterbalance the ozone you produce.

Switch on the steamer just after completing the skin analysis so that it's ready for use when you need it. Apply damp cotton pads to your client's eyes to prevent stinging and irritation and bring the couch into a semi-reclined position. The length of time and distance of the steamer will be determined by your client's skin type and condition; this will also determine whether or not you apply **ozone**. Only use distilled or purified water in the steamer as regular tap water can reduce the life of the equipment. Mechanical steaming is suitable for all skin types and conditions, although settings will vary and are outlined below.

The following settings are a guideline only; refer to the manufacturer's instructions to ensure the safe use of your steamer.

Skin type/condition	Time	Distance
Dry, dehydrated and mature skin	5 minutes	15 inches
Sensitive skin	3–5 minutes	15 inches
Combination skin	5–7 minutes	12 inches
Oily skin	10 minutes	10 inches

You should only apply ozone to an oily or combination skin type as it's designed to produce an antibacterial effect on the skin. This helps to dry out the complexion and speed up the healing process of pustules and papules.

If you need to apply steam for longer because of your client's skin type or condition, you can exfoliate at the same time and manage your time effectively. When the steam treatment is complete, tone and blot the skin.

COMEDONE EXTRACTION

If extractions are required, don't tone the skin after steaming, just blot it dry with a tissue. To extract comedones, you can use either use a comedone extractor or you can do it manually.

MECHANICAL EXTRACTION

Take your comedone extractor out of the Barbicide and dry on a tissue. Using gloves, gently stretch the skin around the target area with your free hand and apply gentle pressure by manipulating the skin so that the comedone is encouraged to release the blockage. Remember comedones can be stubborn and difficult to remove so you need patience and perseverance. Keep checking your client's skin and communicate with them so they know you aren't causing further damage.

MANUAL EXTRACTIONS

Take two clean tissues and wrap around your index fingers, stretch the skin around the comedone and gently squeeze underneath it to release the blockage. Always stretch and squeeze as this prevents the spread of infection in the skin. Wipe down rather than up as this too will prevent the spread of infection between hair follicles.

FACIAL MASSAGE

Massage produces the following effects and benefits:

- produces relaxation
- induces a feeling of wellbeing
- calming
- relieves stress and anxiety
- relieves muscular tension by easing out **lactic acid**
- stimulates blood circulation
- stimulates lymphatic circulation, removing waste products
- revitalises the complexion, bringing a healthy glow.

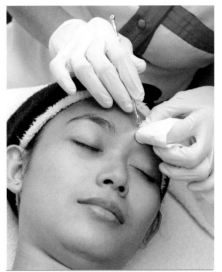

Comedone extraction

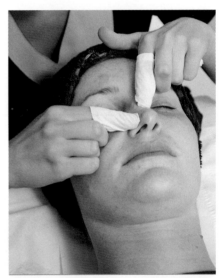

Manual extraction

Lactic acid

A waste product produced by the muscles during stress, exercise and fatigue.

MASSAGE MEDIUM

There are generally two types of massage medium available when you're performing a facial massage: oil and cream. Choose the one that best matches your client's skin type and condition.

Massage Oil

These are light in consistency and generally contain a mixture of essential oils supported by a suitable carrier oil, such as grapeseed or sweet almond oil. They allow for suitable slip and glide throughout the massage so you only need a small amount, otherwise the skin will feel greasy and clogged afterwards. Massage oils are ideal for use on the following skin types and conditions:

- combination skin
- oily skin
- sensitive skin.

Massage Cream

These are much heavier than oils and hydrate the skin. They can provide adequate slip and glide throughout the massage, although you might need to add more. Again, they usually contain a blend of essential oils to enhance the effects of the massage, and are ideal for use on the following skin types and conditions:

- dry skin
- mature skin
- dehydrated skin
- sensitive skin.

MASSAGE TECHNIQUES

Before looking at the massage routine, familiarise yourself with each of the massage techniques available and the effects they have on the skin and underlying structures:

- effleurage
- petrissage
- tapotement
- vibrations/frictions.

Effleurage

Effleurage means to 'skim' or 'lightly touch' and is the movement used to begin and end a massage. It's a suitable way of introducing your touch to your client and indicating that the massage has finished. This movement is also used to link other movements to provide flow, and is performed with the palm of the hand or the pads of the fingers, applied either lightly or firmly without dragging the skin. Effleurage is designed to calm and relax your client and the underlying structures while preparing the area for further treatment. It's a term used to describe the following movements:

- deep effleurage
- superficial effleurage
- circular motions
- stroking.

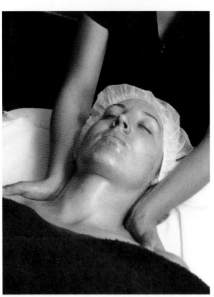

Effleurage

Effleurage is warming and relaxing for the skin and muscles and makes muscles more responsive to deeper movements. It stimulates localised blood and lymphatic circulation and delivers fresh blood, oxygen and nutrients to the area. This encourages cell renewal and gives the skin a healthy glow. It also encourages desquamation of the dead skin cells and reveals a healthy, even appearance and texture. Effleurage is most suited to oily or combination skin types as it helps drain impurities from the skin via the lymphatic system. It's also beneficial for a sensitive skin condition because of its calming and soothing effects.

Petrissage

This movement follows effleurage as the skin and muscles have been prepared for a deeper movement. By moulding the hands, this technique compresses the muscles in the target area and is a deep movement that you should apply slowly and deliberately using the palm of the hand, the thumbs or the index and middle fingers. The following movements are all variations of petrissage:

- Kneading – imagine you're kneading bread, and use a rhythmical motion.
- Knuckling – similar to kneading but the knuckles are used to lift and knead in upwards, circular motions.
- Rolling – the thumbs or fingers are used to manipulate the skin over the muscles.
- Wringing – imagine you're wringing out a cloth. This is a more superficial movement than the others where you grasp the skin in both hands and move back and forth alternately.
- Picking up – similar to kneading but much more deliberate and is aimed at 'picking up' the muscles away from the bone.
- Scissors – another superficial movement where you use the index and middle fingers on flat areas only. Place the fingers opposite each other before slowly working them towards each other to lift and release the skin.

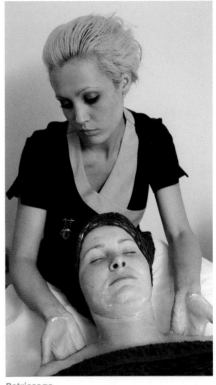
Petrissage

As petrissage is a deeper movement, it provides a toning effect in the muscles and the layers of the skin. It increases blood and lymphatic circulation, encouraging the breakdown of built-up tension and lactic acid in the muscles, which can cause muscle fatigue. Petrissage also stimulates the sebaceous glands, making this movement effective for dry and mature skin types and dehydrated conditions. However, avoid this movement where there's redness and dilated capillaries.

Tapotement

This is the most stimulating of all the movements and should be the last one you use. It derives from the French word 'tapoter', which means to tap or drum and is more often referred to as 'hacking', although hacking is only one variation of this movement where you use the outer edges of the hands in an alternate motion to gently tap the target area. Other movements include:

- Cupping – make your hands into a cup with the palm facing the target area and tap alternately. It's important you don't flatten your palm otherwise you'll be slapping your client, when instead you want to hear a dull cupping sound that almost echoes on contact with the skin.

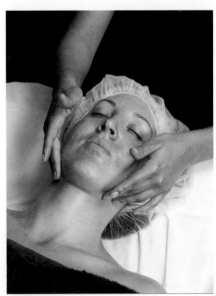
Tapotement

- Pounding – make a fist with your hands and pound the area alternately with a firm motion. Be careful not to bruise the skin.
- Tapping – this is a lighter variation that is only used on the face. Use the pads of either all, or just some, of your fingers to tap the skin, depending on which area of the face you're working on.
- Flicking – again this is a lighter variation that is only used on the face with the pads of either all, or just some, of your fingers, depending on which area of the face you're working on. It's a brisk movement often used along the jawline and around the mouth where the fingers or thumbs quickly flick the skin.

Tapotement is also good at breaking down the build-up of tension in the muscles and has a temporary toning effect on the skin and muscles. It's ideal for mature skin conditions and on lacklustre complexions as it stimulates surface capillaries and brings about a healthy glow to the skin. You might want to omit this movement when you're working on a sensitive condition or over dilated capillaries.

Vibrations/Frictions
Vibrations are considered the deepest of all the massage movements as they affect the nerves endings, and as such there is very little surface stimulation. It is performed by rapidly contracting the muscles of the lower arm and hand to produce a mild trembling movement in the fingers and thumbs. When vibrations are firmly applied they stimulate the sensory nerve endings, but when the application is gentle they provide a soothing effect to the sensory nerve endings.

Frictions involve the skin being rubbed very quickly in order to create heat and warmth. They are also deeper movements applied to localised areas.

Vibrations and frictions are probably the least used movements as part of a facial massage, although can easily be applied to the back of the neck. These movements can be stimulating and soothing and as such are ideal for all skin types.

THE FACIAL MASSAGE ROUTINE
This should generally last 15–20 minutes, and is performed methodically and slowly to ensure complete relaxation for your client. Below is a step-by-step guide to a complete facial massage routine. Each movement in the facial massage is performed three times unless otherwise stated. Please note that this is just one example of a facial massage routine – you may have been taught an alternative method.

It's important to remember that each massage you perform should be catered to the needs of each individual client. Use the massage movements you see here as a guideline and make sure you adapt your massage to suit your client's needs and requirements.

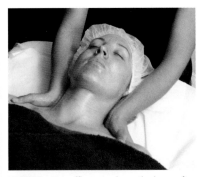

STEP 1 – Use effleurage down the base of the neck towards the sternum, out across the décolleté towards the shoulders and down to the elbow. Move around the shoulders and increase your pressure up the back of the neck at either side of the spine.

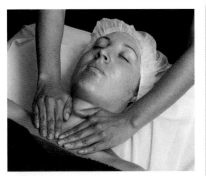

STEP 2 – Move on to petrissage, applying finger kneading in the same direction and ensuring your pressure increases as you come up the back of the neck.

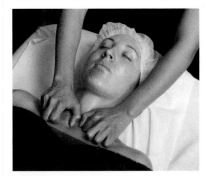

STEP 3 – Use gentle knuckling movements across the décolleté in the same direction, making sure the movement is a little deeper on the upper arms and deeper again up the back of the neck.

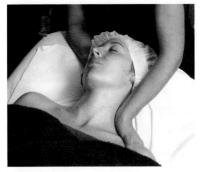

STEP 4 – Hold your client's head in your hands. Tilt it to the left and support with your left hand. Use your right hand to knead from the deltoid up over the trapezius and towards the occipital bone. Stroke back down firmly towards the deltoid.

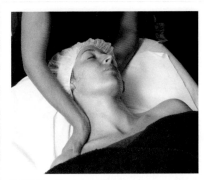

STEP 5 – Repeat on the other side and bring your client's head back to the centre.

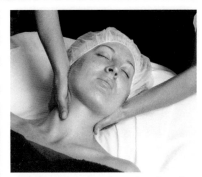

STEP 6 – Manipulate the neck and gently stretch up either side towards the jawline, avoiding the centre.

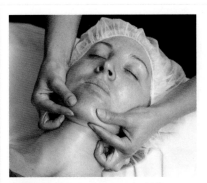

STEP 7 – Use your index and middle fingers to roll the skin of the chin alternately four times before stroking the jaw towards the ears.

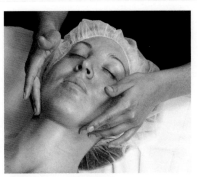

STEP 8 – Use your fingers to apply gentle tapotement movements across the entire jawline as if you're playing the piano.

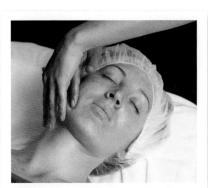

STEP 9 – Apply slow, deep and firm finger rotations with your middle and ring fingers just in front of the ears underneath the highest point of the cheekbones.

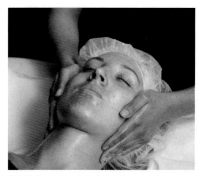

STEP 10 – Use the whole of your palms to stroke in firmly towards the nose until your hands meet in a prayer position. Keep this pressure consistent and stroke back across the cheeks towards the temples.

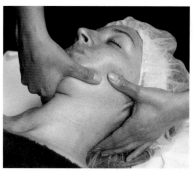

STEP 11 – Thumb knead across both cheeks using a scissor motion, starting at the left and moving over to the right across the chin, and then back again.

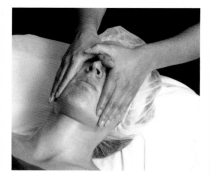

STEP 12 – Stroke up over the eyes with your whole palm and move out across the forehead towards the temples.

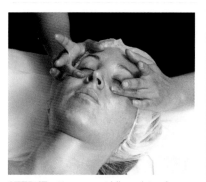

STEP 13 – Use your middle and ring fingers to gently stroke around the eyes, coming in from the temples and stroking out across the eyebrows.

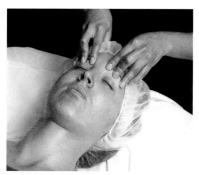

STEP 14 – On the last circle, stroke up the nose to the eyebrows with your ring finger followed by your middle then index fingers and apply a lifting pressure at three points across the eyebrow.

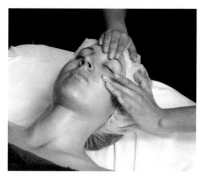

STEP 15 – Apply slow, deep and firm finger rotations with your middle and ring fingers just in front of the ears underneath the highest point of the cheekbones.

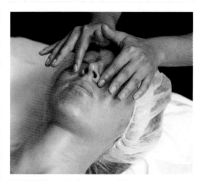

STEP 16 – Stroke around the eyes once more with your middle and ring fingers before coming up on to the forehead with your palms resting at the hairline. Apply gentle tapotement under the eyes in the same way you did over the jawline.

STEP 17 – Cover the eyes with your palms and gently stroke out towards the temples.

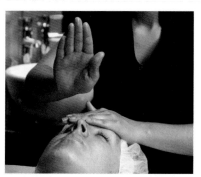

STEP 18 – Use the whole of your palm to apply effleurage from the eyebrows to the hairline, alternating with each hand.

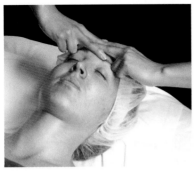

STEP 19 – Use your index and middle fingers to apply scissor movements across the entire forehead from the left to right.

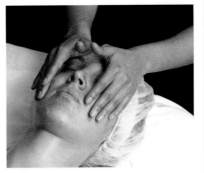

STEP 20 – Rest your palms on the hairline once more and apply piano movements to the whole face. Move back to the décolleté and apply the three original movements once, finishing with effleurage.

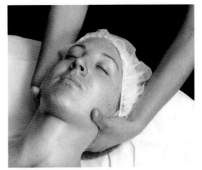

STEP 21 – On the final movement, grasp your client's head in both hands and stretch the neck three times, ensuring your client's legs are not crossed and you're fully supporting the neck and head.

Remove any excess massage medium with heated mitts or warm, damp disposable sponges or cotton pads, apply an appropriate toner and blot with tissue.

FACIAL MASKS

Before you apply your mask, choose the right one to suit your client's skin type and condition. Masks generally come in two forms:

- setting
- non-setting.

SETTING MASKS

These are applied to the skin in a thin layer to allow for easy removal. They can set completely or partially depending on the ingredients and are popular for their deep cleansing and drying effects. Setting masks include the following:

- peel-off masks
- thermal masks
- clay masks.

Peel-off masks

These usually contain ingredients, such as gel or **latex**, but **paraffin wax** masks also fall in this category. They create warmth in the skin as it's encouraged to sweat but the perspiration cannot escape, and surface debris is also absorbed. Remember, if you're applying paraffin wax as a mask, protect the eyes with damp cotton pads and build up three or four layers over gauze, which allows for easier removal.

Thermal masks

These masks come in powder form which is then mixed with water before it's applied to the face and neck. On contact with the skin, they heat up and set solid so they need to be applied quite quickly.

Mask application with a brush

Latex

A common ingredient in peeling masks, making them pliable so they don't crack.

Paraffin wax

A luxurious treatment used for moisturising and softening the skin.

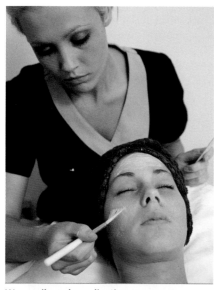

Warm oil mask application

Humectant

Attracts moisture.

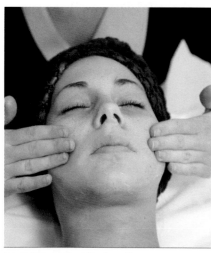

Applying mask with clean fingers

Clay masks

These also come in powder form; however, these masks are mixed with a suitable active lotion to create different effects on the skin:

- Flowers of sulphur: bright yellow in colour, this must be mixed only with a witch hazel toner and applied to pustules and papules for a maximum of five minutes because of the drying effect they can have on the skin.
- Fuller's earth: a dull, dark green colour, this must be mixed only with witch hazel as it's stimulating and can cause erythema. Most suitable for an oily skin type.
- Kaolin: a creamy green colour, this clay is absorbent and is a popular ingredient in most pre-made setting masks. It can be mixed with witch hazel if the skin has a tendency towards oiliness, or orange flower water if there's a tendency towards dryness or dehydration.
- Magnesium carbonate: white in colour, this powder can be mixed with orange flower water for dry skin or with rose water if there are signs of sensitivity.
- Calamine: this is a pink colour and designed to be used on sensitive skin mixed with rose water. Ideal for a client who has slight erythema following the massage as it will cool and soothe the skin.

NON-SETTING MASKS

These masks never set and usually have a much higher moisture content. The following are variations of non-setting masks:
- warm oil
- cream.

Warm oil

Magnesium carbonate and calamine can be used to produce a warm oil mask, and are mixed with the following:
- almond oil: hydrates and nourishes the skin
- glycerol: this doesn't necessarily need to be warmed first but because it has an oil-like consistency and is a **humectant**, it's also suitable for rehydrating a dry complexion.

You can also apply warm oil masks with gauze. Warm the appropriate oil, soak the gauze in it and apply to the face and neck. Remember to apply damp cotton pads to protect your client's eyes before application. Some product companies produce their own warm oil to use as a mask product.

Cream

These are becoming increasingly popular for salon and home use as they're pre-made and can be left on for as long as your client wants without causing any contra-actions. As they have a high moisture content and are rich in consistency, they're ideal for use on the following skin types and conditions:
- dry skin
- dehydrated skin
- mature skin
- sensitive skin.

MASK APPLICATION

Choose the mask appropriate to your client's skin type and condition, even if this means using more than one. Apply quickly and evenly to the entire face and neck using your mask brush in long even strokes, taking care to avoid the eye area and hairline. Cover your client's eyes with damp cotton pads and leave for 10–15 minutes (or according to the manufacturer's instructions) and check you haven't missed the area just under the chin. Use this time to complete your consultation card and tidy your work area. If you have time, perform a hand and arm massage or scalp massage to relax your client even more.

Remove the mask with damp cotton wool, disposable sponges or heated mitts, making sure you cleanse all areas properly. You might need to be a little firmer with the setting masks; use slightly warmer water and avoid rubbing the skin as this can cause discomfort and irritation.

WHY DON'T YOU...
Try out some natural mask ingredients, such as honey, oatmeal or cucmber.

HANDY HINTS

The amount of time a mask is left on also depends on your client's skin type. If a client has problem skin, the mask might need to be left on for longer, whereas if your client has a more sensitive complexion, it might need to be removed sooner. Check the skin reaction while the mask is on and communicate with your client to ensure they're comfortable.

MOISTURISING THE SKIN

When you've removed the mask, tone and blot the area. Finish the treatment by applying a suitable eye cream and facial moisturiser to the face and neck. Apply your facial moisturiser with the same techniques you used to apply your cleanser. The moisturiser you choose again depends on your client's skin type and condition, and will be one of the following:

- moisturising lotion
- moisturising cream
- tinted moisturiser.

MOISTURISING LOTION

These are the lightest of moisturisers available with a high water-to-oil ratio, making them ideal for the following skin types and conditions:

- oily skin
- combination skin
- sensitive skin.

MOISTURISING CREAM

Much richer than a lotion because of a higher oil content, these moisturisers are ideal for the following skin types and conditions:

- dry skin
- dehydrated skin
- mature skin
- sensitive skin.

Overall, a day moisturiser is designed to provide a small amount of protection against the environment, while also rehydrating the skin and maintaining its pH balance. Some are prepared with an **SPF** or **broad spectrum protection** to provide sun protection as well.

There are other moisturising preparations available, which are becoming increasingly popular as people become more aware of their skin and how to look after it. They include:

- neck products
- eye products
- lip balms
- medicated skin care.

SPF
Sun protection factor provides a certain amount of protection against UVB damage but not UVA damage.

Broad spectrum protection
Protects against UVA/B and environmental damage.

WHY DON'T YOU...
Research other specialised products, such as night creams, serums, boosters, tinted moisturisers and SPFs to see what benefits they have on the skin and why they should be included in a client's skin care routine.

NECK PRODUCTS

The neck is usually one of the first areas to show signs of ageing so it makes sense that the products should be slightly thicker in consistency and richer in content to help prevent this. Many product ranges will have at least one neck cream as part of their anti-ageing line. They're normally recommended for use from around the age of 25, when the skin starts to mature, as a simple facial cream will not provide adequate moisture.

EYE PRODUCTS

Also designed for use as part of an anti-ageing skin care routine, these products tend to come in three forms: gel, serum and cream. Gel has the lightest consistency and is aimed at cooling the eye area. It's ideal for younger skin, for use in the morning or for those who are at a computer all day. Serums are slightly more advanced with a light, almost liquid consistency, and are designed to penetrate slightly deeper into the epidermis. They are suitable for younger skin and for people who are concerned about ageing. Creams are much thicker in consistency and designed for more mature clients and for use at night to repair the skin.

MEDICATED SKIN CARE

Specifically designed for use on problem skin or for skin with acne vulgaris, these products can take many forms, such as gels, creams and washes. They are prescribed by a GP who will diagnose a condition and can range from gels and lotions to solutions. Retin-A is the most common topical product available and Roaccutane is the most common oral medication available. They have a thinning effect on the skin and cause increased sensitivity. If a client is using medicated skin products, take care during facial treatments especially with skin warming and exfoliation techniques.

LIP BALMS

These are designed to rehydrate the lip area and support the fragile skin. Common ingredients include mint extracts for a cooling and invigorating effect, although more soothing ingredients, such as lavender and aloe, may also be included to provide a calming effect. Lip balms are increasingly being developed with SPF protection.

PROVIDE AFTERCARE ADVICE

When you've finished the facial, remove the towel protecting your client's hair and tell them the treatment has ended. Bring the couch into a semi-reclined position and offer them some water before leaving them to get changed. Ensure they're satisfied with the results and ask them for feedback on the treatment.

Now's the time to give your client the appropriate aftercare advice to ensure they maintain the results. You should give the same aftercare advice to every client after a facial. You should also give home care advice to every client but this will be more specific to their individual needs, and will include product recommendations and advice on skin care routines.

HANDY HINTS
When the facial is finished, remember to complete the consultation card to include the end result. File the card in the right place so it can be accessed and referred to when your client returns for a follow-up treatment.

THE CITY & GUILDS TEXTBOOK

AFTERCARE ADVICE

The reason why aftercare advice is so important is because the skin and the underlying structures have been stimulated, bringing newer cells to the surface and encouraging cell renewal in the epidermis. Therefore, it's important to ensure your client doesn't stimulate the skin even more as this could cause a contra-action. The advice should be:

- Avoid applying make-up to the area.
- Avoid heat treatments, such as steam, sauna or hot tubs.
- Avoid swimming.
- Avoid UV treatments or sun exposure.
- Drink plenty of water, ideally two litres a day.
- Avoid caffeine, alcohol and smoking.
- Eat a light, healthy diet.

HOME CARE ADVICE

This is more client specific and will include skin care recommendations, product recommendations, tips for any necessary lifestyle changes and treatment frequency. As a result, this advice will vary from client to client depending on their skin type and condition, and their current routines. An example of this type of advice is outlined below.

CASE STUDY

A male client is 35 years old and has an oily skin type with a dehydrated condition. His skin care routine involves just soap and water, which he uses to shave with on a daily basis. He leads a busy life and doesn't have time to spend on his skin every day. He eats a healthy diet and exercises three times a week. However, he doesn't like water and drinks a lot of coffee and fizzy drinks.

Aftercare advice following a facial

The approach you need to take with this client is 'quick and simple'. Give him a routine he feels is easy and doesn't involve too much time otherwise he won't stick to it. Tell him to bin the soap the minute he gets home and to invest in a face and body wash he can use in the shower every day – and take to the gym. Explain the soap is part of the problem as it's dehydrating his skin, stripping it of its protective barrier, the acid mantle, and leaving it open to infection. Recommend a shaving cream he can apply with his fingers, which will help to 'lift' the hairs before shaving and allow for a much closer shave. Finally, advise him to invest in a moisturising lotion as this will provide the moisture his skin needs to rehydrate without making the skin feel greasy.

Praise your client for his healthy lifestyle and diet. Encourage him to maintain this as it's good for his health but also encourage him to take steps to reduce his caffeine intake, eg by only having coffee in the morning and one fizzy drink per day, as this will be affecting his sleep patterns and concentration levels. Advise that he needs to drink two litres of water each day to maintain hydration levels. Suggest diluting juice initially or even trying flavoured water. He might experience 'withdrawal' symptoms from not consuming as much caffeine, for example, headaches and migraines, mood swings and possibly stomach upsets, but encourage him to persevere as it will have a positive effect on his skin and overall health.

With regard to treatment frequency, advise your client to have a weekly facial for six weeks if he can commit and afford it; if not maybe twice a month, or at most monthly. After the sixth facial, tell him you'll reassess the skin condition and take any necessary action. As he begins to notice and feel the results, you can start to introduce other products into his skin care routine at home, such as weekly exfoliation and a mask to prepare the skin for that closer shave and smoothe the texture of his skin. Anti-ageing products could also be introduced in time, such as eye creams and anti-ageing moisturisers to protect and repair the skin.

It's important to provide advice on a home care routine as this will enhance the benefits of the facial and ensure your client sees the results more quickly. There's no point having regular facials if your client is going to use soap on their skin every day at home because this will undo all your hard work and your client won't see the results they want. You're doing a disservice to your clients if you don't give appropriate product recommendations; remember it's not 'hard selling', it's skin care advice!

When you're recommending frequency between facial treatments, you need to consider the following factors:

- skin type
- skin condition and severity
- your client's schedule
- your client's income
- cell reproduction.

ACTIVITY

Think about the home care advice you would give to the following clients:

Client A: a 25-year-old female who leads an active lifestyle, with a demanding career and a busy social life. She often eats out and socialises as part of her job and drinks a lot of alcohol as well, although does make the effort to balance this with a high water intake during the day. Her skin type is a combination of dry and oily with signs of sensitivity across the cheeks and dark circles under the eyes.

Client B: a 40-year-old mother of two teenage children who works part time and rarely gets a moment to herself. She has no idea when it comes to skin care and doesn't have a great deal of money to spend on herself. She wants to look after her skin as she is beginning to notice fine lines and wrinkles around her eyes and mouth; she also feels she looks older than she is. She doesn't sleep well but does eat a healthy diet. However, she doesn't exercise and smokes, on average, ten cigarettes a day.

HANDY HINTS

Why not produce a simple aftercare leaflet for your client to take home.

HANDY HINTS

Cell reproduction usually occurs every 21–28 days so a client should have a facial at least every month to ensure there's an improvement; less often and you'll be 'starting from scratch' every time. A client shouldn't have a facial more than once a week to avoid overstimulating the skin.

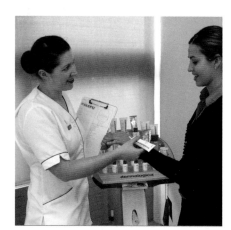

Recommend products based on your client's lifestyle

CONTRA-ACTIONS TO FACIALS

The following contra-actions might occur during or after a facial. Keep an eye out for such reactions so you know how to deal with them and what advice to give your client to make sure the effects are reduced. These can include:

- excessive erythema
- irritation.

EXCESSIVE ERYTHEMA

This could be a result of your client being touch sensitive; you would have noticed this quickly in the skin. Adjust your pressure throughout the treatment accordingly, especially during the facial massage to avoid aggravating this further. If excessive erythema occurs during the treatment, stop immediately and apply a cold compress to the area to reduce the heat and bring down the erythema. Apply a calamine mask made with a rose water toner to cool and soothe the skin. Advise your client to continue applying cool compresses over the next 24 hours, by which time the reaction should have gone; recommend they seek GP assistance if it hasn't. Excessive erythema can also accompany irritation.

IRRITATION

This is usually caused by a stimulant in a product and is more common in product-sensitive skin, although it can happen to anyone. If this contra-action occurs during the treatment, stop immediately and remove the product with cool water to reduce the heat and temptation to scratch the skin. Follow this with a calamine mask made with a rose water toner to cool and soothe the skin, or apply a cool compress to the area for the same effect. Apply aloe vera gel to soothe the skin and advise your client to continue this process over the next 24 hours. Recommend they seek GP assistance if the reaction doesn't go away after this time.

Apply aloe vera gel to irritated skin

END OF UNIT SUMMARY

Now you've reached the end of the unit, you should feel confident in the theory and practical aspects of all areas of facial treatments. Use the checklist below to see if there are any areas you feel you need to recap before beginning the end of unit assessment:

- maintain safe and effective methods of working when improving and maintaining facial skin condition
- consult, plan and prepare for facials with clients
- improve and maintain facial skin condition
- provide aftercare advice.

TEST YOUR KNOWLEDGE B4

Using the questions below, test your knowledge of Unit B4 to see how much information you've retained. These questions will help you to revise what you've learnt in this chapter.

Turn to pages 400–401 for the answers.

1 Why is it important to create the right environment for a facial?

2 What health and safety measures do you need to follow?

3 How do you sterilise your metal implements?

4 Explain why you need to disinfect all non-metal and disposable implements and work surfaces.

5 Why is it important to establish your client's current skin care routine?

6 Describe **three** contra-indications to a facial that require medical referral and explain why.

7 Explain how you would prepare your client for a facial treatment.

8 What is the difference between a superficial and deep cleanse?

9 Why is it important to perform a skin analysis and what might the consequences be if you don't do this?

10 Why should you recommend your clients exfoliate?

11 What are the benefits of skin warming?

12 Name the benefits of using ozone on the skin.

13 Describe how to perform a manual comedone extraction.

14 What **three** techniques are used in massage and what are their benefits on the skin?

15 What is the difference between a setting and non-setting mask?

16 Why is it important to tone the skin?

17 What **two** components make up the acid mantle?

18 How often should a client have a facial and why?

19 Name and describe the **two** contra-actions that might occur during a facial and explain how you would deal with them.

20 What aftercare advice should you give to every client after a facial and why?

WHY DON'T YOU...
Test your knowledge further by logging into SmartScreen and completing the revision activities before attempting the sample GOLA revision questions.

B5
ENHANCE THE APPEARANCE OF EYEBROWS AND LASHES

The eyes are said to be the window to the soul, so naturally your clients want to ensure they look their best at all times, and there are plenty of products to assist with this. As a beauty therapist, you'll advise your clients on the various treatments available.

In this chapter you'll learn how to:

- maintain safe and effective methods of working when enhancing the appearance of eyebrows and eyelashes
- consult, plan and prepare for the treatment with clients
- shape eyebrows
- tint eyebrows and lashes
- apply artificial eyelashes
- provide aftercare advice.

Tint colours
Tubes of permanent dye that are designed to colour brow and lash hair. They are made for use around the delicate eye area and are activated by being mixed with hydrogen peroxide.

Hydrogen peroxide
A chemical that is mixed with the tint to create a permanent hair colour change.

Dappen dish
A small glass or plastic dish used to mix the tint colour and hydrogen peroxide.

Manual tweezers
Normal tweezers used to remove individual hairs and define the overall shape.

Automatic tweezers
Tweezers that have a 'spring-like' action to remove hairs from the bulk of the brows.

MAINTAIN SAFE AND EFFECTIVE METHODS OF WORKING WHEN ENHANCING THE APPEARANCE OF EYEBROWS AND EYELASHES

As with all beauty treatments, it's important you understand and adhere to the relevant health and safety legislation throughout to ensure you perform a safe and enjoyable treatment for your client. The main legislation affecting eye treatments is:

- Data Protection Act (DPA)
- Disability Discrimination Act (DDA)
- Control of Substances Hazardous to Health (COSHH)
- Reporting of Injuries, Diseases and Dangerous Occurrences Regulations (RIDDOR).

Each of these Acts is described fully in Unit G20 along with all other health and safety legislation.

SETTING UP YOUR WORK AREA
Before you can provide eye treatments, you need to be prepared with all the necessary equipment and materials to provide an effective treatment. It will also help you to portray a professional image of yourself and the salon.

Before beginning a treatment, make sure your work area has been properly set up. Clean all surfaces of your trolley with an appropriate disinfecting product, protect it with couch roll and place the products, materials and equipment you'll need for the treatment on the top shelf. These include:

- eye make-up remover or a rehydrating cleanser
- a gentle toning lotion
- a selection of **tint colours**: usually black, blue/black, grey and brown
- **hydrogen peroxide**
- a **dappen dish**; ideally glass but plastic will suffice
- petroleum jelly
- a tinting brush
- an eyebrow/lash brush
- an orange wood stick
- disposable spatulas
- **manual tweezers** and/or **automatic tweezers**
- scissors
- a small jar of Barbicide
- a small bowl with damp and dry cotton pads

- cotton swabs
- tissues
- antiseptic soothing lotion, such as aloe vera
- a selection of **strip lashes** and **individual lashes** in various sizes and colours
- **lash adhesive**
- **artificial lash remover**; often called solvent
- a small square of kitchen foil; to line the dappen dish for artificial lash application
- rehydrating eye product (optional).

On the second shelf you should have a small towel, a headband, a hand-held mirror and a small bowl of cool water.

On the bottom shelf you should have the client record card and any aftercare advice leaflets you might want to give to your client following the treatment.

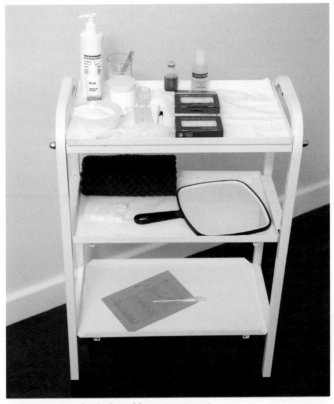

A trolley set up for lash and brow treatments

As you're setting up your trolley, make sure your product bottles are clean by wiping them down with disinfectant. Sterilise your tweezers and scissors using an autoclave or glass bead steriliser before immersing them in Barbicide to maintain the effects. Disinfect any other materials, such as tinting and eyebrow/lash brushes and place them in the UV cabinet until you need them. Also check your magnifying lamp is in working order, has passed a PAT test less than 12 months ago and has been cleaned with the appropriate disinfectant.

To prepare the treatment couch, protect it either with a sheet or towels and cover with couch roll. Provide adequate neck support at the head in the form of a pillow or a small rolled-up towel.

Strip lashes

Very dramatic artificial lashes that are applied to the length of the eye.

Individual lashes

One or two artificial lashes grouped together to produce a more natural look.

Lash adhesive

A glue that is used to ensure the artificial lashes 'stick' and remain in place.

Artificial lash remover

A type of solvent that is used to remove lash adhesive.

HANDY HINTS

Remember that you'll need informed and signed parental or guardian consent if your client is a minor aged under 16 years and a parent or guardian should be present throughout the treatment.

WHY DON'T YOU...

Refer to the Habia guide to pre-16 restrictions, which states that minors cannot receive sensitivity tests or come into contact with chemicals, such as tints, perm lotions and lash adhesives.

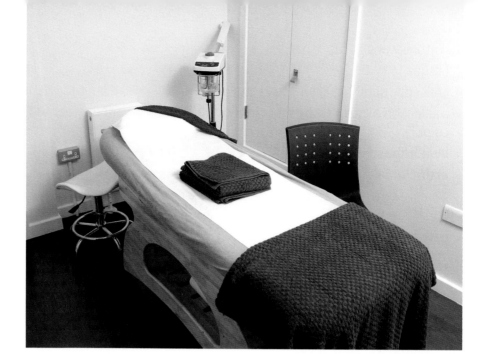

When you're happy with the trolley and treatment couch, check your own comfort by adjusting the chair so it supports your back, and is the right height so you can reach everything you need without having to stretch. Remember to check for any other health and safety implications.

SALON ENVIRONMENT

To create the right environment for the treatment, focus your attention on the lighting and your client's general comfort. As your client will be lying supine or in a semi-reclined position, make sure the overhead lighting is not too bright that it glares in their eyes, but is bright enough for you to see what you're doing. If it helps, use a magnifying lamp for removing those lighter, finer hairs from the eyebrows. Provide enough pillows or small towels nearby to support your client's vertebrae and maintain their comfort throughout the treatment.

Before greeting your clients, remember to check you own appearance and that you'll give them the right first impression. Refer to Unit G20 for guidance on personal preparation and presentation.

It's vital that your treatments are cost effective and adhere to the industry accepted times so you don't reduce your salon's profits. The table below identifies how long each eye treatment should take. These times exclude consultation.

WHY DON'T YOU...
Refer to Unit G20 for further information on creating the right environment.

Treatment	Times
Eyebrow shape	15 minutes
Eyelash tint	20 minutes
Eyebrow tint	10 minutes
Full set of artificial lash application (strip)	10 minutes
Partial set of artificial lash application (strip)	10 minutes
Full set of artificial lash application (individual – flares)	20 minutes
Partial set of artificial lash application (individual – flares)	10 minutes

CONSULT, PLAN AND PREPARE FOR THE TREATMENT WITH CLIENTS

It's always important to perform a consultation and obtain your client's signature before you begin any treatment to safeguard yourself and the salon. During the consultation, focus your attention on the following points depending on which eye treatment your client has booked:

- products used to enhance the eyes, such as mascara, liner, brow pencil
- previous methods used for maintaining/shaping eyebrows
- previous tinting treatments (if any)
- is the treatment for a special occasion?
- your client's natural hair colour and eye colour
- has your client received a skin sensitivity test at least 24 hours ago? If so, is there evidence of this?

When you've identified these points, give your client any advice they could benefit from so that the treatment they receive is the best one you can offer. For example, a client could be getting married and want strip lashes. These produce a dramatic result so advise them that individual lashes are more natural and will enhance their make-up. This will give your client the option of which to choose and, if they're still unsure, you could let them see both effects by applying one type to each eye. It's also important to explain the treatment procedure to your client so they know exactly what to expect.

As part of the consultation, you need to identify whether or not your client has any contra-indications that prevent or restrict the treatment. The following are contra-indications that require medical referral:

- Severe skin conditions: risk of making the condition worse or risk of cross-infection.
- Stye: this is a bacterial infection of the lash follicle and the risk of cross-infection is increased.
- Conjunctivitis: this might be a viral or bacterial infection of the eye and brings a risk of cross-infection.
- Blepharitis: this is chronic inflammation of the eyelid and, although it's not contagious, the treatment could exacerbate the condition, causing unnecessary discomfort.

The following are contra-indications that prevent eye treatments:

- Inflamed skin: the skin could be more reactive and sensitive to products.
- Known allergies to tint, adhesives, solvents: risk of an **allergic reaction**, and risk of developing contact dermatitis (this is described fully later on in the unit).
- Bruising: as the skin is fragile.
- Recent scar tissue: as the skin is healing, avoid eyebrow shaping in particular because you might damage the skin.
- Recent operations on or around the eye area: treat as above.
- Hyper-sensitive skin: risk of a reaction or risk of developing contact dermatitis.

HANDY HINTS

Remember that anyone aged under 16 years old is considered a minor and therefore cannot receive an eye treatment as chemicals, such as tints, adhesives, solvents and peroxides cannot be applied to their skin. This means a skin sensitivity test cannot be performed and as a result neither can tinting or the application of artificial lashes.

HANDY HINTS

More information on these contra-indications can be found in the anatomy and physiology chapter.

Allergic reaction

An adverse (bad) reaction that the body has to a particular substance in the environment or when a substance comes in contact with the skin. Most substances that cause allergies are harmless and have no effect on other people. Some common allergies are contact dermatitis and hay fever.

Exacerbate

To worsen.

- Hay fever: eyebrow shaping could **exacerbate** the condition.
- Watery eyes: lash tint application might not be as intense and artificial lash adhesive might not adhere effectively. Also adhesive or tint could enter the eyes.
- Highly nervous clients: there's a risk of product entering your client's eyes if your client finds it difficult to relax. Their eyelids will 'flutter' or they could accidentally open their eyes during product application.

If your client has any of the above contra-indications, explain to them that the treatment cannot go ahead as you've identified a possible contra-indication. Make sure that you NEVER name the contra-indication, and tell your client to see their GP if medical referral is required. If not, offer your client another treatment and advise them to return when the condition has gone.

The following are contra-indications that restrict eye treatments and require you to make modifications:

- Eczema: if the skin is open and weeping, you shouldn't proceed with the treatment. If it's not open and weeping, continuously check the skin's reaction and communicate with your client throughout, taking care not to damage the skin.
- Psoriasis: treat in the same way as eczema.
- Bruising: work around the area and avoid applying too much pressure.

To prepare your client, ask them to lie supine and place a medium towel over their décolleté to cover their clothing. Protect their hair with a headband or use a small towel, tucking in two tissues to protect it from staining. Ask your client to remove all jewellery from the area and place it in their handbag.

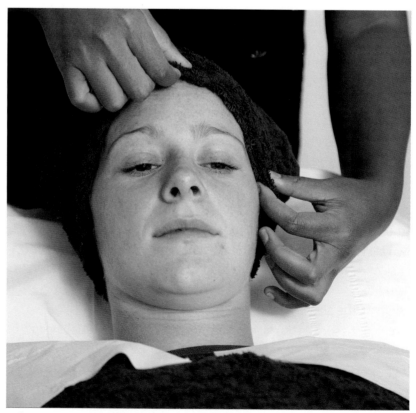

A therapist preparing a client for an eye treatment

Before starting an eye treatment, you need to prepare the eye area by removing make-up and grease so you can achieve the best results. Follow the step-by-step guide below for both eye and eyebrow cleansing.

CLEANSING THE EYE AREA

STEP 1 – Take the make-up remover (or a rehydrating cleanser) and apply to two damp cotton pads. Place them over the eyes and apply gentle pressure with your fingers. Hold this for a couple of minutes to emulsify all waterproof make-up.

STEP 2 – Gently rotate the cotton pads to encourage the breakdown of any stubborn make-up.

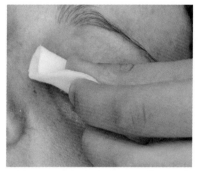

STEP 3 – Gently stroke down and outwards across the eye towards the temple to avoid getting any product in the eye. Repeat on the other eye.

STEP 4 – Take some more eye make-up remover or cleanser and apply to two more damp cotton pads. Apply in small circular motions from the temples coming up over the eyebrows until they meet in between the brows and gently stroke back towards the temples.

STEP 5 – Add a gentle toner to two more damp cotton pads and stroke from the temples under the eyes. Stroke over and out across the eyelids back towards the temples.

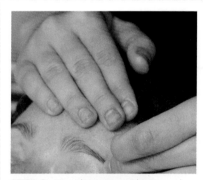

STEP 6 – Turn the cotton pads over and stroke over the eyebrows in the opposite direction to the hair growth and back towards the temples.

You're now ready to perform an eye treatment.

SHAPE EYEBROWS

This is performed with tweezers only and provides a suitable alternative to waxing for those who could be sensitive to wax or who simply prefer this method. Your client might book in for a brow reshape which will need them to grow their brows for anywhere between six weeks to six months depending on their hair growth. A brow reshape is where a new eyebrow shape is created to define the eye area and frame the face. You might also have a client who simply wants their original brow shape maintained; this requires you to remove any stray and unwanted hairs from the area.

A perfect brow shape

DETERMINING YOUR CLIENT'S FACE SHAPE

Bring your client into a sitting position and move to the end of the couch so you're directly opposite them. Study their face and eyes to determine their shape so you can decide on the best eyebrow shape to frame the eyes and enhance their facial features. Below are the different face shapes you'll come across and the best eyebrow shapes to suit them.

LONG FACE

The ideal eyebrow shape for this client is almost straight to divide the length of the face, draw attention across the face and give the illusion of width. The brow should be of medium thickness, tapering slightly at the outer edge.

SQUARE FACE

The ideal eyebrow shape for this client is a smooth tapering arch to create the illusion of softer features. The brows need to be of average thickness so they're not lost in the strong bone structure.

Long face shape
with straight brows

Square face shape
with tapering brows

HEART-SHAPED FACE

The ideal eyebrow shape for this client is an arched brow that tapers off at the outer edges, and is neither too thin nor too thick to create the illusion of balance in the face. This is called an oblique shape.

ROUND FACE

The ideal eyebrow shape for this client is a high angular arch to create the illusion of extra length and detract from the roundness of the face. The brow should be thicker at the inner corner, tapering into the angular arch.

DIAMOND-SHAPED FACE

The ideal eyebrow shape for this client is a curved brow with a high arch at the outer corners. This creates the illusion of softening this face's angular features. The same approach can be used for a pear face shape as well.

Heart face shape and oblique eyebrows

Round face shape with high arch brows

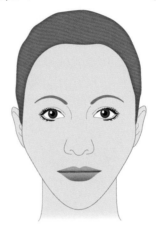

Diamond face shape with curved, arched brows

EYES

Now you've established your client's face shape, look at their eyes so you know whether or not to reduce the length of the brows.

CLOSE-SET EYES

Try to create the illusion of space by extending the length of the brow beyond the normal length line and increasing the distance between the eyes equivalent to a third eye space.

WIDE-SET EYES

Try to balance the shape of the eyes and face by creating less space between the eyes and shortening the length of the brow inside the normal length line.

As part of the consultation, you need to perform a 'mirror consultation' while your client is on the couch. Ask your client to hold the mirror, and brush the eyebrows into shape with the brow/lash brush. Take the orange wood stick and measure the eyebrows at three points.

WHY DON'T YOU...
Have a go at completing SmartScreen worksheet 3 without looking at the information above to see how much you can remember.

SmartScreen B5 worksheet 3

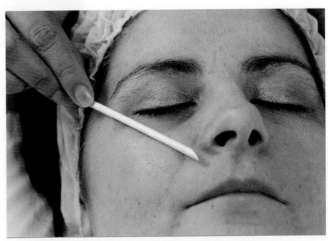

A therapist measuring the length of the brows

1 Begin with the orange wood stick resting next to the right nostril pointing straight up so it's aligned with the inner end of the right eyebrow. Any hairs to the left of the orange wood stick need to be removed to neaten the space between the brows.

2 Asking your client to look up, bring the orange wood stick to an angle so it's still resting against the right nostril but the other end is resting directly over the iris. Where it ends over the brow will indicate where the arch needs to be.

3 Bring the end of the orange wood stick to the outer corner of your client's eye. Any hairs to the right of the orange wood stick need to be removed to prevent 'bringing the eyes down'.

Agree the ideal shape with your client and check they're happy with your recommendations before you proceed with the treatment.

SHAPING THE EYEBROWS

Below is a step-by-step guide to shaping the brows using tweezers only and should be followed for both reshaping and maintenance treatments:

1 Bring the head of the couch down so your client is lying flat or semi-reclined.

2 Take both sets of tweezers out of the Barbicide and dry thoroughly with a tissue.

3 Take the tweezers and stretch the skin between the brows with your index and middle fingers, removing one hair at a time in the direction of hair growth. Work quickly and methodically to remove the bulk of the hair from between the eyebrows.

Removal of eyebrow hairs with automatic tweezers

4 After you've removed a small amount of hairs, wipe the tweezers on a tissue so they don't become overloaded.

5 Move out along the length of each brow, remembering to stretch your client's skin with your index and middle finger and remove the hairs in the direction of hair growth.

6 At this point, focus on developing the specific shape of the brows. Use the magnifying lamp to check that you haven't missed any of the finer hairs.

HANDY HINTS

Use automatic tweezers for bulk removal of thick, dense areas.

HANDY HINTS

Avoid removing hairs from above the brow as this might cause them to appear flatter and lose their arch.

HANDY HINTS

Try working from the side of the couch; you could find the tweezing technique easier to manage.

HANDY HINTS

Remember to stretch the skin throughout the whole treatment to avoid unnecessary discomfort and catching your client's skin in the tweezers.

Removal of eyebrow hairs with manual tweezers

7 Check the shape by coming to the front of the couch and looking at your client straight on.

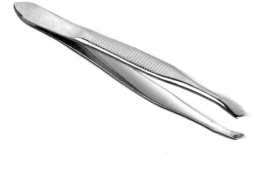

AFTERCARE

When you're finished, hand your client the mirror and ask them for feedback on the finished result. If you need to, go back and make any amendments according to your client's wishes. When both you and your client are satisfied with the result, apply rose water or witch hazel toner to the area to tighten the pores, followed by a soothing agent, such as aloe vera to calm and reduce erythema. It might be necessary to soothe the brows during the shape if erythema occurs quickly, in which case apply a soothing toner using damp cotton pads. Remove the towels protecting your client's hair and clothing, place the used tissues in the waste bin, and ask your client to look at the finished result. Make sure they're happy with the shape you've created before you provide aftercare and home care advice.

HANDY HINTS

Some people are allergic to aloe vera. If you use it after an eyebrow shape, it could cause an allergic reaction and continued use can lead to contact dermatitis. Instead, apply a soothing toner with damp cotton pads followed by another soothing agent, such as after-wax or calamine lotion, which will have the same calming and cooling effects. Remember to check the ingredients so you know it doesn't contain any aloe vera.

Tint can give eyes a very dramatic effect.

Keep your tweezers in a pouch or case to prevent them from becoming blunt and losing their alignment. This will ensure they last longer and work effectively.

TINT EYEBROWS AND LASHES

Before beginning the tint, establish with your client how dark they want to go. This might be your client's first tinting treatment and they might need some guidance from you as to what will suit them best. You need to make sure the brows and lashes complement the colour of their hair and eyes.

TINT COLOURS

salonsystem
Eyelash Dye
STARTER KIT

There are only four tint colours available for a tinting treatment but they can be mixed to create all different types of shades and effects. The colours are:

- grey
- brown
- black
- blue/black

Grey would only be used on a person with grey or white hair and is the lightest colour available. It could be used alone or mixed with brown to produce more depth.

Brown is ideal for people with fair or red hair. It could be used alone or mixed with grey or black to produce more depth.

Black is a dark tint designed to be used on those with very dark brown or black hair. It can be mixed with brown or blue/black to produce more depth.

Blue/black is darker again and is specifically designed to be used on black hair to enhance the natural colour. It should only be mixed with black to produce the darkest shade available: blue/black plus black is a raven black that has a great deal of depth to its colour. It produces a dramatic effect that shouldn't be used on the faint hearted!

SELECTING TINT TO SUIT THE NATURAL HAIR, SKIN AND EYE COLOUR

To produce the most effective result, you need to consider your client's hair, skin and eye colour as this will allow you to choose the right mixture of tint to produce either a natural effect, which will define the eye area, or a more dramatic effect to both enhance and define. Ultimately, the aim is to draw attention to the eye area in a good way!

Before lash tinting

After lash tinting

BLONDE HAIR

People with blonde or fair hair usually have blue eyes and might not necessarily suit a very dark tint. Instead, mix brown with black to provide definition to the eyes without the result being too obvious. However, you might have some clients with white blonde hair and blue eyes who you just know will suit the dramatic effect of black or blue/black and black applied to the lashes. Remember to check with your client that they're happy to go ahead with this. For the brows, you should use only a brown tint to ensure a natural result.

RED HAIR

This is the most stubborn of all the hair colours and is more resistant to the tint. Therefore, you'll need to leave the tint on for longer according to the manufacturer's instructions to produce the most effective result. People with red hair might suit a dramatic effect as well, in which case you can apply blue/black and black or just black on its own to the lashes. If your client doesn't want to have such dark lashes, mix black with brown instead so the eyes are still defined but the result is more natural. For the brows, use a brown tint for a more natural result.

GREY/WHITE HAIR

This hair colour is also resistant to tint because there's no pigment in the hair at all. Depending on your client's personality, they might prefer a natural effect, in which case use a grey tint, or mix the grey with the brown tint to provide more depth. If your client wants a more dramatic result, apply black to the lashes. For the brows, use either a grey, brown/grey or black tint depending on the shade of hair colour and your client's preference.

BROWN HAIR

The depth of your client's hair is will determine the mixture of tint you should use on the lashes and brows. If your client has light brown hair, generally a black tint is ideal for the lashes and a brown for the brows. Whereas if your client has dark brown hair, they might suit blue/black and black on the lashes for added depth, and brown/black on the brows.

BLACK HAIR

As this client has very dark hair, they will naturally suit a darker tint on the lashes and brows. Apply black tint to the brows or, for a deeper shade, mix the black tint with blue/black. Apply the same colour to the lashes for a full effect.

Clients with dark hair will really suit dark lashes

SKIN SENSITIVITY TEST

Before every tinting treatment, your client needs to have a skin sensitivity test at least 24 hours prior to treatment to see if they're allergic to any of the ingredients in the mixture. To do this properly, mix the tint according to the manufacturer's instructions and apply a small amount behind the ear or to the crease of the elbow and leave to dry. If your client doesn't have a skin sensitivity test, there's a risk that your client could be allergic to one or more of the ingredients in the mixture, which could cause a reaction on or around the eye area and, in worse case scenarios, leave your client permanently blind. Permanent damage to the lash follicles can cause the lashes to fall out and not grow back; this can be a traumatic experience for your client. You must safeguard yourself by performing a skin sensitivity test and record it on your client's file as proof the test has taken place. Some salons even go as far as obtaining a signature from their clients as proof they've agreed to the test, further safeguarding them from any **litigation**.

Litigation
Legal action.

Mixing tint

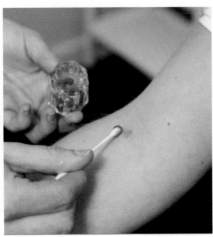

Tint test to the crease of the elbow

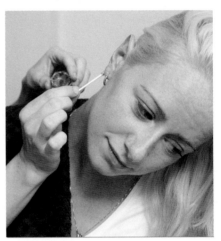

Tint test behind the ear

When the skin test is complete, give your client the necessary advice to follow so they don't affect the results of the test. This should include:

- Avoid cleansing the area after the sensitivity test for at least 24 hours.
- Check for any changes in the appearance of the skin, such as redness, inflammation, irritation, a rash, tingling and burning sensations.
- Inform the salon should any such reactions occur.

There are two results that can occur from a skin test: positive and negative.

POSITIVE RESULT

If your client presents a positive result to a skin sensitivity test, this means they have an allergy to the mixture or an ingredient in the mixture. As a result, the tint cannot go ahead under any circumstances for health and safety reasons, in which case you should offer another treatment.

NEGATIVE RESULT

If your client presents a negative result to a skin sensitivity test, this means they've had no reaction to the mixture or any of the ingredients and the treatment can go ahead safely.

HANDY HINTS

Remember that a skin test is required at least 24 hours before any tinting treatments can take place even if your client is a regular and has had tints done in the past.

DEVELOPING THE TINT

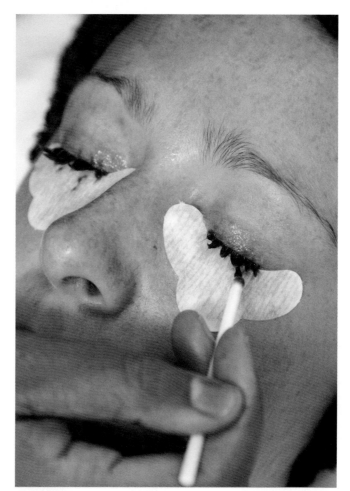

Application of tint to the lashes

Two products are used in the development of the tint: hydrogen peroxide and the tint colour. Hydrogen peroxide is an oxidant, which causes a chemical reaction to take place when it comes into contact with the tint colour. That process is called oxidisation. The tint colour is made up of molecules of permanent dye, which are 'activated' when they come into contact with the hydrogen peroxide.

OXIDISATION
When the tint colour and hydrogen peroxide are mixed together, oxidisation occurs, which produces molecules of pigment that can penetrate between the scales of the cuticle of the hair. These molecules swell and become trapped in the cuticle, permanently changing the colour of the hair until it grows or falls out. To ensure the tint produces the best result, always mix the peroxide and tint colour after you've prepared the skin, and apply immediately after the two products have been mixed into a paste. The longer the mixture is left exposed to the air, the more the oxidisation process will affect the results of the treatment and make the colour less intense.

APPLYING AN EYEBROW TINT
On the next page is a step-by-step guide to tinting the eyebrows.

STEP 1 – Take some petroleum jelly out of the pot with a spatula and apply it around the brow area using a cotton swab. Make sure it doesn't get on any of the actual brow hairs. This provides a barrier between the tint and the skin and prevents staining during the treatment.

STEP 2 – Mix the tint colour and peroxide according to the manufacturer's instructions and your client's preference.

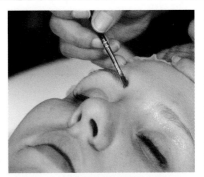

STEP 3 – Lift a small amount of tint from the dappen dish with your tinting brush, and apply against the direction of hair growth, moving from the outer to inner edges of the brows. Take care not to get any tint on the skin. This will ensure the tint lasts that little bit longer as it's applied to the whole hair.

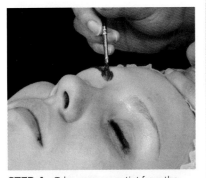

STEP 4 – Take some more tint from the dappen dish and apply in the direction of hair growth from the inner to outer edges of the brows. Make sure each hair is covered without getting any tint on the skin. At this point, you could use an orange wood stick to lift the hairs so you don't stain the skin.

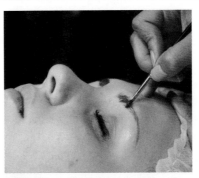

STEP 5 – Repeat this process on the other eyebrow while the tint develops on the first one.

STEP 6 – When you've covered both eyebrows with tint, go back to the first one and remove with damp cotton pads. Make sure all the tint has been thoroughly removed from the brows and the skin isn't stained before you remove the tint from the second brow. If the tint isn't dark enough, repeat the process until you achieve the correct depth of colour.

STEP 7 – Brush the eyebrows into shape.

STEP 8 – Let your client see the finished result and give aftercare and home care advice. Remove the towels and place the tissues in the waste bin. Remember to book your client in for an eyebrow tint in 2–4 weeks to maintain the effects.

APPLYING AN EYELASH TINT

Below is a step-by-step guide to tinting eyelashes.

Before you begin the treatment, bring your client into a semi-reclined position. This reduces the risk of tint running into their eyes.

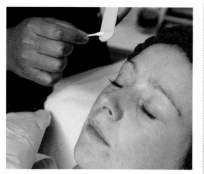

STEP 1 – Take some petroleum jelly out of the pot with a spatula. Petroleum jelly provides a barrier between the tint and the skin so it doesn't get stained.

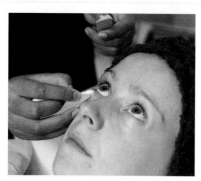

STEP 2 – Ask your client to look up towards the ceiling. Use a cotton swab to apply the petroleum jelly to the lower eyelid, just underneath the lower lashes.

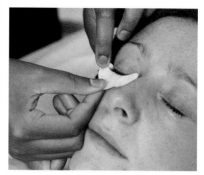

STEP 3 – Gently place an eye shield underneath the lower lashes.

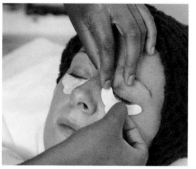

STEP 4 – Ask your client to slowly close their eyes and to keep them closed until you tell them to open them again.

STEP 5 – Apply petroleum jelly to the upper eyelid along the lashline, avoiding the hair.

STEP 6 – Mix the tint colour of your client's choice with hydrogen peroxide according to the manufacturer's instructions.

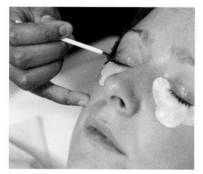

STEP 7 – Using a tinting brush, apply a small amount of tint to the outer edge of the eye at the lashline, and stroke down along the length of the lashes.

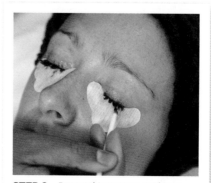

STEP 8 – Repeat this process until every lash has been tinted. Move on to the other eye and repeat these steps. Remind your client to keep their eyes closed and double check you haven't missed out any of the lashes.

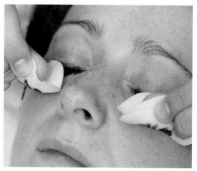

STEP 9 – Leave the tint on for approximately 12 minutes (see the manufacturer's instructions) and ask your client to let you know if they feel stinging, itching or burning.* Remove the eye shield and place it in the waste bin.

STEP 10 – Focus on the first eye you worked on and gently remove the tint by rolling damp cotton swabs along the length of the lashes. Start at the outer edge and move in towards the inner edge of the eye.

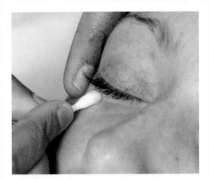

STEP 11 – When you've removed all the tint from the upper lashes, ask your client to keep their eyes closed. Take another damp cotton swab and stroke it along the lower lashes. Repeat this process until you've removed all the tint from both eyes. Ask your client to open their eyes and look towards you.

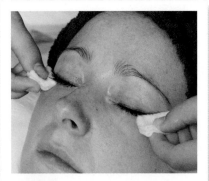

STEP 12 – Take another damp cotton swab and stroke along the lower lashes of each eye. Ask your client to look down and stroke a damp cotton swab along the upper lashline to remove any tint from between the lashes.

STEP 13 – Take two damp cotton pads and gently wipe your client's eyes to remove any traces of the petroleum jelly. You could apply a rehydrating eye product at this point.

STEP 14 – Let your client see the finished result before you give aftercare and home care advice. Remember to book your client in for an eyelash tint in 4–6 weeks to maintain the effects.

HANDY HINTS

If you accidentally stain the skin with tint, use a simple carrier oil, such as grapeseed, and apply to the area with a cotton swab with gentle pressure and the stain will gradually disappear. However, it's important that this doesn't happen continuously as chronic contact dermatitis could occur because of overexposure, which is why adequate protection is required prior to tint application.

* At this point you should complete the consultation card and record the tint colour(s) you've used. If you have spare time, offer your client a soothing scalp massage.

Sometimes you'll find there's too much mixture left in the dish, so you need to check that each hair has been completely covered with tint before you get rid of what's left over. When you're satisfied that each hair has been completely covered, use a paper towel to remove the remaining tint from the dish and place it in the waste bin. Use another paper towel to remove any remaining tint from the brush and wash both in warm soapy water.

WHY DON'T YOU...

Have a go at SmartScreen worksheet 2 to see how much information on eyelash tinting you can remember.

 SmartScreen B5 worksheet 2

HANDY HINTS

Remember to always keep the dappen dish on the trolley. NEVER hold it near your client or place it on the couch next to them as there's a risk of accidentally staining the skin.

WHY TINT MIGHT NOT COLOUR SUCCESSFULLY

Tint might not colour successfully for the following reasons:

- grease on the brow and lashes
- old tint
- the tint was removed too soon
- mascara left on the lashes
- tint mixed incorrectly
- uneven application.

HANDY HINTS

Look and see the different varieties of strip lashes available. Try out different styles.

APPLY ARTIFICIAL EYELASHES

Artificial lashes are becoming increasingly popular. Strip lashes are ideal for an evening out to enhance the overall look, while individual flare lashes are more suited to a bridal look for a more natural effect.

APPLYING STRIP LASHES

STEP 1 – Separate the lashes by brushing them with the brow/lash brush.

STEP 2 – Measure the strip lash against your client's natural eye shape. The shorter lashes fit the inside of the eye and the longer lashes fit the outer eye area.

STEP 3 – Cut the width to fit the natural eye with a pair of scissors. Reduce the length of the lashes using a feathering technique with the scissors to maintain a natural effect.

STEP 4 – Place a small amount of adhesive in a foil-lined container.

STEP 5 – Apply a small amount of adhesive to the base of the lash using the rounded end of the orange wood stick and following the manufacturer's instructions. The adhesive is white initially but dries clear and takes up to five minutes to set.

STEP 6 – Hold the strip lash with sterile tweezers. Position the strip lash as close as possible to the base of the natural lashes, approximately 2 mm from the edge of both the inner corner and outer edge of the eyelid.

STEP 7 – Gently press the strip lash and natural lashes together from corner to corner of the eye. Repeat this process on the other eye.

STEP 8 – Brush the lashes gently from under the natural lashes to blend both false and natural lashes together.

STEP 9 – Ask your client to check the finished result in the mirror and provide aftercare and home care advice.

Why not try experimenting with fashion and special occasion lashes? Application is exactly the same as above.

REMOVING STRIP LASHES

Follow the steps below to remove strip lashes. Remember to wash synthetic lashes in warm soapy water and rinse them in warm water before storage. If strip lashes are composed of natural hair, follow the manufacturer's instructions on how to clean them without causing damage.

You can also use a storage stand to retain the curl of strip lashes. Instead of using tweezers, grip them with a lash placement tool for easier application.

STEP 1 – Support the eyelid at the corner of the eye and gently peel the strip away from the lid, working from the outer to inner corner of the eye. Using tweezers, gently peel the adhesive off the strip lashes.

STEP 2 – To maintain the curl of the lashes when they're clean, place them side by side on a tissue. Wrap them around a pencil and secure in place with a rubber band.

STEP 3 – When the curl has been established, return the lashes to their original container for storage.

When you've removed the lashes, apply a rehydrating eye product to your client's eye area.

WHY DON'T YOU...
Read through SmartScreen handout 10 for further details on the application and removal of strip lashes.

 SmartScreen B5 handout 10

APPLYING INDIVIDUAL FLARE LASHES

In this step-by-step guide, you'll learn how to apply individual flare lashes to the entire width of the eye. However, this can be both time consuming and expensive, so individual flare lashes tend to be applied at the outer corners to enhance the natural lashes.

STEP 1 – Separate the lashes by brushing them with a brow/lash brush.

STEP 2 – Select the shorter lashes to fit the inside of the eye, using the longer lashes to fit the outer eye area.

STEP 3 – Place a small amount of adhesive in a foil-lined container or on a disposable spatula.

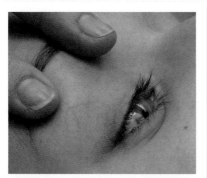

STEP 4 – Ask your client to look down and, with one hand, lift the brow to support the eyelid area.

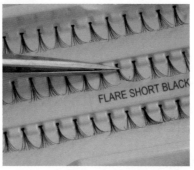

STEP 5 – Use sterilised tweezers to remove the shorter lashes from the tray, holding each lash as close to the centre as possible.

STEP 6 – Pass the 'bulb' of the lash through the adhesive, following the manufacturer's instructions. The adhesive is white initially but dries clear and takes up to five minutes to set.

STEP 7 – Start the application 2 mm in from the inner corner of the eyes.

STEP 8 – Use a stroking movement to apply false lashes on top of natural lashes. Use sufficient adhesive to cover at least half of the length of the natural lashes.

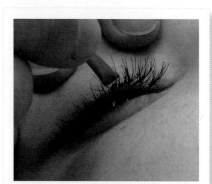

STEP 9 – Secure the false lash as close to the root of the natural lash as possible to create a natural effect.

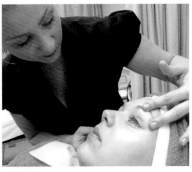

STEP 10 – Check the lash is positioned correctly before moving on and repeating this process along the width of the eye. If the lash is incorrectly positioned, remove it while the adhesive is still wet and reapply.

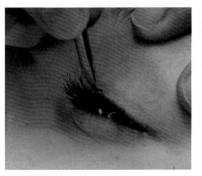

STEP 11 – Continue to apply lashes one at a time, working each eye alternately. Use the appropriate length to follow the contour of the eyes and this will ensure application is even, smooth and gradual.

STEP 12 – Ask your client to check the result in the mirror.

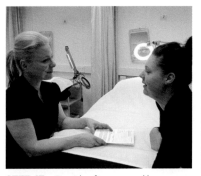

STEP 13 – Provide aftercare and home care advice.

WHY DON'T YOU...
Find out what types of strip and individual flare lashes are available to buy both online and in the shops, and think about what occasions or make-up styles they would suit.

REMOVING INDIVIDUAL FLARE LASHES

STEP 1 – Place damp cotton pads under the lower eyelashes. Ask your client to close their eyes for the duration of the removal process to avoid getting any product in their eyes.

STEP 2 – Support the eye area with your free hand.

STEP 3 – Dip the end of a cotton swab into adhesive remover/solvent and gently apply down the length of the false lash until the adhesive has fully dissolved.

STEP 4 – As the adhesive dissolves gently, stroke down with the cotton swab so the false lash is resting on the cotton pad.

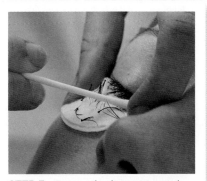

STEP 5 – Remove the damp cotton pad with the false lashes and place in the waste bin.

STEP 6 – Apply a damp cotton pad to soothe the eye area and repeat this process on the other eye.

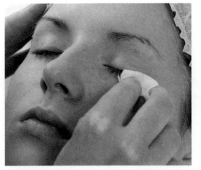

STEP 7 – You could apply a rehydrating eye product at this point to complete the treatment.

WHY ARTIFICIAL LASHES MIGHT NOT ADHERE

Artificial lashes might not adhere successfully for the following reasons:

- grease on the lashes
- mascara left on the lashes
- not enough adhesive on the artificial lashes
- too much adhesive on the artificial lashes that won't dry.

WHY DON'T YOU...
Have a go at SmartScreen worksheet 4 to see how much you can remember about artificial lashes.

 SmartScreen B5 worksheet 4

Some of your clients will want to experiment with alternative styles; some will want a natural look.

PROVIDE AFTERCARE ADVICE

The following aftercare advice is specific to each individual treatment and should be given before your client leaves to ensure they don't experience any contra-actions and the effects last as long as possible. Remember home care advice is client specific and will vary depending on your client's personal requirements and hair growth. For example, a client with fair hair who prefers dark eyelashes might need to return sooner than six weeks for an eyelash tint, whereas a client who has individual lashes for a special occasion, such as a wedding, will need specific advice on how to look after them so they last as long as possible.

AFTERCARE ADVICE FOR EYEBROW SHAPING

Erythema is a normal reaction after an eyebrow shape due to the stimulation of the hair follicles. This usually goes down after the first couple of hours depending on your client's skin sensitivity. Give the following aftercare advice after every eyebrow shape to stop the reaction getting worse, and suggest that your client follows it for up to 24 hours:

- Avoid heat treatments including sauna, steam and hot tubs as the pores are open and infection could occur.
- Avoid UV exposure as hyper-pigmentation might occur and infection might enter open pores.
- Avoid swimming as irritation might occur.
- Avoid applying make-up to the area as infection could occur.
- Apply a soothing antiseptic cream, such as aloe vera, to calm and soothe erythema.
- Groom the eyebrows into shape daily using a brow/lash brush, although a clean toothbrush will also do the job!
- Return for the next treatment in 4–6 weeks depending on previous hair removal treatment results.

AFTERCARE ADVICE FOR EYEBROW AND EYELASH TINTING

- Avoid using an oil-based eye make-up remover as this will affect the longevity of the tint.
- Avoid rubbing and touching the eyes as this could cause cross-infection.
- For eyebrow tinting, return for the next treatment in 2–4 weeks depending on the rate of growth of your client's hair.
- For eyelash tinting, return for the next treatment in 4–6 weeks depending on the rate of growth of your client's hair.

AFTERCARE ADVICE FOR ARTIFICIAL LASHES

- Do not touch the eyes for two hours following treatment to allow the adhesive to dry fully.
- Avoid rubbing the eyes in general as this will loosen artificial lashes.
- Avoid using an oil-based eye make-up remover as this will dissolve the adhesive.

- Avoid heat as it could affect the lashes, making them frizzy if they're synthetic.
- Do not attempt to remove individual lashes – this will result in a loss of natural lashes. Instead, return to the salon for a safe and effective removal of any artificial lashes.
- Use an oil-based eye make-up remover to dissolve the lash adhesive when removing strip lashes. This avoids tearing out any natural lashes.
- If you lose an eyelash, return to the salon for a replacement fitting.

CONTRA-ACTIONS

The following contra-actions are specific to each individual treatment, so if they occur during or immediately after the treatment, it's important you know how to deal with them so that your client isn't injured in any way.

CONTRA-ACTIONS TO EYEBROW SHAPING

- Excessive erythema: occurs because the hair has been removed from the root of the follicle and is a minor histamine response. Apply an antiseptic agent, such as aloe vera, to soothe the area and reduce erythema; or, if severe, apply a cold compress first. You can prevent excessive erythema by stretching the skin properly.

CONTRA-ACTIONS TO EYELASH AND EYEBROW TINTING

- Watery eyes: this could be caused by tint entering the eyes.
- Smarting of the eyes following treatment: this can be a natural occurrence for some clients but, to be safe, check that no tint has entered the eyes.
- Allergic reaction to petroleum jelly.
- Allergic reaction to the tint.
- Tint entering the eyes if your client opens her eyes during the treatment.
- A tingling sensation is normal during an eyelash tint; however, burning, irritation and stinging aren't and can be caused by tint in the eyes.

The contra-actions listed above should be dealt with in the same way. Use an eyebath of purified or distilled water to rinse any product that has entered the eye in the following way:

1 Tilt your client's head to one side and support with a small rolled-up towel.
2 Place a small bowl of cool water beside the temple.
3 Rinse from the inner to the outer edge of the eye with a sponge or a cotton pad and repeat until you've soothed the area and removed all the product.
4 Repeat on the other eye before you apply damp cotton pads to each eye to soothe the area.

CONTRA-ACTIONS TO ARTIFICIAL LASHES

- Watery eyes: this might be due to adhesive entering the eyes and should be treated with an eyebath.

Applying an eye bath after identifying a contra-action

- Lashes sticking together: apply adhesive remover to the lashes with a cotton swab and run along the lashes until the adhesive has dissolved enough to separate the lashes. If this isn't possible, continue until all the adhesive has dissolved and restart the treatment.
- Adhesive or adhesive remover entering the eye: apply an eyebath and damp cotton pads as outlined previously for an eyelash tint.

CONTACT DERMATITIS

This is the skin's response to an allergen or irritant it has been exposed to for the first time (acute) or over a period of time (chronic). It's identified by dryness and cracking, a rash, blisters or weals and is accompanied by irritation or burning, depending on the severity. If this occurs during any eye treatment, stop the treatment immediately and act fast to reduce the reaction as best you can:

- Apply a cold compress to the affected area (after applying an eyebath if this occurs during an eyelash tint) until the reaction has begun to subside.
- Apply a soothing lotion to the area, such as aloe vera. This will help heal and cool the skin and reduce erythema.

Ensure you give your client the following advice to stop the condition getting worse:

- Apply a soothing lotion, such as calamine or aloe vera, to soothe the area.
- If blisters occur, continue applying cold water compresses for around 30 minutes, three times a day.
- Antihistamines can relieve swelling and irritation.

Contact dermatitis is the result of exposure to an irritant or allergen, which is why it's so important to stop the treatment as soon as you recognise a reaction. Explain to your client clearly what's going on and stress the importance of them following the aftercare advice. If your client suffers from contact dermatitis and you discover this on consultation, try to identify what the cause is before going ahead with the treatment to ensure this reaction doesn't occur. As a therapist, make sure you're adequately protected when you're using chemicals, such as hydrogen peroxide and lash adhesive, by wearing gloves or a barrier cream to protect your skin. In the event of any chemical coming into contact with your skin, wash your hands immediately and dry properly.

HOME CARE ADVICE

This is more client specific and will vary from client to client depending on what treatment they've received, the rate of growth of their hair and their particular needs. The home care for each treatment is detailed below.

HOME CARE ADVICE FOR EYEBROWS

- Continue to apply a soothing agent if the area still feels warm over the next 24 hours.
- Use an eyebrow pencil to enhance the eyebrow shape and add volume to thin eyebrows.

HOME CARE ADVICE FOR EYELASH AND EYEBROW TINTING

- Apply a clear mascara to enhance the intensity of the tint, especially for darker tints.
- If your client has had only an eyelash tint or an eyebrow tint, recommend they think about having both treatments in future to enhance the eye area and give a more polished result.
- Use an eyeliner to draw even more attention to the eyes and further enhance an eyelash tint.
- Use an eyebrow pencil to give added volume to thin eyebrows.

HOME CARE ADVICE FOR ARTIFICIAL LASHES

- As far as strip lashes are concerned, apply mascara afterwards to blend the artificial lashes with the natural lashes.
- Apply thick liquid liner to the upper lashes to enhance the dramatic effect created with this look.
- As strip lashes are generally designed to last for one occasion and not necessarily for any length of time, advise your client to be careful when they remove them if they cannot come back for professional removal. Suggest they use an oil-based make-up remover to dissolve the adhesive and gently remove the artificial lashes without pulling out any natural ones.
- Individual lashes are designed to last a little longer than strip lashes. Recommend the use of mascara to blend the artificial lashes in with the natural lashes.
- If your client is unable to return for professional lash removal, give them the same advice as you would for strip lash removal.
- Apply eyeliner to enhance the eyes further and draw more attention to them.

END OF UNIT SUMMARY

Now you're at the end of the unit and before you test your knowledge with the end of unit assessment, check the following list to see if you feel confident in all the areas covered. If there are still any areas you're unsure of, go back over them in the book and ask your tutor for additional support:

- maintain safe and effective methods of working when enhancing the appearance of eyebrows and eyelashes
- consult, plan and prepare for the treatment with clients
- shape eyebrows
- tint eyebrows and lashes
- apply artificial eyelashes
- provide aftercare advice.

Now you feel confident in the eye treatment procedures and the theory behind them, let's test your knowledge to see how much you've retained. These questions will help you to revise what you've learnt in this chapter.

Turn to pages 401–405 for the answers.

1 Why is it important to ensure adequate lighting for all eye treatments?

2 Explain why you should perform a mirror consultation before an eyebrow shape.

3 List the contra-indications to eye treatments that require medical referral.

4 List the contra-indications to eye treatments that require modifications, and explain how you would apply these modifications.

5 Why is it important to ensure the eyebrow shape complements a person's face shape?

6 Explain how and why we measure the eyebrows before shaping them.

7 What type of eyebrow shape is most suited to a heart face shape?

8 Why do square face shapes suit a tapered arch of medium thickness?

9 What corrections would you make to the eyebrows for a client with wide-set eyes?

10 Explain the term oxidisation.

11 Why are red and grey hair the most resistant to tinting?

12 Explain why it's important to make sure the finished tint result complements the natural hair colour.

13 What type of look would individual lashes complement the most?

14 Explain how strip lashes are applied and removed.

15 When would you recommend strip lashes?

16 Explain how you should care for and store strip lashes.

17 How should you apply individual lashes?

18 Explain the aftercare advice you would give to a client after each eye treatment.

19 Identify **one** contra-action to each eye treatment and state how you would deal with it.

20 Explain how you would identify contact dermatitis, how you would deal with such a reaction and how this affects the treatment.

WHY DON'T YOU...
Test your knowledge further by logging into SmartScreen and completing the revision activities before attempting the sample GOLA revision questions.

B6
CARRY OUT WAXING SERVICES

Waxing will be one of the most popular and profitable treatments you perform as a beauty therapist. There are many products available for temporary hair removal but none provide the finish and result that is delivered by a professional waxing treatment. In this chapter you'll discover how and when to apply the appropriate wax to suit a person's hair growth and skin and how to give appropriate aftercare and home care advice so your client can maintain the benefits.

In this chapter you'll learn how to:

- maintain safe and effective methods of working when removing hair by waxing
- consult, plan and prepare for waxing treatments with clients
- remove unwanted hair
- provide aftercare advice.

HANDY HINTS

When you're providing a waxing treatment, it's important to use the skills you've learnt in the following units:

Unit G20   Ensure responsibility for actions to reduce risks to health and safety

Unit G18   Promote additional services or products to clients

Unit G4   Fulfil salon reception duties.

HANDY HINTS

Permanent methods of hair removal are known as epilation, and temporary methods of hair removal are known as depilation.

WHY DON'T YOU...

Familiarise yourself with the Acts listed here before continuing with this unit.

WHY DON'T YOU...

Check out habia.org for the latest edition of the waxing code of practice. It's recommended that you work to this code of practice as it outlines the National Occupational Standards (NOS) and guidelines for performing effective and safe waxing treatments. This includes information on personal presentation, PPE, maintaining hygiene and safety throughout the waxing treatment, and why it's important for all beauty therapists to adhere to this code of practice.

WHY DON'T YOU...

Work through SmartScreen worksheet 4 to identify the differences between sterilisation and disinfection and when you would use them in preparation for a waxing treatment.

SmartScreen B6 worksheet 4

MAINTAIN SAFE AND EFFECTIVE METHODS OF WORKING WHEN REMOVING HAIR BY WAXING

When you're providing any waxing treatment, you must maintain high standards of hygiene and adhere to the relevant health and safety procedures and legislation. The following legislation comes into play as part of this unit:

- Data Protection Act (DPA)
- Disability Discrimination Act (DDA)
- Control of Substances Hazardous to Health (COSHH) Regulations
- Reporting of Injuries, Diseases and Dangerous Occurrences Regulations (RIDDOR)
- Personal Protective Equipment (PPE) at Work Regulations.

Each of these Acts is described fully in Unit G20 along with all other health and safety legislation.

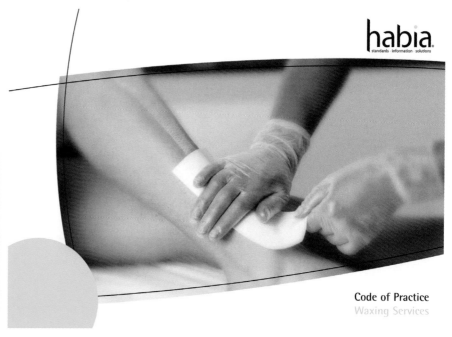

habia.
standards · information · solutions

Code of Practice
Waxing Services

SALON ENVIRONMENT

Now you have an understanding of the health and safety procedures affecting waxing treatments and the code of practice you should follow, focus your attention on the salon environment and setting up your work area. To prevent the risk of cross-infection, sterilise all your metal implements in an autoclave or glass bead steriliser. Disinfect all work surfaces with a suitable disinfectant before you set up your work area with the following equipment on the top shelf:

- wax heater(s)
- wax (warm and/or hot)
- wax strips (paper and/or muslin)
- disposable spatulas (large and small)

- an orange wood stick
- a small bowl with dry cotton pads and cotton swabs
- tissues
- an eyebrow brush
- talc-free powder
- disposable gloves.

Place the following items on the second shelf:
- a jar containing Barbicide
- an apron
- disposable panties
- pre-wax lotion
- after-wax lotion
- after-wax oil
- barrier cream, such as petroleum jelly
- manual tweezers
- scissors
- a hand mirror
- a headband.

On the bottom shelf you should have a small towel, the client record card and any aftercare advice leaflets you want to give to your client at the end of the treatment. When you've set up your trolley, check the wax heater is in a level position and will not fall, and that it has passed a PAT test less than 12 months ago. Turn it on and make sure the dial isn't too high. Follow the manufacturer's instructions when you're using wax heaters as they all have different thermostats and, as a result, different temperature settings. You'll need to continually check the temperature of your wax before and during all waxing treatments.

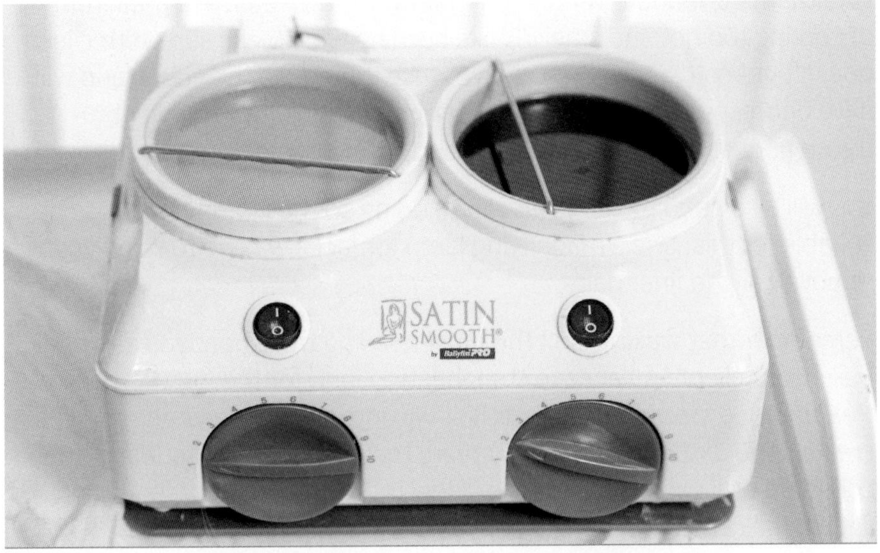

HANDY HINTS

Petroleum jelly can be applied to certain contra-indications that restrict a waxing treatment so you know the wax won't stick to the hair. A hairy mole on the lower calf is a perfect example of when to use petroleum jelly.

HANDY HINTS

Refer to Unit G20 for how to sterilise and disinfect your equipment.

HANDY HINTS

Small towel: same size as the hand towels you might see in a bathroom.

Medium towel: double the size of a hand towel.

Large towel: about the same size as a bath towel.

Make sure your wax heater is in a level position before you start the treatment.

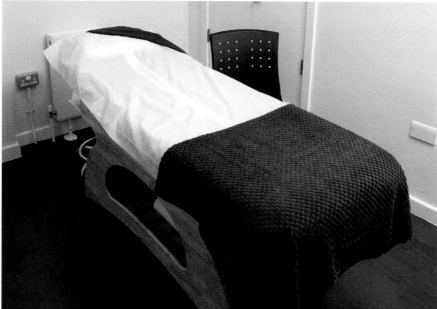

A treatment couch ready for a waxing treatment

HANDY HINTS

Remember that you'll need informed and signed parental or guardian consent if your client is a minor aged under 16 years and a parent or guardian should be present throughout the treatment.

Protect the treatment couch with a sheet; plastic sheets are recommended as they're easily maintained and you can remove wax spillages with an appropriate disinfectant. Place a pillow at the top of the sheet to support the neck and cover both lengthways with couch roll, split in half to minimise waste and protect the treatment couch. Place a large or small towel on the couch for your client to cover themselves with. The size of towel should reflect the treatment you're performing and maintain your client's modesty.

Check the overall environment by referring back to 'Creating the right environment' in Unit G20, and focus your attention on ventilation. Remember that the wax can get very hot very quickly and give off fumes. This heat can warm the treatment area up just as quickly so make sure there's adequate ventilation to prevent the treatment area from becoming too hot and smelling like burning wax. Make sure your client doesn't get cold as they're inactive while they're on the couch and will have undressed to some degree. Communicate with your client throughout to check they're warm and comfortable.

You will also need to see what you're doing so the lighting needs to be suitable for this. Use a magnifying lamp for facial waxing to see if you've removed all the finer hairs.

Remember that waxing isn't the most relaxing treatment you can offer. Make your client feel at ease straight away (and for the duration of the treatment), especially if it's their first waxing, and the environment you create should reflect this. If you create the right environment and appear confident and calm, your client will feel relaxed in your presence and this should make the experience enjoyable for both of you.

Waxed legs can give your clients the confidence to wear whatever they want!

Check you have a lined metal pedal bin for all your hazardous waste and move it to an appropriate hazardous waste bin when it's full. This is also referred to as a clinical waste bin and is yellow or orange in colour. Disposal of such waste must meet local authority requirements.

The following items are considered hazardous or contaminated waste as they might carry bodily fluids and even blood. They must be disposed of in the hazardous waste bin and kept separate from general waste to prevent cross-infection:

- large and small disposable spatulas
- wax strips
- gloves
- aprons
- cotton pads
- tissues
- disposable panties
- couch roll.

When your client has left, wash laundry from the treatment couch at 60°C to ensure it's hygienically clean and all bacteria has been killed.

Check your own comfort by making sure all the equipment and materials you need are close by to prevent overstretching, and that your chair (if required) has adequate back support and is height adjustable. If you need to stand up for the treatment, make sure your posture is correct to avoid fatigue and injury. Look at Unit G20 for further details on personal preparation.

HANDY HINTS

Paper wax strips: less expensive than muslin but can be difficult to use. Ideal for the experienced therapist or a client who is allergic to muslin.

Muslin wax strips: more flexible and easier to use than paper strips and better for inexperienced therapists. However, they're also more expensive.

HANDY HINTS

Remember to NEVER re-dip spatulas that have blood or bodily fluids on them during a waxing treatment as this carries the risk of cross-infection; place them in the hazardous bin after use. Re-using wax strips during a treatment is acceptable; just remember to throw them away at the end of each treatment.

CONSULT, PLAN AND PREPARE FOR WAXING TREATMENTS WITH CLIENTS

As you know, it's always important to perform a consultation prior to any treatment and to obtain your client's signature before beginning the treatment.

Some clients book waxing treatments when they're menstruating so it's important that you advise them that this will affect their skin sensitivity. For example, many clients find they're more sensitive and have a lower pain threshold, while others find their skin can become more reactive to products. Discuss this with your client and re-schedule the appointment if necessary. To prepare your client for the treatment, tell them what clothing they need to remove, if necessary and, for bikini line waxing, give them the option of wearing disposable panties as well.

WHY DON'T YOU...

Read through SmartScreen handout 8 for more details on client consultation for waxing treatments.

SmartScreen B6 handout 8

HANDY HINTS

Remember you'll meet clients from many different cultural backgrounds so it's important at the consultation to make them fully aware of any disrobing required to enable the treatment to be performed to its full potential. That way if your client has any concerns or questions, they can be discussed without causing any embarrassment or unease.

CONTRA-INDICATIONS

As part of the consultation, check your client has no contra-indications, although you might not find this out until you come to examine the area to be treated. The following is a list of the contra-indications that will prevent waxing treatments, and require medical referral:

- Severe and infectious skin conditions: the treatment could make the condition worse, secondary infection could occur and there's a risk of cross-infection.
- Severe varicose veins: painful for your client and could cause the veins to burst and cause an ulcer.

Do not under any circumstances carry out a waxing treatment if your client displays any of the above contra-indications. Explain to your client that they're displaying signs of a contra-indication, without naming it, and that to work over it could worsen the condition or cause infection. Refer them to their GP where necessary.

The following contra-indications also prevent waxing treatments but do not necessarily require medical referral:

- Thin or fragile skin: chance of bruising or tearing the skin open.
- Scar tissue under six months old: risk of opening the scar and causing a secondary infection.
- Certain medication, such as steroids: these thin the skin and increase the likelihood of the skin tearing or reacting.
- Heat rash: skin will not tolerate more heat if it's already hot and irritated.
- Sunburn: skin will be hot and painful and there could be a risk of further burning.
- Known allergies: many clients are allergic to ingredients such as rosin, which is found in sticking plasters and wax. An allergic (histamine) reaction could cause the skin to swell, become hot and irritated.

The following conditions could restrict a waxing treatment:

- Diabetes: lack of tactile sensation could allow burning to occur and the skin is often thin and fragile which can make tearing and bruising more likely.
- Moles: have their own cellular structure and waxing could alter this.
- Infected ingrowing hairs: will be painful and sore with the risk of secondary infection.
- Skin tags: could be removed with waxing and will bleed with the risk of secondary infection.
- Medication: could irritate the skin and make it fragile.

You also need to make your client aware of the possible contra-actions that might occur as a result of the waxing treatment so they're not alarmed in any way. Descriptions of such contra-actions can be found under 'Provide aftercare advice'.

SKIN TESTS

Before all waxing treatments, you should carry out a test patch and skin sensitivity test to identify whether or not the treatment can go ahead, or whether it needs to be modified. Usually, these tests are carried out prior

HANDY HINTS

Cross-infection occurs as a result of poor hygiene practices and poor knowledge of skin conditions that carry the risk of cross-infection. This is why you must familiarise yourself with the various conditions that are infectious so you know that you're not putting yourself and others at risk of becoming infected. This also explains why you must wear PPE and wash your hands before, during (if required) and after every treatment.

HANDY HINTS

More information about contra-indications can be found in the anatomy and physiology chapter.

to the intended wax treatment. Perform a skin sensitivity test on, or close to, the area to be treated. Apply pre-wax and wipe away, then apply a layer of wax and remove with whichever wax strip you plan to use during the treatment. Apply after-wax oil and lotion to soothe, advising your client to inform you of any reactions over the following 24 hours. If your client does report a reaction, they're allergic to something, be it a product or the wax strip, in which case the treatment cannot go ahead as overexposure could lead to contact dermatitis.

However, with facial waxing, it's better to perform the test on the inside of the wrist. Explain to your client that warm wax will feel warm and nothing more, while hot wax will feel instantly hot but the heat should not linger or burn.

VISUAL EXAMINATIONS

When you've completed the consultation and your client is suitably prepared, carry out a visual examination of the skin and the hair. You'll need to identify:

- hair growth patterns
- density of hair growth
- hair type
- skin type and condition
- direction of hair growth.

Identifying these points allows you to choose a suitable wax for your client's skin hair type and helps you apply it in the right direction.

BEFORE THE TREATMENT

Sometimes, you might need to trim the hair first if it's too long or it could result in discomfort and bruising. Place the trimmed hair on a clean tissue before putting it in the bin. Now you're ready to start the treatment, agree a plan with your client so they know what to expect and are happy with your approach. Place them in a suitable position for the treatment and ask them to remove all necessary clothing and jewellery. Make sure the rest of their clothing and hair is adequately protected.

Below is a table of the industry accepted times for different waxing treatments. It's important you adhere to these times to ensure cost effectiveness and to keep your clients happy. These times exclude consultation.

Treatment	Times
Full leg wax	45 minutes
Half leg wax	30 minutes
Bikini line wax	15 minutes
Underarm wax	15 minutes
Eyebrow wax	15 minutes
Upper lip wax	10 minutes
Chin wax	10 minutes

A skin sensitivity test before waxing

WHY DON'T YOU...
Work through SmartScreen worksheet 5 to test your knowledge on the differences during the hair growth cycle.

SmartScreen B6 worksheet 5

Make sure your waxing treatments stick to industry accepted times, otherwise your clients won't return.

REMOVE UNWANTED HAIR

When you've completed the consultation and your client is ready for their treatment, check you've chosen the right type of wax for the hair type and skin condition. You need to choose from hot or warm wax and know the effects and benefits of each so you can make an informed decision.

HOT WAX

The main ingredients in hot wax are beeswax, derived from honeycomb, and resin. Soothing agents, such as azulene or chamomile can also be present; tea tree is also a common ingredient because of its antibacterial properties. Below is a general guideline to the application of hot wax, but you should check the manufacturer's instructions prior to use to ensure you're using it correctly.

Hot wax melts at around 50°C, with the working temperature at approximately 55°C. As the wax cools on the skin, it solidifies and adheres to the hair rather than the skin. This means there's less of a risk of bruising and the hair removal is much more effective. This treatment is more beneficial for coarse, deep rooted terminal hair found in the pubic regions, although it can be used on the eyebrows as well.

Layer the hot wax on the treatment area in patches, approximately 5 cm by 10 cm depending on the area being worked on, keeping the edges slightly thicker for easier removal. Apply the first layer against the direction of hair growth. Apply thickly and add subsequent layers in a 'figure of eight' motion to build up the thickness of the wax, until it's several layers thick. Make sure the lower edge is always a little thicker and is spread on to a hair free area, so that when you remove the wax, it's less painful for your client. Leave the wax to cool for a minute and tap to check it's 'tacky' in consistency, then flick up the thicker edge with your fingers until you have enough to grasp with your hand. Ask your client to stretch the skin and use your own free hand to stretch beneath the treatment area. Remove the wax in the opposite direction to the hair growth and place the wax in a lined bin for hazardous waste. Repeat this process until you've removed all the hair, making sure you don't wax the same area twice.

HANDY HINTS

Always check the manufacturer's instructions for working temperatures as these can vary.

HANDY HINTS

With modern hot waxes and their refined ingredients, it's not necessary to build up so many layers as the wax is more pliable and grips the hairs better. Remember the first layer is always applied against the direction of hair growth.

HANDY HINTS

Apply a light dusting of talc-free powder prior to hot wax in the opposite direction to the hair growth to lift the hair and allow for better adhesion of wax to the area and a smoother result.

HANDY HINTS

As hot wax is more expensive than warm wax, it's not cost effective to use on larger areas, such as the legs, but is nearly always used for bikini and underarm wax treatments.

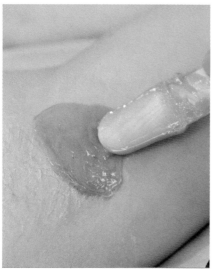

Application of hot wax to underarm

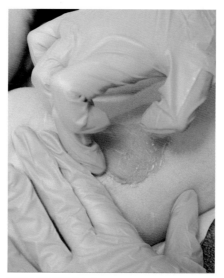

Removal of hot wax

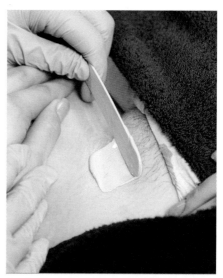

Application of hot wax to bikini line

WARM WAX

The main ingredients in warm wax don't necessarily include wax; instead, they include rubber latex, honey and solvents. Soothing agents, such as aloe vera, lavender or cucumber can be added to reduce skin reaction.

Warm wax doesn't set in the same way as hot wax and so application is completely different. Below is a general guideline to the application of warm wax, but you should check the manufacturer's instructions prior to use to make sure you're using it correctly.

To provide the most effective treatment, apply a thin layer of wax, keeping the spatula at a 90° angle, following the direction of hair growth (NEVER apply warm wax against the direction of hair growth as this will be painful for your client) and place a wax strip on top. Use your free hand to stretch the skin beneath and quickly remove the wax strip in the opposite direction to the hair growth.

The melting temperature of warm wax is 47°C, with the working temperature at 43°C; it should feel warm on application but not hot. As warm wax is relatively inexpensive, it's much more cost effective on larger areas, such as the legs and more effective at removing **vellus hair** as this has shallow roots and isn't as stubborn as **terminal hair**. However, it can be used on more intimate areas if a client's hair isn't that stubborn and deep rooted.

Always apply pre-wax lotion to the treatment area prior to waxing to cleanse the skin of grease and debris. After-wax oil is designed to remove wax left on the skin at the end of the treatment. After-wax lotion soothes and rehydrates the skin after the treatment, and often contains soothing and cooling agents, such as cucumber and aloe vera.

HANDY HINTS

Warm wax can also be applied via a roller system or tube system, which enables the therapist to work much more quickly than with the spatula method, although it's not as skilled. Some developments even eliminate the risk of cross-infection as a 'gate mechanism' stops the wax from re-entering the tube.

Vellus hair

Soft fine downy hair found on the face and body.

Terminal hair

The eyebrows, eyelashes and scalp hair, as well as pubic hair.

WHY DON'T YOU...
Refer to the anatomy and physiology chapter to refresh your memory on the hair growth cycle and the structure of the hair.

B6 WAXING

THE WAXING TREATMENT

As you become more experienced, you'll feel more confident in your ability. This will enable you to improve your technique and the speed at which you work.

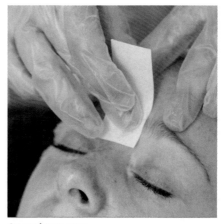

An eyebrow wax

FACIAL WAXING

Now that you're ready to begin the waxing treatment, ensure both you and your client are properly prepared. Below are the steps you should follow before a facial waxing:

- Check your client is lying supine and has adequate support. Place a pillow or bolster under the neck or knees to support the vertebrae.
- Wrap your client's hair in a small towel for protection.
- Wash your hands so they're disinfected (refer to Unit G20 for further information on the importance of this).
- After you've performed a visual examination and determined if there are any contra-indications, apply the pre-wax lotion to a dry cotton pad and wipe over the treatment area to cleanse. Blot dry with a tissue.
- Take a small disposable spatula and test the temperature of the wax on your own and your client's intended treatment area or wrist. If it's OK, you can begin the treatment. This is in keeping with the testing stated on pages 148–149.
- Remember to maintain the correct posture throughout for your own comfort.
- Check client comfort and wellbeing throughout the treatment.

Note that the following waxing procedures are designed for warm wax application only.

Eyebrow wax

Cut your wax strips to the right size by folding the wax strip in half and cutting; fold in half again and cut; fold in half one last time and cut. This is the perfect sized wax strip for an eyebrow shape.

- Perform a measure and mirror consultation as outlined in Unit B5 to determine the most suitable eyebrow shape.
- Begin at the centre of the eyebrows and apply an even layer of wax in the direction of hair growth.
- Take a small wax strip, place it directly on top of the wax and apply firm pressure with the pads of your fingers.

HANDY HINTS

When you're removing wax, avoid pulling the strip directly up at the same time as this will cause the hair to snap at the surface.

HANDY HINTS

Remember to communicate clearly with your client throughout the treatment to ensure they're comfortable and know exactly what you want them to do.

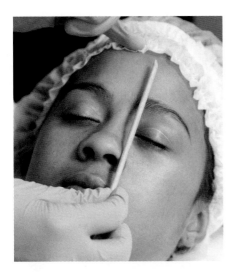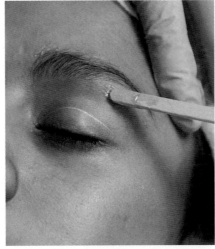

- Using one hand, stretch the skin and lift the eyebrows with your index and middle fingers. This will minimise client discomfort.
- With your other hand, quickly remove the wax strip in the opposite direction to the hair growth.
- Repeat this process until you've removed the bulk of the hair in this area, taking care not to wax the same area twice.
- Move to the side of the eyebrows and apply an even layer of wax in the direction of hair growth at the outer edge of the eyebrow.

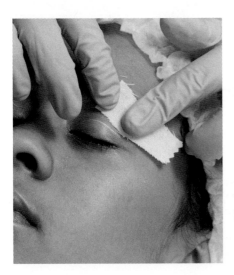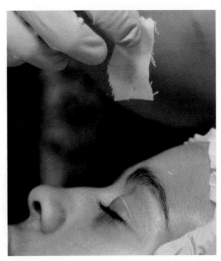

- Apply a new wax strip to the area with the pads of your fingers. With your free hand, stretch and lift the eyebrow before quickly removing the wax strip in the opposite direction to the hair growth.
- Repeat this process, working your way towards the inner edge of the brow before moving on to the other eyebrow.
- You might find there are still some strays, in which case use manual tweezers to remove them.
- Brush the eyebrows into shape before applying after-wax oil to remove any left-over wax, followed by after-wax lotion to soothe the skin.
- Check client satisfaction by letting them see the finished result in the mirror.
- Give aftercare and home care advice (see page 163).
- Rebook your client for 2–4 weeks' time.

HANDY HINTS

Initially, you might find it easier to use a new small wax strip for each area of the brow. However, with experience comes confidence and you might find that in time you're able to perform an eyebrow wax with only one or two small wax strips.

Upper lip wax

- Begin at the side of the mouth and ask your client to bring their tongue to the cheek to stretch the skin, telling them not to move unless otherwise instructed. This ensures the skin is adequately stretched and will minimise client discomfort.
- Apply an even layer of wax to the side of the mouth following the direction of hair growth, and take care not to get any on the actual lip.
- Apply a small wax strip firmly over the wax with the pads of your fingers and stretch beneath the strip with the thumb of your free hand. Quickly remove the wax strip in the opposite direction to the hair growth.

 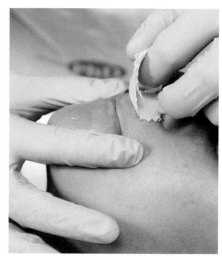

- Repeat this process at both sides of the mouth until there's only the centre of the upper lip left.
- Apply the wax and wax strip as before, only this time stretch with the index and middle fingers of your free hand in the same way you would at the centre of the eyebrows. Ask your client to purse their lips together before removing the wax strip in the opposite direction to the hair growth.
- Remove any stubborn hairs with tweezers and apply after-wax oil to remove any left-over wax, followed by after-wax lotion to soothe the area.
- Check client satisfaction by letting them see the finished result in the mirror.
- Give aftercare and home care advice (see page 163).
- Rebook your client for 2–4 weeks' time.

Chin wax

- Place a small rolled-up towel or bolster under your client's neck to tilt the head back, stretch the skin and minimise client discomfort.
- Apply an even layer of wax to the area in the direction of the hair growth.
- Place a small wax strip over the wax.
- Stretch beneath the wax strip using the thumb of your free hand and quickly remove in the opposite direction of hair growth.
- Remove any stubborn hairs with tweezers before applying after-wax lotion to soothe the area.
- Check client satisfaction by letting your client see the finished result in the mirror.

HANDY HINTS

Advise your client that excessive erythema is a common reaction to an upper lip wax and this usually diminishes quickly.

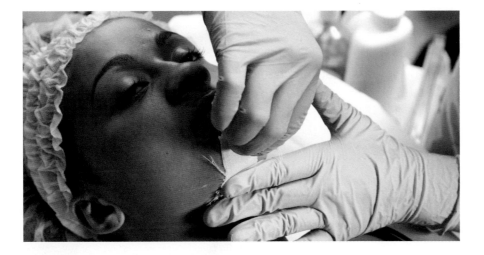

- Give aftercare and home care advice (see page 163).
- Rebook your client for 2–4 weeks' time.

BODY WAXING
Full and half leg wax

Before beginning any waxing, make sure you've washed your hands, performed a visual examination of the area to be treated, applied pre-wax lotion to the treatment area to cleanse and carried out a skin sensitivity test. Remember to maintain your client's modesty throughout as some amount of undressing is required and some clients are more nervous than others; you need to be sensitive about this.

- Ask your client to lie in the supine position, and check they've removed their shoes, socks and trousers. Place a small towel over their feet and a medium towel above the tops of their legs to maintain their modesty.
- You must pre-wax the area and make sure it's dry.
- Bring your client into a semi-reclined position while you work on the front of the legs.
- Start at the lower leg and apply an even layer of wax from mid-calf down, following the direction of hair growth.
- Apply a full wax strip directly over the wax and stretch beneath the area with your free hand. Quickly remove the wax strip in the opposite direction to the hair growth.

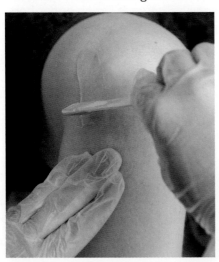

- When you reach the knee, ask your client to bend it so the skin is sufficiently stretched and continue applying the wax as before. For a half leg wax, finish just above the knee.
- Keeping the knees bent, continue to wax the top of the legs as before.

> **HANDY HINT**
>
> Hair on the chin can be sparse so only apply wax to the areas with sufficient hair to avoid stimulating blood circulation, which could result in denser hair growth.

- To wax the inside of the top of the leg, ask your client to bring their foot to the opposite knee to provide additional stretch to the skin.

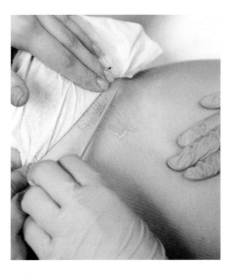

- Use tweezers to remove any stubborn hairs.
- When you're happy that you've removed all the hair from the front of the legs, apply after-wax oil to remove any wax, followed by after-wax lotion down the centre of the leg.
- Bring the head of the couch down so your client is supine before lifting the towel and asking them to turn over slowly and lie in the **prone** position.
- Ask your client to bring their feet on to their tiptoes to provide additional stretch and help minimise discomfort.
- Begin at the ankles and apply wax in the same way as before, stopping just below the back of the knee for a half leg wax.

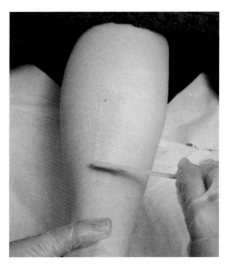

- NEVER apply wax to the back of the knee as there are lymph nodes here and the skin is significantly thinner, making it more prone to bruising.
- Apply after-wax oil to the entire legs to remove any left-over wax, followed by after-wax lotion to soothe the area.
- Check client satisfaction by letting them see the finished result.
- Give aftercare and home care advice (see page 163).
- Rebook your client for 4–6 weeks' time.

Prone
Lying face down.

HANDY HINTS

A good tip is to begin on the back of the legs when you're new to waxing as you're less likely to talk to your client during the treatment. This means you can focus on the treatment, your technique and most importantly the pace at which you work.

WHY DON'T YOU...
Read through SmartScreen handout 17 for further guidelines on warm wax procedures.

 SmartScreen B6 handout 17

HANDY HINTS

Always ask your client if they want their feet and toes waxed as well. Also remember to check the direction of hair growth on the upper legs as it's likely to grow in many different directions.

Underarm wax

Your client should lie supine or in a semi-reclined position for this treatment.

- Place a large or medium towel over your client's décolleté to maintain their modesty and protect it by tucking tissues into the sides of the bra.
- Pre-wax and apply a thin application of talc-free powder to the area to allow the wax to adhere to the hair and prevent perspiration.
- Pre-wax and apply an even layer of wax in the direction of hair growth before placing a wax strip directly on top.
- Ask your client to stretch the skin by using the palm of their hand to pull at the side of their bust. Stretch the area and quickly remove the wax strip in the opposite direction to the hair growth. Ask your client to assist with stretching to minimise discomfort.

HANDY HINTS

Never apply wax to the entire underarm in one go as the hair usually grows in many different directions; instead, apply it in a patchwork motion. This reduces the risk of pain, bruising and spot bleeding.

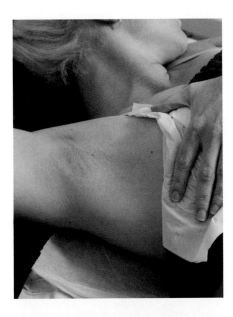
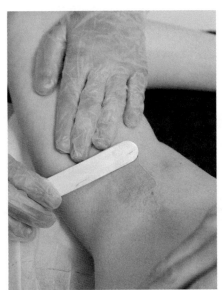
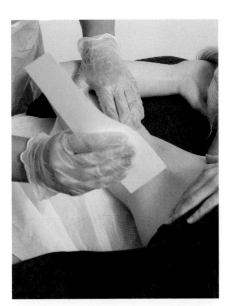

- Repeat this process until you've removed all the hair from both underarms and tweeze any stubborn hairs.
- Apply after-wax oil to remove any left-over wax, followed by after-wax lotion to soothe the skin.
- Check client satisfaction by letting them see the finished result.
- Give aftercare and home care advice (see page 163).
- Rebook your client for 2–4 weeks' time.

HANDY HINTS

Talcum powder can cause allergic reactions and aggravate respiratory disorders. Instead, use a talc-free powder, such as cornflour.

HANDY HINTS

Immediately after waxing an underarm, place a cotton pad soaked with aloe vera on the treated area. This will immediately soothe the area while you work on the other underarm. Repeat on the second underarm and apply after-wax oil and lotion to both.

B6 WAXING

Bikini line wax

This treatment is more effective with your client lying supine as it allows for further skin stretching, but they can lie in a semi-reclined position if they prefer. You can also give them the option of wearing disposable pants.

- Ask your client to remove their shoes, socks/tights, trousers/skirt and ask them to lie in the supine position. Place a small towel over their feet and a medium towel above the tops of the legs to maintain their modesty.
- Fold the towel in half to reveal one side of the bikini line. If your client is wearing their own pants, bring them to above the hip to produce a straight line, securing tissues in place for protection.
- Ask your client to bend their leg at the knee and relax it so the foot is resting against the opposite knee. This will stretch the area even more. Ask them to place both hands on top of their pants to apply and maintain firm pressure throughout the treatment and minimise discomfort.

HANDY HINTS

If a client requests an intimate bikini wax, use hot wax rather than warm wax as it's less painful and produces longer-lasting results with a smoother finish. Many salons now offer hot wax for such treatments as the results are more effective.

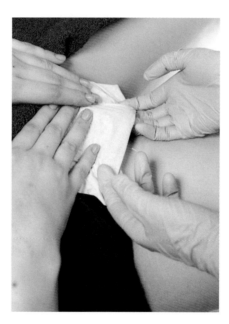
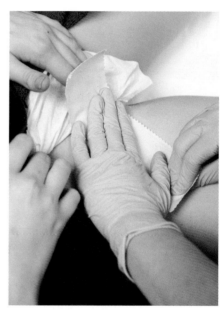

- Wipe over with pre-wax then apply talc-free powder to the area to allow the wax to adhere to the hair and prevent perspiration.
- Apply an even layer of wax in the direction of hair growth. Place a wax strip on top and apply firm pressure.
- Stretch beneath the wax strip with your free hand to further support your client's stretch, and quickly remove the wax strip in the opposite direction to the hair growth.
- Repeat this process until the hair is removed from both sides of the pants and use tweezers to remove stubborn hairs.
- Apply after-wax oil to remove any left-over wax before applying after-wax lotion to soothe the skin.
- Check client satisfaction by letting them see the finished result.
- Give aftercare and home care advice (see page 163).
- Rebook your client for 2–4 weeks' time.

HANDY HINTS

Always remember to use your disposable gloves to protect you and your client from the risk of cross-infection.

HANDY HINTS

NEVER apply wax to the same area twice, especially on intimate areas and the face. The skin is prone to bruising and spot bleeding in these areas.

WHY DON'T YOU...

Think about why it's important that you leave the work area ready for further treatments when you're finished. Use SmartScreen worksheet 6 to assist you with this.

SmartScreen B6 worksheet 6

LIMITATIONS OF WAXING

Waxing provides an instant result and is the preferred method of hair removal for many people. It means they don't have to worry about removing the hair themselves and can relax in the knowledge that a professional will give them the results they want. However, there are limitations as the results are temporary and, depending on a person's hair growth rate, will only last 2–6 weeks. While waxing is an adequate method of hair removal for the majority of clients, it might not be suitable for everyone, which is why a consultation is so important. For example, if a client has an underlying medical condition, it could be affecting their hair growth, resulting in more hair in certain areas, such as the upper lip and jawline. Advise your client that the result waxing produces cannot be guaranteed and, if they want a more permanent result, they would need to look at other methods of hair removal.

CONDITIONS THAT AFFECT HAIR GROWTH

- Polycystic ovaries: a hormonal imbalance whereby cysts form on the ovaries.
- Polycystic ovary syndrome (PCOS): similar to the above condition. A woman might display the symptoms of having polycystic ovaries, such as being overweight, suffering with breakouts along the jawline and male hair growth patterns on facial areas and sometimes on the chest and back. However, this person might not necessarily suffer with cysts on the ovaries.
- Pregnancy: at this time a woman's hair growth becomes synchronised, causing them to grow more hair than usual. This often returns to normal after six months of giving birth.
- Menopause: as a woman goes through the menopause, both male and female hormone production decreases dramatically. However, the female hormones decrease far more than the male hormones, and this can result in facial hair growth that follows male hair growth patterns.
- Puberty: as the body changes, hormone imbalances could result in more hair growth than normal.
- Stress: when under continuous stress, the body stops functioning normally, leading to an imbalance in hormone production.
- Hirsuitism: a hormonal imbalance causing the hair to follow male hair growth patterns.
- Hormonal imbalances: can cause hair to follow male hair growth patterns, and lead to increased hair growth on the body.

While your client might be happy with the temporary results of waxing, others might require something a little more permanent. It's your responsibility to have an understanding of all other types of hair removal available in salons, clinics and on the high street, so your client can make an informed decision as to which is the best method for them. You also need to understand how the results of these other methods compare with the results obtained with waxing and how waxing can affect them. These methods are discussed below.

TEMPORARY HAIR REMOVAL

TWEEZING

Manual or automatic tweezers are used to remove the hairs one by one from areas such as the eyebrows. The hair is grasped in the tweezers and quickly plucked from the root of the follicle, delaying regrowth for approximately four weeks. Tweezing is used along with waxing to remove stubborn hairs.

ELECTRICAL DEPILATORY

These electrical hand-held devices produce a plucking motion to remove hair. The device contains pincers that grasp several hairs at a time, tearing them from the follicle, which can lead to distortion of the follicle. It can be quite painful for some but is ideal when you're in a rush and is generally applied to dry skin. If a client uses this in conjunction with waxing, it could reduce the effectiveness of waxing by stimulating hair growth.

DEPILATORY CREAMS

These creams are another method of removing the hair from the skin's surface. The cream is an alkaline solution that is left on the skin for 5–10 minutes and dissolves the hair. Both hair and cream are removed with a spatula before rinsing clean. Sometimes this method can stimulate hair growth and so shouldn't be used in conjunction with waxing.

SHAVING

This is one of the most common and cheapest methods of temporary hair removal. A shaving foam is applied to the treatment area, most commonly the legs and underarms, before the hair is removed from the skin's surface with a sharp razor that is stroked over the area following the contours of the body. For some clients with eczema, shaving aggravates the condition, and so waxing is ideal. Shaving shouldn't really be used in conjunction with waxing as it can reduce the effectiveness of the treatment.

An electrical depilator

THREADING

This method of hair removal is an old Indian method that is becoming more popular among clients. A cotton thread is rolled over the skin, grasping hairs as it goes and plucking them from the root. The effects are similar to waxing and tweezing; however, it's much more effective at removing fine blonde hairs.

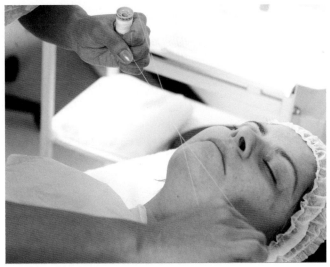

Threading the chin

ABRASIVE MITTS

Another cheap and effective method available on the high street, the mitts are gently rubbed over the treatment area, exfoliating the skin and removing the hair from the skin's surface. Too much rubbing can cause an erythemic reaction and so care must be taken to avoid this.

Using an abrasive mitt

SUGAR PASTE AND STRIP SUGAR

This method is less common nowadays in comparison to hot and warm wax. Its origins come from the Far East where sugar, lemon juice and water were boiled in a pan to create a paste. This sticky paste was applied to the area with the fingers before being rolled and flicked away, bringing with it the unwanted hair. These days, it doesn't need to be boiled in a pan and has been developed to be safer to use in the salon. However, because the sugar paste can be reapplied to the treatment area to make sure all the hair has been removed, there's a risk of cross-infection.

The advantage of using sugar paste is it contains no additives and is much gentler for use on sensitive skin. Strip sugar is similar to warm wax in consistency and method of use; it's applied with a spatula and removed with a muslin strip. The effects of sugar paste and strip sugar usually last between 4–6 weeks depending on your client's hair growth rate.

LASER HAIR REMOVAL

A laser is applied to the treatment area and is attracted to the melanin in the hair, warming the melanin and the hair follicle without heating the skin around it. Laser works best on light skin and dark hair, so those with fair hair usually take supplements to enhance melanin production prior to treatment. Laser is not a method of permanent hair removal as it doesn't destroy the blood supply which encourages hair growth. Instead, it's referred to as 'permanent hair reduction' because the hair regrowth is often finer than it was originally. Clients who choose laser hair removal are encouraged to shave between treatments rather than wax.

INTENSE PULSED LIGHT (IPL)

This is a cheaper and faster alternative to laser hair removal that uses xenon flash lights rather than a laser. The method uses heat to reduce hair growth as it's attracted to the melanin in the hair follicle. Clients are encouraged to shave between treatments rather than wax.

PERMANENT HAIR REMOVAL

ELECTROLYSIS/ELECTRICAL EPILATION

This method of hair removal is permanent and uses a galvanic, short wave diathermy or blend current, which passes into the hair follicle via a tiny probe. The blood supply to the hair is destroyed to prevent regrowth from the follicle. This method of hair removal can be applied almost anywhere on the body and, although some see it as a dated method, it's still the only method of permanent hair removal available. This method is ideal for clients with unwanted hair growth in obvious areas, such as the upper lip or jawline. Waxing shouldn't be used at the same time as it can stimulate hair growth and make the electrolysis less effective.

An electrolysis treatment

THE CITY & GUILDS TEXTBOOK

A therapist providing an aftercare advice leaflet following a waxing treatment

PROVIDE AFTERCARE ADVICE

At the end of the treatment, it's vital you provide your client with all the aftercare and home care advice they need so they can maintain the results and avoid infection and reaction. Tell your client that the advice you give MUST be followed for at least 24 hours otherwise a contra-action might occur, which could lead to infection or an allergic reaction.

The reason for this advice and why it's so important for clients to follow is because the pores have been opened as the hair has been removed from the follicle. If your client doesn't follow your advice or you forget to give them advice, the skin could become infected and you'll be the first person they come to if this happens.

WHY DON'T YOU...
Think about why it's important to follow this aftercare advice.

AFTERCARE ADVICE

This is given to every client after every type of waxing treatment and must be adhered to for at least 24 hours:

- Avoid make-up (facial waxing only).
- Avoid showers or baths.
- Avoid heat treatments, such as steam, sauna, hot tubs and infra-red.
- Avoid sun exposure and UV treatments.
- Avoid applying perfumed and chemical-based products.
- Avoid deodorant or antiperspirant (underarm waxing only).
- Avoid touching the area.
- Avoid tight clothing as this will rub and cause friction and heat (body waxing only).

- Avoid tanning products or talcum powder.
- Avoid swimming and exercise.
- Avoid other beauty treatments that involve working on the treated area.

Advise your clients to be careful about the products they use after waxing.

HOME CARE ADVICE

This advice is more client specific and will vary from client to client but should follow the same theme:

- Exfoliate between one and three times a week to prevent ingrown hairs.
- Moisturise at least once a day to keep the skin hydrated and prevent the hair from becoming brittle.
- Increase water intake so that the skin is hydrated; two litres per day is the recommended amount.

If your client must wash in the next 24 hours, recommend a tepid shower to avoid the application of heat on heat and use only unperfumed products to minimise the risk of infection.

If your client's skin is red afterwards, advise them to use aloe vera over the next 24 hours to cool and soothe the area, or apply a cold compress.

CONTRA-ACTIONS – NORMAL SKIN REACTIONS

Waxing is an effective method of hair removal that will cause an instant reaction on the skin as the hair is removed from the follicle. It's important you make your client aware of these reactions so they're not alarmed. Some clients will notice more of a reaction than others. It depends on your client's skin type and their skin colour so it's your responsibility to keep an eye on the skin reaction throughout the treatment. The following indicates what a normal skin reaction to waxing would be:

- erythema
- red spots around the follicle.

ERYTHEMA

This is the correct term for redness. As heat has been applied to the area, local blood circulation has been stimulated, encouraging the skin to become erythemic. This often diminishes in the first couple of hours and is a perfectly normal reaction to waxing. Calm erythema by applying after-wax lotion or a soothing agent, such as aloe vera. If you identify excessive erythema during the treatment, stop immediately and apply a cold compress followed by a soothing agent, such as aloe vera, which will calm the skin and reduce the reaction.

RED SPOTS AROUND THE FOLLICLE

As the hair has been removed from the follicle, there has been trauma to the area and surrounding tissue, which is why the skin is sometimes referred to as 'looking like a plucked chicken'. It's a minor, and normal, reaction that diminishes in the first couple of hours and treatment is the same as with erythema. However, if this reaction gets worse throughout the treatment, you might find your client is displaying signs of a histamine reaction.

OTHER CONTRA-ACTIONS

There are other contra-actions to waxing which aren't normal reactions so it's important you understand why they've occurred and how to deal with them:

- spot bleeding
- ingrown hairs
- abrasions
- broken hair
- histamine reaction
- excessive erythema
- excessive or diminished regrowth
- contact dermatitis.

SPOT BLEEDING

This is common in the more intimate areas, especially when a client chooses to replace their current method of hair removal, such as shaving or depilatory creams, with waxing. It's a normal reaction that occurs as a result of coarse, stubborn hair being removed from the follicle and the initial trauma is followed by a small amount of bleeding. As your client continues with waxing, the hair becomes much finer and sparser, meaning this reaction is less likely to occur. If this does occur during a treatment, simply wipe away with a cotton pad which is disposed of into the hazardous waste bin and continue with the treatment, ensuring you apply a soothing agent, such as aloe vera, afterwards.

INGROWN HAIRS

Ingrown hair might occur because of a severe reaction to depilation. Extra cells might be made which block the follicle's exit and result in the newly growing hair to turn around on itself and grow inwards. Sometimes tight clothes and dry skin can also cause the follicle to become blocked.

There are different types of ingrown hairs and it is important to know how to identify and deal with them:

- Ingrown hairs growing along and just beneath the surface of the skin: These are usually quite easy to spot as you can see the hair just below the surface of the skin very often growing in a line. Identify where the end of the hair is by locating its tip, then pierce with a sterile needle, free the tip of the hair but leave it in the follicle so the skin heals around it, thus preventing further infection and damage
- Coiled ingrown hairs: Very often these look like a small dark spot similar to a comedone, as the hair grows deep into the skin rather than along it. Freeing the hair is very simple: wrap some tissue around your fingers and tease the hair from the follicle in the same way you would ease a comedone from a pore. Sometimes the hair falls out completely. If it doesn't ensure the tip is free and allow the skin to heal around it
- Infected ingrown hairs: When an ingrown hair becomes infected the area around it will very often appear red, raised and similar in appearance to a pustule. In order to free the hair and remove the infection, treat in the same way you would a coiled ingrown hair and cover with a sterile dressing to prevent further infection from occurring.

ABRASIONS
This is caused by the wax being too hot and/or the removal being too rough so make sure you take your time with each client. While it's important to build on your speed to ensure cost effectiveness, it's much better to be thorough and have a happy client than cause reactions and provide an ineffective treatment. If an abrasion does occur, treat it in the same way you would a burn.

BROKEN HAIR
The result of incorrect wax removal causes the hair to tear at the surface rather than the root of the follicle which can lead to irritation, infection and ingrown hairs. The technique needs to be improved to ensure the hair is removed from the root and not the surface. To maintain the correct angle, make sure you pull the wax strip quickly in the opposite direction to the hair growth without lifting the wax strip up at the same time.

HISTAMINE REACTION
Sometimes the trauma to the hair follicle stimulates an immune response, causing the mast cells in the dermis to release histamine into the skin. This sets off a chain reaction:

- Irritation and/or pain is caused by stimulation of the sensory nerve endings.
- Histamine is released and vasodilation occurs, stimulating local blood supply.
- With this increased blood supply come fresh oxygen, nutrients and leucocytes (white blood cells) to repair the damaged tissue.
- As a result of all of these points, localised skin temperature increases, making the skin feel warm to the touch.

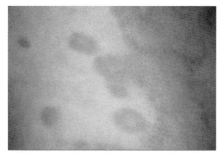
A histamine reaction

THE CITY & GUILDS TEXTBOOK

- There is also a temporary increase in keratinised cells in the area, which results in the skin flaking when the histamine reaction has gone.

If you notice a histamine reaction, stop the treatment and apply a cool compress to the area until the reaction goes down. Advise your client to continue applying a cool compress for the next 12–24 hours and suggest antihistamines that can reduce the reaction even more. If the response continues, advise your client to seek GP assistance.

EXCESSIVE ERYTHEMA

This occurs alongside other contra-actions, such as a histamine response, bruising, burning or abrasions and is the result of an increase in skin temperature. Stop the treatment and apply a cold water compress to cool and soothe the area.

EXCESSIVE OR DIMINISHED REGROWTH

If your client has an underlying medical condition or is taking medication, they might find the regrowth after waxing increases. Suggest that other methods of hair removal might be more suitable and discuss these options with your client. Diminished regrowth is a natural occurrence for many clients who have undergone waxing treatments over a long period of time, and is most common on the legs and underarms.

CONTACT DERMATITIS

This describes the skin's response when exposed to an irritant for the first time (**acute**), or over a period of time (**chronic**). The symptoms include dryness and cracking, a rash, blisters or weals, and irritation or burning. If this occurs during the treatment, stop immediately and apply a cold water compress to the area to cool and soothe before giving your client the following advice:

- Apply a soothing lotion, such as calamine or aloe vera, to soothe the area.
- If blisters occur, continue applying cold water compresses for around 30 minutes, three times a day.
- Antihistamines can relieve swelling and irritation.

As contact dermatitis is triggered by exposure to an allergen, it's important the treatment is stopped immediately and shouldn't be repeated at a later date as the condition could get worse. If the initial reaction doesn't diminish after three days, advise your client to seek GP assistance. If your client suffers with contact dermatitis and you discover this during the consultation, try to identify what the cause is before going ahead with the treatment; rosin (found in plasters and wax) is a common cause of this condition. If your client is allergic to any ingredient, you might need to look at other options or find a different wax. If you're still in any doubt, ask your client to obtain GP approval first. You can avoid contact dermatitis by performing a skin sensitivity test as outlined on pages 148–149. As the therapist, you can also avoid contact dermatitis by protecting yourself with disposable gloves.

Acute dermatitis
Caused by exposure to an irritant and occurs almost immediately.

Chronic dermatitis
Caused by overexposure to an irritant over a period of time, be it days, weeks, months or years.

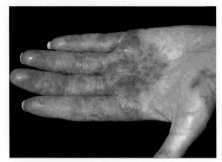
Contact dermatitis

RESULTS OF INCORRECT WAXING

Some reactions are not contra-actions, but the result of mistakes made during the waxing treatment. You must be aware of these so you can avoid making mistakes that result in client discomfort.

BRUISING

This usually occurs as a result of ineffective stretching before wax removal, and is more common on the bikini line and underarms but can happen anywhere. It's vital you give clear instructions on how your client can assist with skin stretching as this will make your job much easier. If bruising does occur, explain to your client what has happened. Apply aloe vera to damp cotton pads, place them over the bruise and leave while you move on and continue with the treatment. Usually the bruising will have reduced by the end of the treatment but it's important you act fast, and usually your client will appreciate your efforts to calm the area. Advise them to follow the aftercare advice to stop the bruise getting worse.

BURNS

Burns are caused by the wax being too hot and can become painful and infected if not dealt with immediately because the skin can tear as well. If this does occur, stop the treatment, place a cold water compress on the area for several minutes and add fresh ones if you need to. When the area has cooled, apply a dry dressing to prevent infection. Tell your client to remove this dressing after three days to allow the skin to heal. If blisters form, tell them not to break them as they're there to protect the skin. If the burn hasn't gone down after three days, advise your client to seek GP assistance.

SKIN REMOVAL

This occurs if the wax is too hot. As a result, the outermost layers of the stratum corneum are taken off, which can look similar to peeling of the skin after sun burn. If this happens stop the treatment and apply a cold compress to cool the skin followed by a soothing agent such as aloe vera or calamine lotion to calm and encourage skin healing.

OVERHEATED AREAS

It's very common for the temperature of the wax to fluctuate during treatments so it's important to constantly check this when you're performing a waxing service as you might cause some areas of the skin to overheat. If this happens, simply stop the treatment and apply either a soothing agent such as aloe vera or calamine, or a cold compress prior to this depending on how hot the skin has become, before resuming the treatment once the wax has cooled. Remember to re-check for sensitivity before reapplying wax to the treatment area(s).

Waxing treatments can help clients feel confident on their holidays!

PRODUCT RECOMMENDATIONS

As with any treatment, you should offer product recommendations after all waxing treatments so your client gets the best from the results. This should include soothing agents, such as aloe vera, for the first 12–24 hours to cool the skin and encourage skin healing. Recommend exfoliators and moisturisers to prevent ingrown hairs and dehydrated skin.

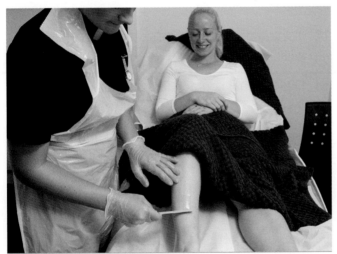

Application of warm wax to the lower leg

END OF UNIT SUMMARY

Now you've reached the end of the unit, you should feel confident in the theory and practical aspects of all areas of waxing. Use the checklist below to see if there are any areas you feel you need to recap before beginning the end of unit assessment:

- maintain safe and effective methods of working when removing hair by waxing
- consult, plan and prepare for waxing treatments with clients
- remove unwanted hair
- provide aftercare advice.

Using the questions below, test your knowledge of Unit B6 to see how much information you've retained. These questions will help you to revise what you've learnt in this chapter.

Turn to pages 405–407 for the answers.

1 Why is it important to ensure hygiene measures are in place for all waxing treatments?

2 List **two** types of PPE that you should use during waxing.

3 What PPE should your client have available during waxing treatments?

4 Why is it important to ensure your client is in the correct position before you start any waxing treatment?

5 Explain how you can minimise waste during waxing treatments.

6 When the spatula you're using has been in contact with bodily fluid, why is it important to use a new one?

7 What is meant by the term 'hazardous waste'?

8 How long should a full leg wax take?

9 Why is it important to adhere to the industry accepted times?

10 What are the contra-indications to waxing, and which ones require medical referral?

11 Why should you do a test patch and skin sensitivity test before you begin the treatment?

12 Why is it important to perform a visual examination of the treatment area prior to waxing the hair and how is this done?

13 Which type of hair is best suited to hot wax, and which is best suited to warm wax?

14 What are the melting and working temperatures of hot and warm wax?

15 List the **two** main ingredients of hot wax.

16 Explain why sugar paste is ideal for use on sensitive skin.

17 List and describe the expected skin reactions to waxing.

18 Explain what contact dermatitis is and how you avoid it.

19 Explain a histamine reaction and how to deal with it.

20 What aftercare and home care advice should you give to each client after a waxing treatment?

WHY DON'T YOU...
Test your knowledge further by logging into SmartScreen and completing the revision activities before attempting the sample GOLA revision questions.

B34
PROVIDE THREADING SERVICES

Threading is an exciting development in beauty therapy and is another way of removing hair. While this is a new development in the West, threading has been used for hundreds of years in Middle Eastern cultures. It's believed to have originated in Persia (today known as Iran), where young girls would have hair from their faces and bodies removed as a rite of passage into womanhood. It's highly skilled and needs patience from both client and therapist. Eyebrow threading is the preferred method of eyebrow shaping in the East, and is fast becoming the preferred method in the West for its precise results.

In this chapter you'll learn how to:

- maintain safe and effective methods of working when providing threading services
- consult, plan and prepare for threading services with clients
- remove unwanted hair
- provide aftercare advice.

HANDY HINTS

When you're providing a threading service, it's important to use the skills you've learnt in the following units:

Unit G20   Ensure responsibility for actions to reduce risks to health and safety

Unit G18   Promote additional services or products to clients

Unit G8   Develop and maintain your effectiveness at work

Unit B6   Carry out waxing services

Unit B5   Enhance the appearance of eyebrows and lashes.

HANDY HINTS

Check your salon's insurance policy to see if you're covered for threading and identify the current guidelines for the delivery of this service.

MAINTAIN SAFE AND EFFECTIVE METHODS OF WORKING WHEN PROVIDING THREADING SERVICES

As with all beauty treatments, it's important you understand and adhere to the relevant health and safety legislation throughout to ensure you perform a safe and enjoyable treatment for your client. The main legislation affecting threading services is:

- Data Protection Act (DPA)
- Disability Discrimination Act (DDA)
- Reporting of Injuries, Diseases and Dangerous Occurrences (RIDDOR)
- Personal Protective Equipment (PPE)
- Manual Handling Operations.

Each of these Acts is described fully in Unit G20 along with all other health and safety legislation.

SALON ENVIRONMENT

Before beginning a treatment, it's important you set up your work area properly.

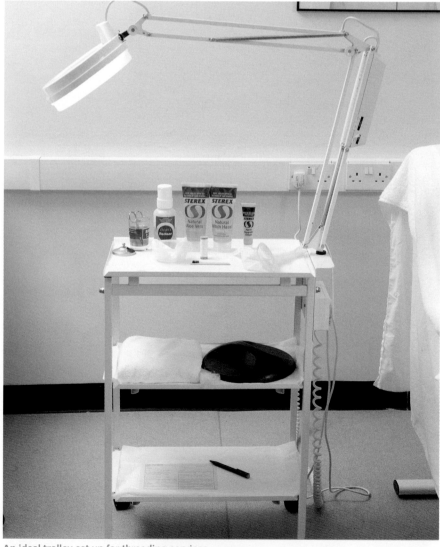

An ideal trolley set up for threading services

To reduce the risks of cross-infection, disinfect all non-metal implements and work surfaces and sterilise all metal implements; check Unit G20 for further assistance with this. Starting with the trolley, disinfect all surfaces with an appropriate product and protect the trolley with couch roll before placing the following items on the top shelf:

- an appropriate skin cleansing solution, such as pre-wax lotion
- a small bowl containing dry cotton pads
- an orange wood stick
- a disposable mascara wand/disposable eyebrow brush
- a jar containing Barbicide
- scissors
- a cotton reel
- an appropriate soothing agent, such as after-wax lotion or aloe vera.

On the second shelf you'll need the following:

- a small towel
- a headband
- a mirror.

On the bottom shelf you should have the client record card and a pen, and any aftercare advice leaflets you might want to give your client before they leave.

You might also need a magnifying lamp to help with a visual examination of the treatment area.

HANDY HINTS

Remember to use a new piece of thread for each treatment area you work on to avoid the risk of cross-infection, and make sure all used thread is disposed of in the appropriate hazardous waste bin.

PREPARING THE TREATMENT AREA

Make sure you cover the treatment couch with a protective sheet. Place a pillow at the head with a small towel on top to protect it, then cover this with couch roll. Check that you have pillows, blankets and towels for additional comfort and support. You'll also need a lined metal pedal bin for all your waste. As you'll be standing for this treatment, maintain your posture by keeping your legs shoulder width apart and slightly bend your knees. Check the couch is height adjustable and the trolley is nearby to avoid any unnecessary stretching; this could result in fatigue or injury. Make sure you're aware of repetitive strain injury (RSI) and how you can prevent this condition.

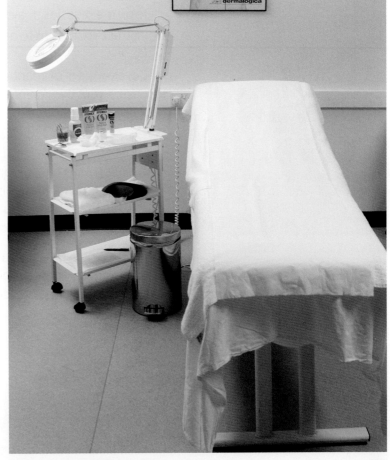

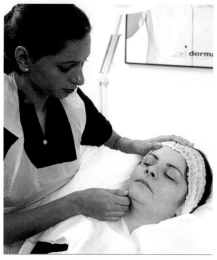

You must be especially mindful of your posture during threading services

REPETITIVE STRAIN INJURY (RSI)

This is a chronic musculo-skeletal disorder that can affect any area of the body. It's caused by working, moving and positioning yourself in the same way over a period of time without adequate recovery time in between. It's often work related and stress can make the condition worse. However, RSI is preventable and treatable but it's important to identify the symptoms earlier rather than later. Symptoms include:

- numbness in the limbs
- dull aches and shooting pains
- swelling of the affected area
- weakness
- cramps
- headaches and migraines.

To avoid developing RSI during threading services, you must maintain a suitable posture as you'll be standing throughout the treatment. You'll also be using your mouth to hold the thread, your neck to keep the thread taut and your hands to move the thread over the target area. To prevent RSI:

- Keep your back straight at all times to avoid putting pressure on the spine.
- Avoid slouching or hunching your shoulders.
- Keep your neck straight to avoid putting pressure on the spine.
- Avoid performing too many threading services in one day; spread them out over the day so you have sufficient recovery time in between.
- Warm up your limbs by performing a few exercises and learning to relax the muscles to avoid building up tension.
- Instruct your client to assist you where possible to avoid muscle fatigue.
- Develop ways of adapting and changing the techniques you use to ensure your own comfort.

CREATING THE RIGHT ENVIRONMENT

It's important you make sure the treatment area is relaxing and welcoming and suitable for you to work safely and comfortably. The main areas you need to think about are the general comfort of your client and the lighting. You need to see what you're doing and your client needs to feel relaxed and comfortable.

Check the industry accepted times so you don't overrun and keep other clients waiting. The table below displays the times you should use as a guideline. These times exclude consultation.

Treatment	Times
Eyebrow threading	20 minutes
Upper lip threading	10 minutes
Chin threading	10 minutes

HANDY HINTS

The treatments included in the table are the most popular threading treatments. But you might also be asked to thread the following areas: sides of face, top of nose, forehead, neck, male brows and upper cheek.

ADVANTAGES AND DISADVANTAGES OF THREADING

Below is a table outlining the advantages and disadvantages of threading; the advantages far outweigh the disadvantages. However, it's important you're aware of both so you can provide the best treatment and achieve optimum results.

Advantages	Disadvantages
Completely safe and hygienic as you dispose of the cotton thread after use	If applied incorrectly, the hair can be broken at the skin's surface causing quicker regrowth
No application of chemicals to the skin	It can sometimes be hard to find an experienced therapist outside large cities
Doesn't affect the skin in the same way as other hair removal techniques so is safe for clients with medical conditions	If the treatment area is not stretched, the skin might be pinched in the lasso
As the therapist becomes more experienced, the service becomes less time consuming	
Cost effective because you need little equipment and consumables	
With experience, this can be much less painful than other hair removal methods	
Allows for a more precise finish on the brow area as the hairs are removed in rows	
Ideal for sensitive complexions as you only remove the hair. The skin isn't affected at all.	

CONSULT, PLAN AND PREPARE FOR THREADING SERVICES WITH CLIENTS

It's always important to carry out a consultation and obtain your client's signature before beginning any treatment to safeguard yourself and the salon. As part of a threading service, you need to discuss your client's expectations with them and the shape they'd like to achieve if having an eyebrow treatment. Explain the procedure and the assistance required from your client to ensure there's as little pain as possible. Remember that you're likely to meet many clients from different cultural and religious backgrounds, as well as different genders. Make sure that you don't cause upset or offence by assuming which areas your client would like treated, or assuming your client will remove certain clothing to make your job easier. It's your duty to adapt your treatment to suit your client's needs and make sure they're happy and comfortable. This way, they're more likely to return for another treatment.

HANDY HINTS

Remember that if your client is under the age of 16 years, you'll need informed and signed parental or guardian consent. The parent or guardian must also stay for the duration of the service.

HANDY HINTS

See the anatomy and physiology chapter for more information on contra-indications.

CONTRA-INDICATIONS

You now need to identify whether or not your client has any contra-indications that could prevent or restrict threading services. Below is a list of contra-indications that would prevent this treatment:

- contact lenses: your client is required to apply pressure to the eye area to stretch the skin effectively, which might cause discomfort
- contagious skin conditions, such as impetigo or conjunctivitis: risk of cross-infection
- recent scar tissue: the skin is fragile and could be damaged by the procedure
- sunburn: as above
- eye infections: risk of cross-infection
- skin allergies: risk of an allergic reaction.

If you identify one of the above contra-indications, explain to your client the treatment cannot go ahead, but don't name the condition in case you're wrong. Instead, tell your client that you've identified a contra-indication and that performing the threading service could make it worse; then advise them to see their GP for a proper diagnosis. If you continue with one of the above contra-indications, you're putting yourself at risk of cross-infection and your client at risk of skin damage, which could lead to legal action.

The contra-indications that restrict threading services are:

- moles: work around the area, avoiding it completely
- skin tags: as above.

The treatment can still go ahead if you identify one of the above contra-indications but, if you work over a mole, you could make it bleed and change the cellular structure. If you work over a skin tag, it could bleed copiously and cause unnecessary skin damage and pain for your client.

HANDY HINTS

It's also recommended that you explain the possible contra-actions to this service, without causing undue alarm, so your client doesn't become concerned. Refer to the section 'Provide aftercare advice' for details on the possible contra-actions to threading services and how to deal with them.

A therapist performing a consultation for threading services

THE CITY & GUILDS TEXTBOOK

PREPARING THE CLIENT AND TREATMENT AREA

To prepare your client, ask them to remove their shoes and lie supine on the treatment couch. Protect their hair by wrapping it up in a small towel or use a headband to sweep the hair off their face. If necessary, support the spine by bringing the couch into a semi-reclined position. This will also ensure that you don't hunch or slouch throughout the treatment.

When the consultation is complete and your client is prepared, you're ready to prepare the treatment area. Conduct a visual examination to identify the direction of hair growth, the type of hair growing and the skin condition; you can use a magnifying lamp for this. Prepare the area by applying a cleansing solution, such as pre-wax lotion, with dry cotton pads before discussing and agreeing a proposed treatment plan with your client.

You're now ready to begin the treatment.

REMOVE UNWANTED HAIR

Before you begin offering threading services, it's a good idea to practise the techniques on yourself or a friend, working on larger areas of the body, such as the legs and arms. This will allow you to increase your speed and your **dexterity**.

Dexterity
Skill in using the hands.

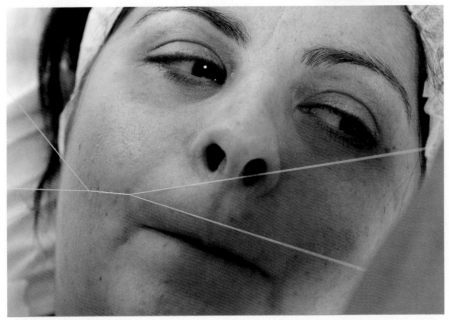

Threading to the upper lip

When you're ready and you've agreed the treatment plan with your client, make sure you know how to perform threading on the most common areas:

- upper lip
- chin
- eyebrows.

THREADING TECHNIQUES

There are three techniques you can use when you're providing threading services:

- the hand technique
- the neck technique
- the mouth technique.

THE HAND TECHNIQUE

STEP 1 – Take 24 inches (61 cm) of cotton thread and form a loop. An easy way to determine the length of the thread is to measure it against your arm length.

STEP 2 – Tie the two free ends together and secure the loop in place.

STEP 3 – Hold the cotton thread in both hands with your thumb and first three fingers and twist eight to ten times.

STEP 4 – Move the wound section of cotton by widening both hands alternately so that it works like a mini lasso, plucking the hairs from the root against the direction of hair growth. Remember to use a new piece of thread for each area you work on.

THE NECK TECHNIQUE

1 Wash your hands thoroughly.

2 Take 24 inches (61 cm) of cotton thread.

3 Anchor the thread around your neck.

4 Loop the other end around your fingers and thumbs.

5 Use this end to thread the hair from the treatment area.

6 Remember to use a new piece of thread for each treatment area.

7 Wash your hands when you've completed the treatment.

THE MOUTH TECHNIQUE

1 Wash your hands thoroughly.

2 Take 24 inches (61 cm) of cotton thread.

3 Place the free ends between your teeth and form a loop with your thumb and first three fingers.

4 With your thumb and fingers still in this position, twist the cotton several times.

5 Take one free end from your teeth and hold it with your free hand. Make sure the distance between the wound cotton and your teeth is enough so you're not too close to your client. You must also keep the cotton as tight as possible during the service.

6 Remember to use a new piece of thread for each treatment area.

7 Wash your hands when you've completed the treatment.

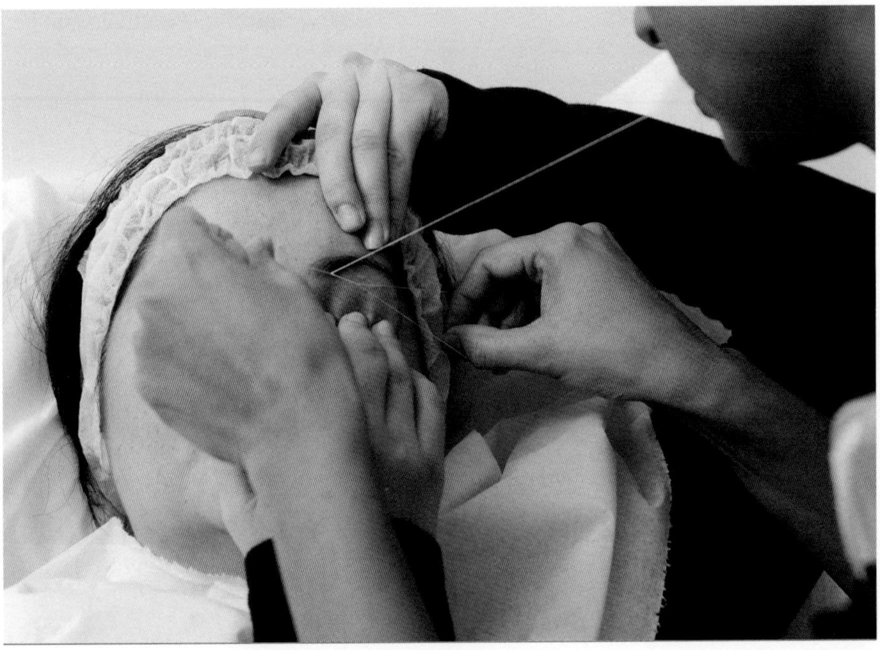

Threading to the brows using the mouth technique

HANDY HINTS

When you're using the mouth technique, keep your neck straight to avoid unnecessary strain on the muscles. This also ensures the thread is kept taut throughout the service and that you're not invading your client's personal space.

HANDY HINTS

It's important to avoid the mouth technique if you have a crown or braces as the thread might get caught in your teeth. This would affect your skills and impact on the threading service.

HANDY HINTS

It's important to adapt your threading techniques when you're working on male clients who want to have external hair removed from their ears and nose. For example, practise the hand technique by twisting the cotton thread fewer times than usual for a more precise finish.

UPPER LIP THREADING

STEP 1 – Ask your client to assist you by pursing their lips together as they would for an upper lip wax.

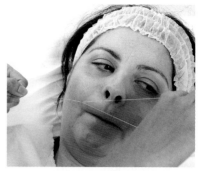

STEP 2 – To remove unwanted hair, widen one hand to push the wound section towards the other hand, pulling the hairs from the root.

STEP 3 – Check the results and continue until you've removed all the unwanted hair.

STEP 4 – Place the used cotton thread in the bin.

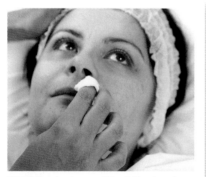

STEP 5 – Apply a soothing lotion to calm the skin.

STEP 6 – Allow your client to see the finished results in the mirror.

STEP 7 – Discuss aftercare and home care advice and rebook your client in for 2–4 weeks' time.

CHIN THREADING

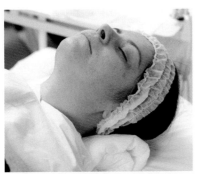

STEP 1 – To stretch the skin, place a bolster or a small rolled-up towel under your client's neck.

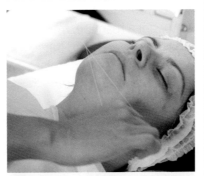

STEP 2 – Remove all unwanted hair by widening one hand and pushing the wound section of cotton towards the other hand, pulling the individual hairs from the root.

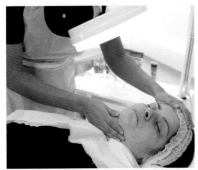

STEP 3 – Check the results and continue until you've removed all the unwanted hair.

STEP 4 – Place the used cotton thread in the bin.

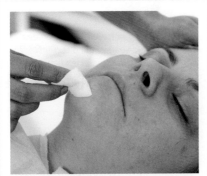

STEP 5 – Apply a soothing lotion to calm the skin.

STEP 6 – Allow your client to see the finished results in the mirror. Discuss aftercare and home care advice and rebook your client in for 2–4 weeks' time.

WHY DON'T YOU...
Refer to Unit B5 to remind yourself which eyebrow shapes suit the different face shapes.

EYEBROW THREADING

When you're performing eyebrow threading, it's important you determine whether your client requires a complete reshape or simple maintenance. If they want a reshape, make sure you suggest the ideal eyebrow shape to define the eye area and frame the face. The step-by-step guide below can be applied to both a complete eyebrow reshape or eyebrow maintenance.

STEP 1 – Take an orange wood stick and perform the appropriate measurements as you would for an eyebrow shape. This will determine where the brows should start, where the arch should be and where the brows should end.

STEP 2 – Using a mirror, discuss the shaping with your client and agree on the best shape to suit their face.

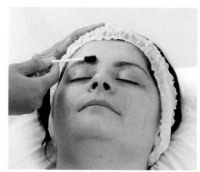

STEP 3 – Brush the eyebrow hairs upwards with the disposable mascara wand.

STEP 4 – Keeping the brush in place, trim any eyebrow hairs that lie above it with scissors. This will groom the brows and produce a more defined shape.

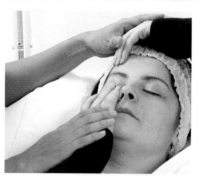

STEP 5 – Ask your client to assist you by holding one hand above and one hand below the brow and stretching.

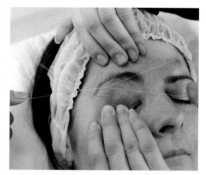

STEP 6 – Start with the right eye. Widen your right hand so the wound section of cotton moves towards your left hand. Remove hair from the root against the direction of hair growth.

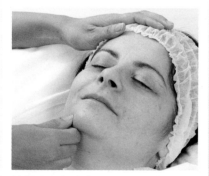

STEP 7 – Check the results before continuing.

STEP 8 – When you work on the left eye, widen the left hand so the wound section of thread moves towards the right hand, remembering to remove the hair against the direction of hair growth. Repeat this process until you've achieved the desired result on both brows. Make sure they appear well balanced, proportioned and defined.

STEP 9 – Place the used cotton thread in the bin.

STEP 10 – Apply a soothing lotion to calm the skin.

STEP 11 – Allow your client to see the finished results in the mirror. Discuss aftercare and home care advice and rebook your client in for 2–4 weeks' time.

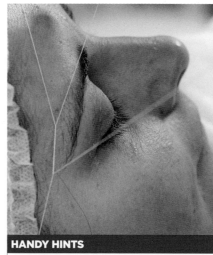

HANDY HINTS

Although it's not normally recommended that you remove hair from above the brows, it can form part of a threading service. This is something you might want to consider as you gain more experience and your skills develop. It might also be a specific request from a client.

OTHER METHODS OF HAIR REMOVAL

While your client might be happy with temporary results, others might want something a little more permanent. It's your responsibility to have an understanding of all other types of hair removal available in salons, clinics and on the high street. This way, your client can make an informed decision as to which is the best method for them. You also need to understand how these other methods can affect the results obtained with threading and how threading can affect them. Refer to Unit B6 for information on the following methods of hair removal:

- tweezing
- shaving
- depilatory creams
- electrical depilatory
- abrasive mitts
- laser and intense pulsed light (IPL)
- waxing
- electrical epilation/electrolysis.

As threading works in the same way as waxing and tweezing, by removing the hair from the root, these methods actually complement each other; there shouldn't be any effect on hair growth if these methods are combined. The only precaution to remember is that waxing covers a larger surface area so isn't as precise as threading; it also removes a layer of skin during the process and can make the skin more prone to reaction.

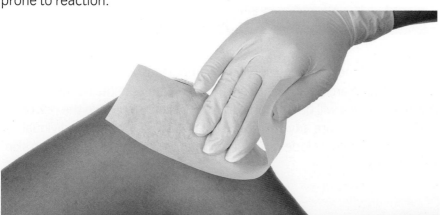

Using an abrasive mitt

As depilatory creams, abrasive mitts and shaving only remove the hair from the skin's surface, they don't complement threading as they encourage the hair to grow back thicker, which defeats the purpose of threading treatments.

Although electrical depilatory devices remove the hair from the follicle, they don't provide a precise result. For most people, they can be painful to use as the hair is literally ripped from the follicle in various directions, which can lead to distortion of the follicle. This makes future threading treatments more difficult.

Electrical epilation/electrolysis is the only permanent method of hair removal available. It's not recommended that your client uses any other method of hair removal, including threading, between treatments as they can stimulate hair growth and reduce the effectiveness of the treatment.

Laser and IPL are permanent methods of hair reduction that use either a laser or intense pulsed light to destroy the melanin or pigment of the skin and hair. Clients undergoing such treatments are advised to shave only between treatments as it stimulates hair growth and makes the laser or IPL treatments much more effective and longer lasting. Hair removal methods that affect the hair beneath the skin's surface, such as threading, can be detrimental to the success of laser and IPL treatments.

PROVIDE AFTERCARE ADVICE

At the end of the threading service, it's important you give the appropriate aftercare advice to ensure your client maintains the results. Aftercare advice will be the same for every client to reduce the risk of infection. Home care advice is more specific to your client's individual needs and should include product recommendations and advice on skin care routines.

AFTERCARE ADVICE

This is given to every client after each type of threading service and must be adhered to for at least 24 hours:

- Avoid make-up.
- Avoid heat treatments, such as steam, sauna, hot tubs and infra-red.
- Avoid sun exposure and UV treatments.
- Avoid applying perfumed products to the area.
- Avoid touching the area.
- Avoid tanning or bronzing products.
- Avoid swimming.
- Avoid other beauty treatments that involve working on the treated area.
- Return in the next 2–4 weeks to maintain the results.

HANDY HINTS

To ensure your client doesn't forget the advice you give, hand them an aftercare advice leaflet for them to take away.

HOME CARE ADVICE

Home care advice is more client specific but should follow the same theme:

- Exfoliate between one and three times a week to prevent ingrown hairs.
- Moisturise at least once a day to keep the skin hydrated and prevent the hair from becoming brittle.
- As your client will no doubt want to wash in the next 24 hours, recommend tepid water to avoid the application of heat on heat and suggest they use unperfumed products to minimise the risk of reaction.

WHY DON'T YOU...
Write a list of the reasons why it's important to follow the aftercare advice.

CONTRA-ACTIONS

While threading is an effective method of hair removal that produces fewer reactions than waxing or tweezing, it's important you make your client aware of the possible contra-actions. You should know how to identify such contra-actions and how to deal with them to prevent any long-term skin damage. These contra-actions are outlined below:

- blood spots
- abrasions
- allergic reaction
- excessive erythema.

BLOOD SPOTS

Blood spots can occur when a deep-rooted hair has been removed or if your client hasn't stretched the area properly. They look like small spots of blood from the follicle. Stop the treatment and apply a damp cotton pad to wipe away the blood. Make sure you dispose of the cotton pad in a hazardous waste bag and not in the general waste. Make sure you provide appropriate aftercare advice to prevent secondary infection of the follicle.

ABRASIONS

Abrasions can occur if you use poor quality cotton or synthetic thread instead of 100 per cent cotton. Poor quality cotton can be a little harsher when it's rolled along the skin and can cause small abrasions or grazes. Make sure you use 100 per cent cotton thread at all times; it's much softer and smoother, and ensures that only the hair is removed and the skin isn't affected. If an abrasion occurs, stop the treatment and apply a soothing agent, such as aloe vera, to promote skin healing and soothe the area. Give your client the appropriate aftercare advice to make sure there's no secondary infection.

ALLERGIC REACTIONS

Allergic reactions can be caused by using poor quality or synthetic thread rather than 100 per cent cotton. Your client will feel an allergic reaction as a tingling or itching sensation, which can lead to a stinging or burning sensation if not dealt with quickly. As your client scratches the area, erythema occurs along with oedema and possibly urticaria. Stop the treatment immediately and apply a cold compress until the reaction diminishes and then apply a soothing agent, such as aloe vera. Advise your client to continue applying cold compresses at home and follow the appropriate aftercare advice to make sure the reaction doesn't get worse.

EXCESSIVE ERYTHEMA

This can occur alongside each of the above contra-actions. It's the result of an increase in skin temperature and causes the skin to appear red, warm to the touch and possibly swollen. Stop the treatment and apply a cold compress to cool and soothe the area.

Before the threading service

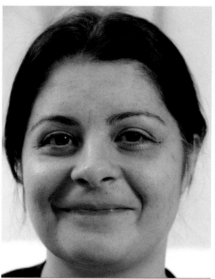
After the threading service

END OF UNIT SUMMARY

Now you've reached the end of the unit, you should feel confident in the theory and practical aspects of all areas of threading services. Use the checklist below to see if there are any areas you feel you need to recap before beginning the end of unit assessment:

- maintain safe and effective methods of working when providing threading services
- consult, plan and prepare for threading services with clients
- remove unwanted hair
- provide aftercare advice.

TEST YOUR KNOWLEDGE B34

Using the questions below, test your knowledge of Unit B34 to see just how much information you've retained. These questions will help you to revise what you've learnt in this chapter.

Turn to pages 407–409 for the answers.

1 Explain why it's important to check your insurance before offering threading services.

2 List the contra-indications that restrict threading treatments.

3 Why is it important not to remove the hairs from a mole?

4 List the advantages and disadvantages of threading.

5 Explain why threading is more suitable for sensitive skin than other temporary methods of hair removal, such as waxing.

6 Describe **two** of the three techniques you can use during threading services.

7 Explain how your client can assist you with stretching the skin.

8 What are the implications of using the mouth technique if you have a crown or a brace?

9 What length of cotton thread do you need for threading?

10 Why is it important not to use the same thread on different areas even on the same client?

11 How do you prepare the cotton thread for the hand technique?

12 How do you prepare the cotton thread for the mouth technique?

13 Why is it important to remove the hair against the direction of hair growth?

14 Explain how threading produces a more defined effect on the brows than tweezing or waxing.

15 What aftercare advice should you give after every threading treatment?

16 When you're providing home care advice, what should it include?

17 What are the possible contra-actions to threading?

18 Explain how to deal with these contra-actions.

19 Why is it important for your client to exfoliate between treatments?

20 How often should your client book a threading treatment?

A manicure is one of the most popular services provided by a beauty therapist and nail technician. It's also one of the first services you're likely to learn as a student. A pedicure is also popular, and you'll probably learn this service alongside or straight after a manicure. Units N2 and N3 have been combined in this textbook as much of the knowledge and skills you need for these services is the same.

During this unit, you'll learn not only how to improve the condition of the skin and nails, but also how to paint nails. For manicures, experimenting with different colours and designs is important; for pedicures, the focus is to make the service relaxing for your client.

In this chapter you'll learn how to:

- maintain safe and effective methods of working when providing manicure and pedicure services
- consult, plan and prepare for manicure and pedicure services
- carry out manicure and pedicure services
- provide aftercare advice.

MAINTAIN SAFE AND EFFECTIVE METHODS OF WORKING WHEN PROVIDING MANICURE AND PEDICURE SERVICES

HANDY HINTS

When you're providing a manicure or pedicure service, it's important to use the skills you've learnt in the following units:

Unit G20 Ensure responsibility for actions to reduce risks to health and safety

Unit G18 Promote additional services or products to clients

Unit G8 Develop and maintain your effectiveness at work.

Before you start a manicure or pedicure service, you must prepare both yourself and your working area. During the service, make sure that your salon environment is safe for both you and your client.

THE SALON

It's your responsibility to be aware of all relevant health and safety legislation to protect yourself, your colleagues and your clients. Both you and your employer must follow all health and safety requirements to make sure the environment is safe before, during and after the manicure or pedicure service.

There's a Code of Practice for nail services that has been created for nail technicians and includes various issues that you must be aware of.

ACTIVITY

Have you ever had a manicure or pedicure? If you have, think about what made it enjoyable or what spoilt the experience. Think about the surroundings, the room temperature and how you were sitting. If you haven't had a manicure or pedicure, think about how you could make the experience more enjoyable.

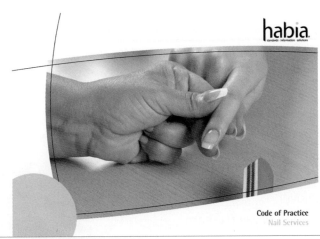

Code of Practice
Nail Services

The Code of Practice is a voluntary code and is available in brochure form at a small cost from www.habia.org.uk.

WHY DON'T YOU...
Read through SmartScreen handout 2 for an introduction to manicure.

SmartScreen N2 handout 2

WHY DON'T YOU...
See SmartScreen handout 1 for guidance
on how to set up your manicure desk.

SmartScreen N2 handout 1

WHY DON'T YOU...
Read through SmartScreen handout 4 for a
list of equipment, and methods of
sterilisation and disinfection.

SmartScreen N2 handout 4

BEFORE YOUR CLIENT ARRIVES

Before your client arrives, make sure your work area is clean and prepared. It's unprofessional if your client arrives and you're not ready for them.

For a manicure, you'll need a specially designed nail desk; for a pedicure, you'll need specially designed salon furniture. There are occasions when a manicure or pedicure will be carried out under different circumstances. For example:

- If the service is a manicure, you might need to work alongside a colleague who is providing a pedicure – and vice versa.
- If a client needs to save time, they might have an eyebrow and eyelash treatment at the same time.

You must make sure you maintain safe and effective methods of working with every treatment. Set up your nail desk or trolley with all the equipment you'll need and keep it in easy reach. Make sure there's adequate lighting and check the salon is warm so both you and your client are comfortable.

Basic equipment

Below are lists of the basic equipment you'll need for manicure and pedicure services. Place them on your tray, trolley or nail station and provide a range of nail polish colours for your client to choose from.

This is a list of the basic equipment and products used for all types of manicure:

- a hand cleanser
- a finger bowl with warm water and nail soak
- towels (to place on your nail station and for drying your client's fingers after the soak)
- files and buffers suitable for natural nails
- disposable tissue for the desk
- nail polish remover
- cotton pads
- a desk mat
- cuticle remover
- hand lotion and/or hand cream
- nail oil
- a base coat
- a top coat
- quick dry (optional)
- a cuticle knife
- cuticle nippers
- orange sticks
- spatulas
- a lidded waste bin
- Barbicide.

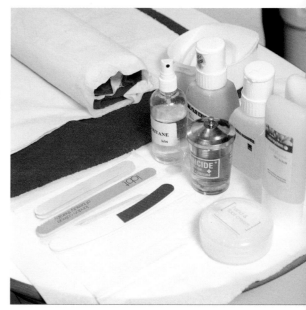
A work station ready for a manicure

This is a list of the basic equipment and products used for all types of pedicure:

- a foot-soak bowl with warm water and an appropriate soak product
- a foot cleanser
- cotton pads
- nail polish remover
- towels
- disposable tissue for the nail and cuticle work
- a desk mat
- cuticle remover
- files and buffers suitable for natural nails
- hard skin remover (abrasive)
- foot lotion and/or foot cream
- nail oil
- a base coat
- a top coat
- quick dry (optional)
- nail clippers
- a cuticle knife
- cuticle nippers
- Barbicide
- orange sticks
- spatulas
- a lidded waste bin.

LUXURY MANICURE AND PEDICURE

For luxury manicures and pedicures, think about the additional products and equipment you'll need.

For a **manicure**, these might include:
- an exfoliator
- a water spray to remove exfoliator and/or mask
- a water bowl
- a hand mask
- warm oil
- a paraffin wax bath
- heated mitts.

For a **pedicure**, these might include:
- an exfoliator
- a foot mask
- massage oil
- a paraffin wax bath
- heated boots.

HANDY HINTS

See Unit G18 for guidance on how to recommend and sell products to clients.

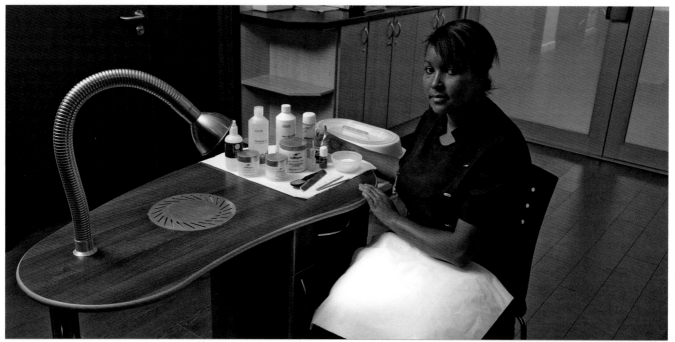
You will need to set up your desk differently for a luxury pedicure.

Other equipment

You also need to make sure that any other equipment you need is easily accessible and placed where it won't create a hazard:

- Suitable lighting: for a manicure, this could be a desk light, either free standing or connected to the desk. Either way, make sure no one will trip over the lead.
- Paraffin wax bath: make sure you can reach it safely. Place it on a firm surface where it cannot be knocked over and check the cable is in a safe position. Turn the heat on just before the manicure starts so it reaches the correct temperature before you use it.
- Heated mitts or boots: place them where you can reach them and leave them plugged in but switched off. Check the cable isn't a hazard and place both mitts or boots side by side to avoid overheating. Switch them on just before you need them as they should heat up quickly.

Access

A salon should be accessible to everyone as far as possible. If appropriate, the salon should provide wheelchair access to try to meet any special requirements. A salon needs to show that it has done this for a variety of disabilities and illnesses.

ACTIVITY

Consider some common conditions and disabilities, such as blindness, hearing impairments and paralysis. Suggest how clients with these conditions could be accommodated. Refer to the Disabilities Discrimination Act (see Unit G20 for details).

Ventilation

Nail polish remover and nail polish contain high levels of **solvents**. It's essential for a healthy environment that there's sufficient ventilation, as too many unwanted vapours can cause headaches, dizziness, fatigue and nausea. If you're just providing manicure and pedicure services, it might be enough to open a window. For nail enhancement services, more substantial forms of ventilation are important because vapours in the atmosphere are more likely.

Extraction is a method of removing polluted air from the atmosphere. See Unit N5 for more details.

See Unit N5 for more details.

Solvents

Liquids that dissolve other solids. Nail polish remover is used to dissolve nail polish. The solvent keeps the polish in a liquid form until it evaporates and leaves behind the solid, dry polish.

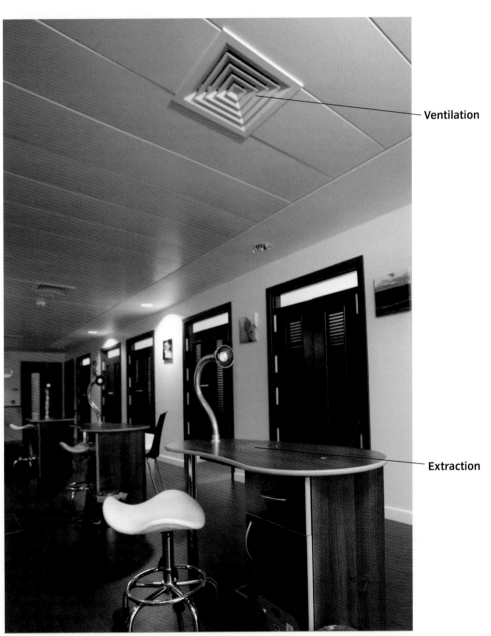

Ventilation

Extraction

An example of a nail station with ventilation and extraction

Your professional appearance

Refer to Unit G20 for guidance on personal presentation.

It's particularly important for nail technicians that you have short, clean nails. Other nail technicians who don't work in a salon might be allowed to have nails that promote services their salon offers. Your nails should be in excellent condition, show a current and fashionable colour or, at the very least, be buffed to a high shine.

Nail services often create some dust. Are your clothes clean and free from dust? Keep jewellery to a minimum. Rings and bracelets can trap products and dust, which can cause allergic reactions.

Personal protective equipment

Sometimes you'll need extra equipment to protect both you and your client. Every employer has a responsibility to provide all forms of personal protective equipment (PPE) and must also provide training in its use. PPE should be available at all times and is designed to reduce the risk of injury.

Sometimes a salon will remove any products and equipment that might result in injury and replace it with a safer option. However, this isn't always possible, so you'll need to use PPE to minimise any potential risk. It's the salon owner/manager's responsibility to carry out a risk assessment to establish where and when you need to use PPE.

It's your responsibility to be aware of any manicure or pedicure products that are potentially hazardous. This information will be available from the salon's risk assessments records.

HANDY HINTS

MSDS are information sheets provided by the manufacturer/supplier that contain information on the ingredients of a specific product. It provides information on toxicity, health effects, first aid and storage requirements.

ACTIVITY

If you have access to the Habia health and safety pack for nail technicians, carry out your own risk assessment using a risk assessment form from the safety pack. Choose a selection of products (eg hand/foot cream, cuticle remover, nail polish remover), collect the Material Safety Data Sheets (MSDS) from the supplier and complete the form.

Types of PPE

1 Gloves: non-latex, preferably nitrile.

Many people are, or can become, allergic to latex gloves or the powder inside them. It's also possible that an individual can be allergic to any of the products used during the manicure or pedicure. The person might have had the allergy for some time, or they might have developed an allergy recently due to overexposure. An existing skin condition could also be irritated by some products.

There are not many products used during a manicure or pedicure that are known to cause allergies. However, if you get an allergic reaction, you must wear protective gloves when you're handling that particular product. You should always wear gloves when you're pouring hazardous products into smaller containers.

Some nail services require you to wear gloves and safety glasses.

2 Safety glasses.

These should be worn when there's any risk of a chemical splash (eg **decanting**) or flying debris (eg clipping toenails). They should be scratch and solvent resistant and provide side protection. Normal spectacles aren't a substitute. Always wear safety glasses when you're clipping toenails. They're usually brittle and can fly up into your eye. Have an extra pair of safety glasses for your client, just in case.

3 Aprons: these should be worn when you're decanting products.

These will avoid any splashes that could damage or stain your clothes or uniform. They will also protect your uniform from dust. You should always wear a waterproof apron for a pedicure service. You'll need to use plenty of water and you might need to hold your client's feet on your lap.

SALON HYGIENE

It's essential you avoid any possibility of cross-infection during manicure and pedicure services. Clients want to see that the salon is clean and that care is being taken to reduce the risk of cross-infection. They want to know that they're not going to leave the salon having picked up a micro-organism that can cause disease and infection.

There are three types of hygiene management that you must follow in the salon:

1 Cleaning: this is the physical process of removing surface debris from tools and equipment. You must clean everything before you disinfect it otherwise the disinfectant won't work properly.

2 Disinfecting: there are many ways of disinfecting, from using an anti-microbial handwash to a strong solution that will destroy most micro-organisms.

3 Sterilising: this process destroys all living organisms and should only be used on metal tools. The only acceptable method of sterilising is using an autoclave where the tools are heated to an extremely high temperature that cannot sustain any life. To find out what this temperature is, check the manufacturer's instructions. This process isn't necessary for nail services as the highest level of disinfection is sufficient.

Decant
To pour liquid from one container to another.

HANDY HINTS
The first signs of an allergic reaction or a developing sensitivity are: redness or itching of the skin; swelling; headaches; runny nose or nausea. These symptoms will subside if the allergen is removed.

N2/N3 MANICURE AND PEDICURE

WHY DON'T YOU...
Read through SmartScreen handout 3 for further guidance on client confidentiality.

 SmartScreen N2 handout 3

Read the nail manufacturers' council and Habia guidelines for cleaning and disinfecting manicuring and pedicuring enhancement equipment, available on the nail services page of the health and safety section at **www.habia.org**.

TOOLS AND EQUIPMENT

The following table shows the appropriate method of cleaning for each piece of equipment involved in the manicure and pedicure treatments.

Equipment	Hygiene method
Towels/linens	Wash after every client at a minimum temperature of 60°C
Hard surfaces	Wipe with a damp cloth to remove debris then use a suitable hard surface disinfectant. Wipe the desk after every client
Metal tools	Use an autoclave or scrub with a brush in detergent to remove any debris and oils. Soak for the recommended time in fresh disinfectant solution
Files and buffers and hard skin removers (immersable)	Brush or scrub under running water to remove any debris and soak in fresh disinfectant solution for the recommended time
Washable files and buffers	Clean files that can be washed (but not immersed) and spray with a tool disinfectant ONLY if they've not come into contact with broken skin
Single-use tools	Throw away anything that cannot be washed and disinfected, eg orange sticks or wooden files after every client
Foot-soak bowls, foot spas, pedicure thrones	Disinfect after every client (see page 197)

An autoclave

Disinfecting

Disinfecting foot-soak bowls, foot spas and pedicure thrones

1 Bowls: simple bowls that you can fill with warm water and are large enough to hold both feet are an inexpensive way of soaking feet. Rinse out several times after each use, clean with a suitable disinfectant and leave to dry.

Remember to follow the manufacturer's instructions when you're using disinfectant. Make up a fresh solution every day and remember to wear PPE when you're handling undiluted disinfectant as it's an irritant.

2 Foot spas: use a professional foot spa with disposable liners rather than the ones you can use at home. This is for several reasons:
  - The liners are for single use so there's no possibility of cross-infection.
  - You won't need to go through a long disinfecting process. The home spas often have a bubbles programme. The tubes can harbour germs and need a thorough clean and soaking with strong disinfectant to make sure all the micro-organisms have been removed.
  - It's much safer and easier to carry a small disposable liner than the whole foot spa.

A pedicure bowl with disposable liner

A professional foot spa will have a heating and vibration facility so the experience will be more pleasurable for your client.

3 Pedicure thrones: these are purpose built chairs with bowls attached for soaking the feet and a foot rest. Some are plumbed into the salon's water supply and others have a removable bowl. If it's a plumbed chair that has the bubbles programme, run a disinfectant solution through the system after every client even if you've not used the programme. The tubes will contain water that can carry germs and also become stagnant. If it

doesn't have this programme, just rinse the bowl with clean water several times and wipe over all the surfaces with disinfectant.

After you've soaked your tools and equipment in disinfectant for the required amount of time, remove them using tongs, pat them dry and store them in a covered container.

You can use UV cabinets to store clean tools. Remember that UV cabinets don't disinfect tools, they simply provide a clean environment for storage.

Some beauty therapists and nail technicians like to keep a jar of disinfectant on their desk. You can place tools, such as nippers and cuticle knives, in the disinfectant but you must scrub and wash them with detergent first. Cuticle knives are often double ended so they'll need to be fully immersed. If any tools or equipment fall on the floor, you shouldn't use them again until they've been properly cleaned.

Paraffin wax baths

Wipe the outside of the bath with a warm, damp cloth that has been soaked in warm soapy water and a little disinfectant. Remember to disconnect from the electricity supply first. Soak the brush used to apply the wax in hot water after every use, then wash in warm, soapy water and a little disinfectant. Clean the inside of the bath after each batch of wax has run out and before you put in a new batch. Always store the bath with the lid on.

Preparing a paraffin wax bath

Heated mitts/boots

You shouldn't need to clean the inside of any heated mitts or boots because the hands/feet are encased in a disposable bag and wrapped in an inner protective bag before they're placed inside. From time to time, wash the inner liner in hot soapy water, rinse and dry. Follow the manufacturer's instructions when you're cleaning the mitts/boots. Make sure you disconnect the mitts/boots from the electricity supply and wipe them over with a clean cloth dipped in warm, soapy water. You can add a small amount of disinfectant to the water but don't use any solvents, such as nail polish remover or an alcohol solution, as this will damage the plastic. Clean the control unit in the same way.

ACTIVITY

Research the various paraffin wax baths and thermal mitts/boots that are available and compare their features, benefits and prices.

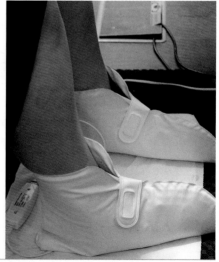

Check the manufacturer's instructions for how to clean heated mitts and boots.

Research the various hygiene products on the market and collect the information in a file. Compare their prices and write a short report on which products would be your first choice to use in a salon.

HAND WASHING

It's essential that you wash your hands before and after every client to avoid cross-infection. It's good practice to use a disinfecting spray or antibacterial gel, but remember to wash your hands first.

For a manicure, ask your client to wash their hands with soap and water, paying particular attention to their nails. It's not your responsibility to clean dirt out from under their nails. Make sure they have access to a sink with hot and cold water, liquid soap, a good supply of disposable (or clean) towels and a waste bin.

During manicure or pedicure services, it's important that you don't touch your face or eyes as you might transfer products from your hands. If you've got a cold, make sure you sneeze into a paper tissue, blow your nose and throw your tissue into a lidded waste bin. Wash your hands with soap and water and use a sanitising spray or gel before you resume the service. If you've got a bad cold, you chould consider wearing a face mask to avoid cross-infection.

DISPOSABLES

During manicure or pedicure services, you'll use quite a few **disposables**. The most common disposables are:

1 Disposable tissue: use a clean disposable tissue to cover the towel on the nail desk (for a manicure) or the foot rest/your lap (for a pedicure). Replace the towel if it gets wet or gets some product on it. Also use a new tissue if you've either clipped the nails or filed them and generated dust.
2 Cotton pads: it's easy to use too many cotton pads so try to use fewer if you can.

When you're using disposables and nail service products, try not to be wasteful. This increases the cost of the service and reduces the salon's profit margins.

Disposables

Single-use products and equipment, such as paper towels, cotton pads, orange sticks, unwashable files and buffers.

Look at a variety of nail polish removers and list their ingredients. Identify the main ingredients and their purpose. Use the Internet to help you with your research.

PRODUCT HYGIENE AND AVOIDING WASTE

You must make sure you keep all products hygienically clean and avoid waste.

1 Polish remover and nail cleansers: pour from their bottles into a specifically designed pump. This makes them easy and safe to use and reduces the risk of spillages.

2 Hand and foot lotions: use a pump dispenser for thinner products. You can usually buy these from your salon's supplier. Make sure you keep the pump clean and free from dried product.

3 Creams and gels: these normally come in tubs. Always use a spatula when you're removing product and never use your fingers as this is unhygienic. Either throw the spatula away or wash it after each use and disinfect. Use an orange stick for small containers and throw away after use.

4 Polish bottles: make sure you screw the cap on tightly when you're not using the bottle, even if you put it down for a few seconds. When you've finished using the bottle, clean the screw thread with a cotton pad dampened with nail polish remover. This will clean any polish from the neck and make sure the cap doesn't get stuck. Be careful though – don't leave any cotton fibres behind.

5 Other nail products: try to apply products, such as oil or cuticle remover, with a pipette. Brushes can pick up debris from the nail and transfer it back into the bottle.

As a general rule, make sure you put lids and caps back on properly. A loose lid or cap can result in spillages and the product can dry up or become contaminated.

DISPOSING OF WASTE

The only acceptable method of disposing your waste is to use a metal waste bin with a lid. This is because metal doesn't absorb vapours and cannot be damaged by solvents. Make sure you put a waste bag inside the bin. The lid will contain the vapours from cotton pads soaked in nail polish remover and prevent them escaping into the room. Remove the liner when the bin is full or at the end of the day. Tie it up and throw it in the main dustbin.

Soak up any liquid spillages with disposable tissue and throw it into the bin. If you spill a large amount of solvent, ask for help from the salon manager as larger quantities of solvents require careful disposal.

Any waste that is contaminated with blood or bodily fluids needs to be collected by the local authority or an approved authorised collection service.

BEFORE YOU BEGIN

SERVICE TIMES

You need to make sure you know and follow the industry accepted times for your treatment. Each type of manicure or pedicure has its own times. If the service is too short, your client will feel you haven't provided a thorough service; if the service is too long, profits will be reduced and the next client will be kept waiting. These times exclude consultation.

Manicure treatment	Times
Shape and paint – a quick shape of the nails followed by a chosen nail polish application	15 mins
Standard manicure – nail and cuticle work, quick hand massage, nail paint or natural buff	45 mins
Luxury manicure – combination of basic manicure plus heat treatment (eg paraffin wax) or exfoliation/mask	60 mins

Pedicure treatment	Times
Shape and paint – cleaning the feet and nails followed by a quick shape of the nails and a chosen nail polish application	20 mins
Standard pedicure – foot soak, nail and cuticle work, quick foot massage, nail paint or natural buff	50 mins
Luxury pedicure – combination of basic pedicure plus heat treatment (eg paraffin wax) or exfoliation/mask	60–75 mins

COMFORT AND AVOIDING INJURY

Sitting in the wrong position for even a short period of time can cause discomfort and possibly injury. Back and neck ache are common injuries caused by incorrect positioning and can result in long-term problems. You could spend a whole day sitting to give nail treatments, so correct positioning is important.

For manicures and enhancements:

1 Manicure work station: this needs to be at a height and width that allows you to work without bending down or stretching.
2 Chair: your chair should be at the correct height at your manicure desk and should support your back and thighs. Always sit straight on the chair and don't lean with one elbow on the desk.
3 Stool and trolley: there might be occasions when you need to provide a manicure at a place other than a desk. You'll need an adjustable height stool and a trolley to hold all your tools and equipment. Make sure the stool is positioned so that you can sit straight without having to bend or stretch.

It's important to use the right furniture for nail services.

For pedicures:

1 Pedicure area: your salon will probably have an area especially for pedicures. It could be as simple as a chair for your client and a stool for you, and you would rest your client's feet on your lap. It could be a pedicure stool for you that has a foot rest for your client, or it could be a purpose built throne.
2 Stool: you must take care to avoid injuring yourself. Check that you're sitting on a stool that supports your legs and is at a height that means you don't have to bend.
3 Tools and equipment: you should also make sure that you can easily reach all your tools and equipment.

CONSULT, PLAN AND PREPARE FOR MANICURE AND PEDICURE SERVICES

The consultation is probably the first contact you'll have with your client. You must make sure that you come across as professional and confident.

We've already discussed your appearance but equally important is your manner and behaviour. It's essential you make a good impression from the start. You need to demonstrate:

1 Courtesy: welcome the client to the salon, offer to take their coat and hang it up if you can. Take them to the treatment area and make sure they're comfortable. Explain that you'll carry out a brief consultation before you start the service. You must be aware of any disabilities your client has and react accordingly. For example, if your client has impaired hearing, make sure you're in a quiet area and speak clearly and slowly. There might also be cultural and religious considerations that could affect your service. For example, a Muslim woman shouldn't receive a treatment from a male therapist.

2 Confidence: your client needs to feel they're in good hands and that the advice and service you're giving is correct. Even as a trainee, you need to demonstrate confidence in your work. As a trainee, your lecturer/teacher/line manager will be available for questions. If there's something you're not sure of, it's better to ask your supervisor for help.

3 Tact: nail services are usually carried out in an open salon. Most clients won't want their personal details overheard by everyone. If possible, ask your client to fill out the record card themselves or carry out the consultation in a more private area. If your client has an unpleasant condition (eg a fungal nail infection), take care not to show any reaction.

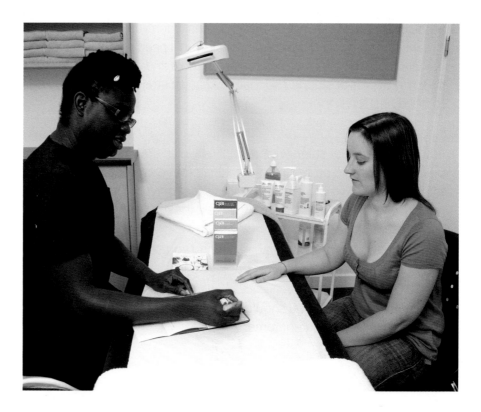

A nail service isn't a medical treatment so it's not necessary to probe too deeply into a client's health. However, there are certain areas where it might be useful to know your client's general health. You need to ask your questions without passing any comment or opinion. Never try to diagnose a client as you're not a qualified medical professional.

CONSULTATION TECHNIQUES

The consultation is an essential first step in providing your client with an appropriate service.

The aim of the consultation is to establish:

- what your client expects from the service
- if your client's expectations are realistic (eg perfect nail and skin immediately when they've got dry nails and overgrown cuticles)
- what service you would recommend and a possible on-going service plan
- if there are possible contra-indications that could restrict or prevent the service
- a realistic time frame
- if there's anything that could affect your recommendations (eg time or lack of money).

When you've found out what your client wants to achieve from their manicure or pedicure service, there are four techniques you need to use before you can make your recommendations.

QUESTIONING AND LISTENING

In a friendly manner and without probing too much, try to ask questions to discover a bit more about your client, the history of their nails and their lifestyle. Listen carefully to what they say as it's important you don't miss anything.

There are two types of questions you can use during the consultation: open questions and closed questions. Open questions give your client the opportunity to explain something in their own words. This type of questioning should give you a better idea of what your client wants to achieve.

Examples of open questions:

- How would you describe the condition of your skin and nails?
- Do you have any problems with your nails?
- Is there anything you're unhappy with about your hands/nails?

Closed questions require a short, definite answer and are useful for identifying any possible contra-indications. They often involve just yes or no answers.

Examples of general closed questions:

- Do you wear gloves when you're washing up/gardening?
- Do you have a hand and nail care routine?
- Do your nails break easily?

If you uncover a contra-indication, ask:

- How long have you had this?
- Are you using any medication or cream?
- Has it been diagnosed by a doctor?
- Is it painful?
- Do you know what caused it?

During the questioning stage, you should find out about your client's lifestyle. Do they have young children, what are their hobbies, what is their job? All of this information will help you plan the correct service and advise them on their home care routine.

Lifestyle has a huge impact on the skin and nails. For example, clients with young children will always have their hands in water; this has a detrimental effect on skin and nails and can dry them out.

An outside job or hobby will affect the hands because of UV light damage, even during winter. Typing can cause the nails to split or peel. Any job that involves constant contact with water can cause problems with both the skin and nails.

VISUAL

To see the condition of your client's nails, you need to take off any nail polish. For pedicure treatments, you need to clean your client's feet before you touch them. Spray them with an antiseptic foot spray or put them into the foot bath for a few seconds to wash them. Look at their nails and skin and continue to ask questions. This will give you an idea of what condition the nails and skin are in and give you a better idea of what recommendations, products and aftercare advice you can give.

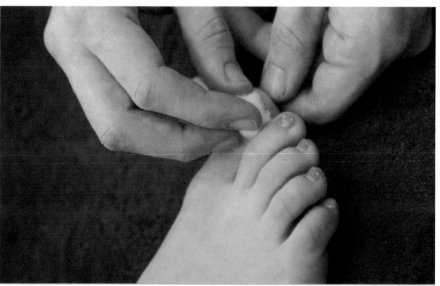

Remove nail polish before you analyse the condition of your client's nails.

MANUAL

Feel the condition of the skin and strength of the nails to give you more information on their condition. You'll learn more from this technique as you gain more experience.

At the end of your consultation, finish writing down the options you've discussed, the condition of their nails and their expectations. Agree on the service plan. Ask your client to sign the record as an agreement that the information you've recorded is correct. Don't forget that you need to sign the card as well.

REFERENCE TO CLIENT RECORDS

Most insurance policies require a signed consultation record for every client to validate the policy. It also makes sure that both you and your client have a record of the service plan and your client is given the correct treatment next time around.

You must write down your notes from every consultation on the client record card. This should include the exact service you've provided, any change to the skin or nail, or any skin or nail condition. Both you and your client need to sign the record card. Make sure your writing is easy to read. A different therapist might carry out the next service and will need to see condition of the client's hands/feet and nails at their first visit and also which products you used.

The client record card can also tell you if your client isn't good at looking after their skin and nails at home, as well as the client's likes and dislikes, how often they've had treatments and how loyal they are to the salon.

If any changes occur during the service, make a note of these and any relevant comments your client makes, plus their choice of nail colour, at the end of the service. Don't make the mistake of thinking you'll remember to do it later. Complete the record immediately and return it to where it belongs.

Records should be locked away securely and should be available only to those who need to see them. There are rules under the Data Protection Act that allow you to record certain essential information. This must only be relevant to your work and shouldn't be shared with a third party unless the individual has given permission.

WHY DON'T YOU...
Research the Data Protection Act on the Internet and write a few sentences about how it affects the recording and storage of client records in a salon.

WHY DON'T YOU...
Design your own client record card, making sure there's space for all necessary information.

ACTIVITY

Conduct two practice consultations: one in pairs in class, and the other at home with a member of your family. Devise a full service plan for each consultation to last several weeks and recommend treatments that will improve their nails and skin.

SERVICES FOR CLIENTS UNDER 16 YEARS

If you have a client who is under 16 years, you must have written consent from their parent or guardian. The consent must include all the details of the nail service: the date and time, the specific service, your client's name and address, and who is providing consent. Keep this document with the record card and create a new document for every treatment unless they're having a course of treatments.

In addition to the written consent, the minor's parent or guardian must stay with them all the time. Make sure you're never left alone with the minor, otherwise your salon's insurance could become invalid, or you could violate the Child Protection and Safeguarding Acts. If you obey the rules, you're protecting both yourself and the minor. It's the parent or guardian's responsibility to supervise each stage of the service and make sure it follows the service plan.

COMMON CONDITIONS AND INFECTIONS

DERMATITIS

This is a condition that causes inflammation of the skin. You should check for dermatitis on yourself and your client. There are several types of dermatitis: atopic dermatitis, which is often hereditary and linked to other conditions, such as asthma and hay fever; and contact dermatitis, which occurs when you come into contact with a particular substance and your skin gets inflamed. There are two types of contact dermatitis.

1 Allergic contact dermatitis is caused by contact with an allergen. An allergen is a substance which causes your immune system to react abnormally. When you're exposed to an allergen for the first time, you become sensitised to it. After that, every time you have contact with the allergen, it causes a reaction.

2 Irritant contact dermatitis is caused by contact with an irritant. An irritant is a substance, product or chemical that damages the skin and makes it inflamed. It can occur in anyone who is exposed to irritants for a sufficient amount of time. Both types of contact dermatitis can cause your skin to become red, blistered, dry and cracked.

INFECTIONS

There are three types of common infection that must be controlled in a salon environment:

1 Bacterial infection: this could be a skin injury that's infected, swollen, red and sometimes has pus. A bacterial infection can also be associated with an upset stomach and food poisoning. Bacterial infections are easily spread by direct and indirect contact.

2 Fungal infection: this is especially relevant for nail services as it appears on the skin and nails. The micro-organisms live on **keratin**. People that have recently taken a course of antibiotics are susceptible to fungal infections, as are diabetics and others with a low immunity. Some common fungal infections are athlete's foot (or tinea pedis), ringworm and some non-specific fungi that thicken and crumble the nails.

3 Viral infections: these are easily spread and include colds and flu, warts (including verrucae), chicken pox, mumps, measles and some types of throat or ear infections. As well as direct contact, indirect contact can spread these infections, such as coughs and sneezes.

SPOTTING A CONTRA-INDICATION

If you notice a contra-indication, you must ask your client about it. Closed questions are more suitable for this as a specific answer is required. The contra-indications might not be obvious. You still need to ask a few basic questions to make sure you're providing the best service.

Questions you should ask include:

1 Do you have any allergies? If your client does have allergies, you need to establish exactly what they are. If the allergy involves anything that you might use during your nail service, you must avoid using it. Some clients might know they're allergic to nail polish and will recognise the signs (sore or puffy eyes, itching around the nails). They might know a brand of polish that they can wear safely and bring it with them.

Keratin
A protein that is a major component of skin, nails and hair. It's present in the epidermis and there's a high proportion of it in nails and hair where the cells have become keratinised.

HANDY HINTS
Make sure you know of all your client's allergies. Nut-based products would cause a bad reaction in someone allergic to nuts.

2 Do you suffer from diabetes? Diabetics often suffer from poor circulation and can have problems with their nails. Also, diabetics have a slower healing time so take extra care to avoid any broken skin and don't press too hard when you're massaging to make sure you don't cause any more damage.

3 Are you taking any medication? Medication can cause changes to the condition of the skin and nails. If your client has been taking the medication for a long time, any changes have probably already happened. If it's short term, such as a course of antibiotics, you could notice a change in the nails in a few weeks' time.

COMMON CONTRA-INDICATIONS

A contra-indication is something that prevents or restricts a service. An infection will prevent a service, while a condition could restrict it. A severe condition, ie nail separation, could get worse during the service.

Diseases that prevent a manicure or pedicure service
Fungal infections
This type of infection is more commonly found on feet and toenails but can also be found on the hands and fingernails.

Skin
A fungal infection of the skin can cause various rashes; some are red, scaly and itchy, whereas others can look like dry skin. The fungus can infect just one area or several areas of the body.

Examples of a fungal infections are:

1 Athlete's foot (tinea pedis): this is usually found on the skin between the toes. The skin can split uncomfortably and smell unpleasant. It's more common on feet due to their environment, ie warm, moist and enclosed in socks and shoes.

2 Ringworm (tinea corporis): this can be found anywhere on the body and looks like a circular rash with a clear centre. This is not a worm; it's called ringworm because the rash is in the shape of a ring.

Particularly at risk from this type of fungal infection are people who:

- have recently taken a course of antibiotics
- are taking steroids
- have diabetes
- are overweight
- have had fungal skin infections in the past
- have a weakened immune system.

Nails
A fungal infection of the nail affects the nail plate. Its correct term is onychomycosis (or tinea unguium). Nails with a fungal infection are thickened, distorted and usually crumbling. This condition takes a long time to heal and will need a topical cream or liquid or oral medication. If you suspect that your client has any form of fungal infection, recommend they see their GP or pharmacist for a proper diagnosis.

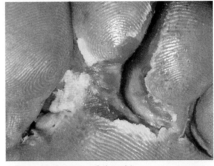
A fungal infection of the skin

HANDY HINTS

A fungal infection of the nail affects the nail plate. A bacterial infection of the nail is either under the nail or on the surface of the nail.

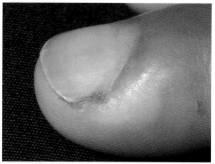

A bacterial infection of the nail

Impetigo

A highly contagious bacterial skin infection normally found amongst pre-school children. It causes painful blisters, usually on the arms and legs.

Eponychium

Also known as the cuticle, this is the thickened layer of skin surrounding the fingernails and toenails.

Hyponychium

Also known as the quick, this is the soft skin beneath the nail plate that forms a seal to protect the nail bed.

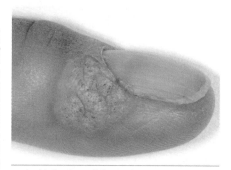

A viral infection of the nail

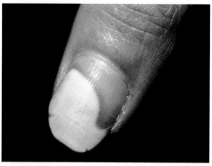

Onycholysis

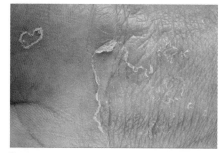

Eczema

Bacterial infections

This type of infection is common on both the skin and the nails. It's usually associated with swelling, inflammation, pain and often pus. It's normally where a micro-organism has invaded damaged skin. The infection is highly contagious. **Impetigo** and boils or infected spots are the most common skin infections.

There are several bacterial infections that can affect the nail. Paronychia is where the skin surrounding the nail, either at the base (**eponychium**) or at the side walls (lateral nail folds), gets damaged. This can be caused by aggressive manicuring or cutting the eponychium. It can also happen when hang nails are pulled instead of cut, or accidental damage. When the skin is broken, bacteria can invade and cause a painful infection in the form of inflammation, swelling and pus. The infection is highly contagious and must be treated with regular antisepsis, eg an antiseptic cream or a salt water soak. A more serious infection must be dealt with by a GP or pharmacist.

Viral infections

The most common type of viral infection on the hands are warts and they're usually found at the sides of the nails. They're highly contagious and you mustn't touch them. Medication is available from the pharmacist.

Parasitic infections

These are rare on the hands and feet. Lice and scabies are the most common parasites on the skin and look like itchy bumps. As a beauty therapist/nail technician, you cannot diagnose these conditions, but make sure you refer any client with itchy bumps to their GP.

Severe nail separation (onycholysis)

The epidermis of the nail bed (bed epithelium) is quite sticky, but the nail plate is held in place mostly by grooves and ridges on the nail bed. A thin, weak nail can easily come away from the nail bed and a damaged nail can have the same problem. If the seal at the **hyponychium** is broken, infection can enter and cause more separation. An allergic reaction to a product can also cause separation. It could also be caused by psoriasis.

If this condition is minor, take extra care when you're filing and buffing the nail. If it's severe (ie a quarter of the nail bed or more has separated), the condition is too delicate to work on as you could cause more separation. It's common on the big toenail if the nail is too long and presses against a tight shoe.

Severe eczema

Some eczema can be minor and only appear at certain times of the year. It can, however, be severe where the skin has open sores. If this is the case, the skin is too delicate to perform a nail service. This could lead to an infection.

Severe psoriasis

Psoriasis on the nails is quite common. If it's severe, the skin can be broken and sore, the nail surface discoloured, pitted and thicker, and the nail bed exposed or infected. The nails can crumble away and leave very little of the nail plate behind. The nail plate can also be rough.

Psoriasis differs from eczema because it has distinct scaly patches. Like eczema, if it's severe, it will prevent a manicure service. Severe psoriasis can also cause nail separation – see above.

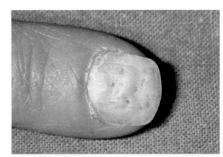
Psoriasis on a nail

Severe dermatitis

Dermatitis is a general inflammation of the skin, often caused by an allergic reaction or overexposure to an allergen. For the same reasons as above, this condition is contra-indicated.

Infected ingrowing toenails (onychocryptosis)

The skin around the big toenail is soft and the nail is tough. Wearing tight shoes can sometimes push a sharp corner on the edge of the nail into the skin. This results in pain and inflammation and often a bacterial infection. An infected ingrowing toenail will prevent a pedicure because it will be too painful and the infection is highly contagious.

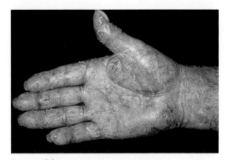
Dermatitis

Conditions that restrict a manicure or pedicure service

There are some minor conditions that won't prevent a service but will mean you'll have to take extra care and modify the treatment to avoid the affected area.

Minor nail separation

If the nail separation is minor, gently file and buff the nail. Don't clean under the free edge as you could cause an infection or further separation. In a pedicure, if a toenail has separated, you could find evidence of a fungal infection. This is because the environment is perfect for an infection to thrive. If you suspect there's an infection, suggest that your client sees a chiropodist or pharmacist as soon as possible.

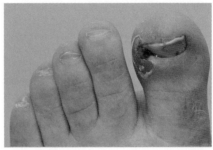
An ingrowing nail

Minor eczema

Take extra care if there's any evidence of eczema and be extra careful with your hygiene. Don't use any exfoliating creams or masks and use gentle pressure movements when you're massaging.

Minor psoriasis

Psoriasis can cause the nails to crumble and leave very little nail plate behind. With minor psoriasis, proceed with caution, but avoid heat treatments and too much friction.

Minor dermatitis

As with psoriasis, be very gentle and avoid heat treatments and applying too much friction.

Severely bitten or damaged nails

Bitten or damaged nails are delicate and must be treated gently. Use gentle filing and little buffing.

WHY DON'T YOU...
Read through SmartScreen handout 13 for treatable nail conditions.

 SmartScreen N2 handout 13

Bitten nails

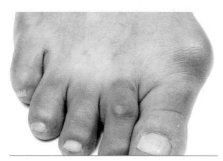
Bunions

WHY DON'T YOU...
Read through SmartScreen handout 7 for conditions that restrict a pedicure.

 SmartScreen N3 handout 7

HANDY HINTS
Did you know that the skin on the fingers of a nail biter will be swollen due to the action of the saliva in the mouth? Saliva is an enzyme that begins the process of breaking down food.

Commercial viability
Making sure you don't spend too much time on tasks. If you take too long doing one thing, your salon loses money because you could be doing something else more valuable for the business. Remember that time is money and you're being paid to be efficient.

Conditions that restrict a pedicure
Bunions
These are a distortion of the joint of the big toe. They're clearly noticeable by a large bump on the side of the foot at the base of the big toe. They can be hereditary or they can be caused by wearing tight fitting shoes over a long period of time. A small bunion can sometimes be straightened by a chiropodist, but the usual treatment is surgery to correct the abnormal joint and replace the cartilage. Bunions don't have to prevent a pedicure but they can be painful so avoid touching the area during the massage.

Corns
Corns are caused by the joints of the toes rubbing on shoes over time. They're a build-up of hard skin that can become painful. Like bunions, avoid the area during a pedicure and you should recommend that your client gets them treated by a chiropodist.

Calluses
Unlike corns, these can be found anywhere on the foot and, again, are caused by rubbing from shoes. There are always areas of hard skin on the heels and the ball of the foot. This is necessary to protect the skin on the feet but most people would rather have soft and more attractive skin. The calloused area on the back of the heels can become hard, dry and unsightly and sometimes crack and be painful. You can treat the hard skin areas during a pedicure but take care not to remove too much and break the living skin beneath the calloused area.

Varicose veins
These are common in people of all ages but particularly older people. Veins that are situated closer to the skin's surface rely on muscle movement to return the blood flow back to the heart. Sometimes the pressure of the blood in the veins causes bulges in the walls of the vein. This can be painful and you must avoid the varicose veins during the massage. Massaging the area could make the condition worse.

DURING THE CONSULTATION
If your client has any of the above conditions, make sure you record everything on the record card. Read it back to your client to make sure you've understood correctly or ask your client to read it through carefully before signing it.

It's important that the consultation is a two-way conversation. Try to keep the consultation to less than ten minutes for **commercial viability**, but encourage your client to ask you anything they need clarifying. This is especially important when you're suggesting a service plan, so that you and your client agree on what the outcomes will be.

ACTIVITY
In pairs, carry out a full consultation with your partner. Make a note of the open and closed questions you use and complete the record card with a full diagnosis of skin and nail conditions.

IDENTIFYING NOT DIAGNOSING

During your consultation, you might discover a condition that you can't deal with yourself and needs medical help. As a beauty therapist/nail technician, you don't have any medical training and you mustn't diagnose conditions. A qualified technician should only identify conditions that need further investigation.

Tact must be used under these circumstances. You must avoid worrying your client unnecessarily. However, depending on the condition, you need to encourage your client to seek medical advice.

Written consent for a nail service usually falls into the category of private medicine and will need to be paid for. However, many clients aren't willing to pay the fee. If the condition isn't contra-indicated but the service is restricted, write down the condition on the record card and ask your client to sign the card to say they agree to the service.

NAIL AND SKIN ANALYSIS

When you're providing a manicure or pedicure service, there are three main areas that you need to consider:

- the skin on the hands or feet
- the skin surrounding the nails
- the nail plate.

THE SKIN ON THE HANDS

Remember from your anatomy and physiology that the hands have two different types of skin: hairy and hairless skin. The hands suffer from many environmental challenges, such as water and chemical damage and exposure to UV light. We don't tend to look after them as much as the skin on our faces, so poor condition is extremely common.

The skin on the palms of our hands can suffer from callouses and hard skin. Callous removal on the hands isn't normally necessary, but the skin does need to be kept soft and protected. The skin on the back of our hands should be treated more like the skin on our face.

Dry skin can have more wrinkles and look dull. You should exfoliate to remove all the dead skin cells and remoisturise. Heat treatments are ideal for dry hands, eg hand masks, heated mitts and paraffin wax baths.

Hand washing can cause skin to become dry

Prematurely aged skin is thin and has lost some of its supporting structure (ie collagen and elastin). It will settle around the underlying structures of blood vessels and ligaments. Plump with moisture and collagen-enhancing products.

Ageing skin can be helped in the same way with extra moisture to help fill out the wrinkles. For sun damage and age spots, exfoliate, moisturise and use daily UV protection.

THE SKIN ON THE FEET

The feet also have the two different types of skin: hairy and hairless. The feet suffer from many challenges that are different from hands, such as tight-fitting shoes, a warm and moist environment and pressure and

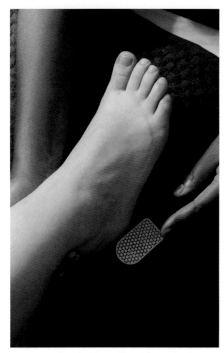

Removing hard skin (callous) from the heels

friction. The skin on the soles of the feet often suffers from hard skin and needs special attention to keep them comfortable and smooth.

THE SKIN SURROUNDING THE NAILS

Generally, you'll focus on the skin surrounding the nails more during a manicure than a pedicure, as the skin surrounding the fingernails will need more work.

The eponychium is the fold of skin that frames the base of the nail. If the cuticle is not regularly removed, this fold of skin can stick to the cuticle and get pulled as the nail grows. It can overgrow and split at the sides if it's pulled too much.

This is one of the most important areas you'll deal with during a manicure, but you mustn't cut it as you'll be cutting living skin. The skin can get dry and split areas can be sore and catch on clothing or hair. If the eponychium is in good condition, it's not especially visible.

At the sides of the nail, the skin can also be dry and you could find hang nails. This applies to both fingernails and toenails. These are spikes of nail that detach from the sides of the nail plate as it grows. Cuticle nippers can effectively remove them. Daily application of nail oil and hand or foot cream will keep the skin in good condition and stop it sticking to the cuticle and being pulled up as the nail grows.

The skin on the feet can be dry and is always prone to blisters. The skin on the feet can also be affected by corns and callouses.

Common cuticle conditions

1 Dry cuticles: these can be seen as whitish areas at the base of the nail plate. Once softened, you can remove them carefully with a cuticle knife. They will continue to grow and should be removed on a regular basis. Use nail oil to stop the cuticle from drying out. Dry cuticles are less common on the skin surrounding the toes.

2 Split cuticles: this refers to the corners of the skin that have been overstretched. Remove the cuticle and moisturise daily to prevent this from recurring.

Split skin around the nail

3 Overgrown cuticles: every nail has some cuticle on it, even a few days after a manicure or pedicure. This is because the dead skin is continually shed from under the nail fold. If this isn't removed, it will stay on the nail as it grows forward, until it's shed naturally. The eponychium often sticks to it and is pulled along with it. This looks unsightly and makes it difficult to apply nail polish.

4 Pterygium: this is a less common condition and is a deformation of the eponychium and nail plate. The skin grows up the nail and sometimes it separates the nail plate. The only treatment is to keep the skin soft but you shouldn't try to remove it.

THE NAIL PLATE

You'll learn about the different nail shapes in anatomy and physiology. These are determined by your genetic make-up and may be similar to those of other members of your family. Nail shape will not alter under normal circumstances. The thickness of a natural nail is also determined genetically and is directly related to the size of the matrix. A deep matrix

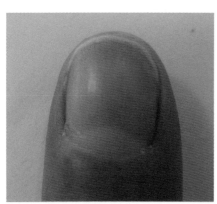

Overgrown cuticle

area will grow a thicker nail than a narrow matrix. However, the thickness of the nail can be affected by how it's treated.

Nail condition is something different. It's something that can change because of several reasons:

1 Lifestyle and environment: water is damaging to nails. If your hands are in and out of water, your fingernails are more likely to be dry, weak or brittle. If you do a lot of manual work, your nails can also get damaged.

2 General health: many changes occur naturally in your body. Hormones change regularly, the body ages and you can get ill. You can take medication from time to time or on a regular basis. There are also long-term conditions, eg vitamin deficiencies, diabetes, etc. All of these and many more can temporarily or permanently change the condition of your nails.

3 Accidental damage: if damage occurs to the nail plate itself, it will probably grow out in time. If damage occurs to the matrix, the damage could be permanent and affect the shape and condition of the nail plate. For example, if a child shuts their finger in a door, it could damage the matrix and permanently disfigure the nail plate. Or there could be a line or ridge running up the nail, or a deeper groove that's always there.

The condition of your nails will probably change several times over your lifetime. Clients can improve many conditions by correct manicuring and pedicuring techniques and following aftercare advice. As a nail technician, you're expected to identify a nail condition during the consultation and treatment. Make sure you don't attempt to diagnose a possible medical problem that has caused the condition. Ask questions that will help you understand the condition. For example, hormonal changes (pregnancy, menopause, etc) can affect the nails. Hormones can make nails stronger if they're weak; or make them weak if they're strong; or thicken them and cause ridges.

A skilled nail technician should be able to solve some conditions and help improve the vast majority of others.

Weak nails

Generally, this relates to fingernails rather than toenails. Questioning and feeling the nail should identify this condition. If the nail is thin, it could be weak, or it could be weak because of environmental or physical damage.

Recommend daily application of nail oil for naturally weak nails to keep them moist and suggest they apply a protective coating of clear or coloured polish. A nail strengthener will also help, but tell your client not to use a nail hardener for longer than 2–3 weeks as it will change a weak nail into a brittle nail. As additional home care advice, suggest a new application of a clear top coat every 2–3 days to maintain the protection.

If the nails are damaged, tell your client to protect them as above until the damage grows out and suggest how they can avoid further damage.

Dry nails

Dry nails are less common on the feet than the hands, but can occur when moisture levels in the nails are low. Dry nails are brittle and usually

Delamination

Where the nail plate layers have separated from each other causing peeling and splitting. This is usually caused by a combination of dryness and trauma to the free edge.

Lunula

The crescent-shaped whitish are of the bed of the fingernail or toenail.

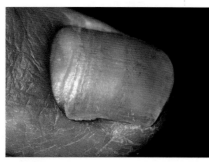

A discoloured nail

peel (**delamination**). Services that use heat and moisturisers/oils for the nail are good for dry nails, eg warm oil soak, heated mitts/boots.

Peeling nails need the protection of nail polish to stop water from getting under the nail plate layers. Gently remove the edge of the nail every week until the damaged area has grown out.

Brittle nails

Brittle nails are usually a symptom of dryness. The lack of moisture stops the nail being flexible enough to withstand accidental knocks. Ageing nails often become brittle, particularly on the big toe. The nail here can become hard and difficult to cut. Heat treatments will help to dramatically change the condition of brittle nails, as will daily application of nail oil.

Ridged nails

Ridges can be caused by several things: damage to the matrix, health issues, damage to the nail, age and hormonal changes.

Longitudinal ridges run from the matrix to the free edge and can signal permanent or temporary damage to the matrix. Longitudinal ridges are often seen in ageing nails.

Horizontal ridges run from side to side. There are two main causes of these:

- Interruption in the nail growth caused by illness: this can be caused by trauma to the matrix; systemic illness or disease; or something that causes trauma to the body, such as a general anaesthetic.
- Damage caused by mechanical methods, such as overbuffing: this can be caused by rough cuticle work which damages the softer nail over the **lunula**; an exposed and large lunula where the nails can get damaged because they're so soft; or swelling at the base of the nail which presses on the soft nail (often seen where the skin has been picked or the nails bitten).

You shouldn't buff ridges unless they're superficial, as buffing will thin the nail plate and lead to severe weakness and possible splitting. Temporary ridges will grow out naturally and you can minimise them by using specialised base coats for ridged nails.

Ridges aren't so common on the smaller toenails but can be found on the big toenail. Here, the ridges are horizontal and caused by physical damage. The most usual damage is from shoes pressing on the end of the toenail. If the nail is too long or the shoe too tight, pressure is put on the end of the nail. This lifts the nail slightly in the matrix. If the nail is thick enough, buff it to smoothe the ridges but not if the nail is too thin.

Thickened nails

Sometimes a fungal infection can cause a nail to become thicker. If there isn't any sign of infection, smoothe a thickened nail with gentle buffing.

Discoloured nails

On the toes, discolouration is often due to a fungal infection, which has caused the nail to become thickened and yellow. Another common cause of discolouration is if nail polish is left on the toes for a long time. Even with a base coat, it can stain the nails. This is easy to recognise if the new nail growth is unaffected. You can buff this off quite easily.

AT THE END OF THE CONSULTATION

When you've finished your assessment, explain to your client what you've discovered. Suggest why you think they have these conditions and explain how this has happened. If you explain everything carefully, your client will be willing to take your advice on the improvements you can make.

YOUR SUGGESTIONS

If you discover any contra-indications or conditions that can restrict the service, you must make recommendations and suggestions to your client by:

- Encouraging them to seek medical advice: if they've got a condition that you feel needs help from a GP, then you must tactfully suggest this course of action.
- Explaining why the service cannot be carried out: a contra-indicated condition means that you're not sufficiently qualified to continue with the service. You need to emphasise that it's for their own benefit that you're giving this advice and that it's your responsibility as a beauty therapist/nail technician to give it.
- Modifying the service: if your client has a condition that means you can provide the service but with certain restrictions, you must explain this carefully.

YOUR SERVICE RECOMMENDATIONS

At the end of your consultation, you should be able to recommend:

- the details for that specific manicure, eg extra attention to the cuticle area, an intensive moisturising treatment for the hands, etc
- the specific products you think will be the most effective
- how your client can achieve the improvements they would like over time by following a service plan
- appropriate home care advice.

AGREEING THE SERVICE PLAN

You must make sure your client understands the conclusions you've reached and agrees with your suggestions. Encourage your client to ask questions if there's anything they don't understand. Write everything down on their record before you and your client sign it.

When everything has been discussed and explained and you both agree on the service options, you're ready to complete the record card and sign it.

Make sure your client understands what they can expect from their chosen service. Explain that the ideal nail condition won't be achieved immediately and your client will need several manicures plus a home care plan. Your client needs to understand and agree to everything to make sure there are no disappointments.

Squoval

The nail is straight across at the free edge with the sides rounded off. An ideal shape for short or bitten nails.

Round

The free edge is rounded and is ideal for short and bitten nails.

Oval

The sides of the free edge are curved to make the nail and finger appear longer and thinner.

Pointed

The free edge is shaped to a point. This places pressure on the sides, weakens the nail and makes it prone to breaking. This is the weakest of all nail shapes.

Tapered

The free edge becomes thinner towards the **distal** edge. Tapered nails are often the weakest nails but, if you don't file down the side walls, you shouldn't make the nail any weaker.

Square

The free edges is straight across and makes the sides sharp and prone to catching on things. This shape makes long nail beds and fingers appear shorter and fuller.

CARRY OUT MANICURE AND PEDICURE SERVICES

ENSURING YOUR CLIENT IS IN A COMFORTABLE AND RELAXED POSITION

You need to make sure that your client is not only comfortable during the nail service, but is also in the correct position to fit in with your working position.

Your client's chair needs to be soft and supportive. For a manicure, it needs to let them rest their forearms on the desk comfortably without stretching or having their arms at an awkward angle. For a pedicure, it needs to let them put their feet on the foot rest or your lap.

For a manicure, place a rolled-up towel under your client's wrist to make their arm more comfortable and make your work easier. Check the towel is clean and cover it with a disposable tissue. Ask your client to remove any jewellery and place it where they can see it, such as a small dish on your desk.

For a pedicure, think about what your client is wearing. Offer them a private area to take off any clothing and place a towel over their knees to maintain their modesty. Make sure you give them pedi slippers so they don't have to walk on the floor bare foot and place a clean towel on the floor by their chair so they rest their other foot on the towel rather than the floor.

MANICURE

Now that all the preparation is complete, we can move on to the service itself. This section will take you through the manicure service, following the steps you must take and the sequence in which you should perform them. (For pedicure services, see the next section, from page 224.)

NAIL LENGTH AND SHAPE

During your consultation, you'll have discussed the style of nails your client would like. The natural shape of the nail and its condition will be relevant in this decision.

If there are any problems with the condition of the nails, it's usually better to keep them relatively short. This will avoid unnecessary breaks.

Many clients have a preferred shape for their nail, regardless of its natural shape. It's unlikely that you'll need to tell them that their preferred shape is inappropriate. If your client is unsure and asks for your advice, choose a shape that mirrors the shape of the nail base.

Nail shapes include tapered, oval, round, squoval, square, pointed, spoon, fan and hook. Spoon, fan and hook are naturally occuring nail shapes. See the anatomy and physiology chapter for descriptions of these.

Distal
The part of the nail that is the furthest away from the centre of the body.

FILING THE NAILS

Use a gentle abrasive when you're filing natural nails. Choose a grit of no lower than 240. File the nails from the sides to the middle and not backwards and forwards; this traumatises the free edge and causes delamination.

Try to angle the file slightly under the free edge, as this will help protect it. When you've reached the chosen length and shape, lightly sweep the file down over the free edge to smoothe the top surface.

If you need to cut or clip nails that are too long, use sharp scissors or clippers. Cut small sections of the nail rather than the whole nail at once, as this distorts the natural nail shape. Cut to slightly longer than the required length and use a gentle file to remove the remaining length and create the shape. This will stop the nail splitting and peeling.

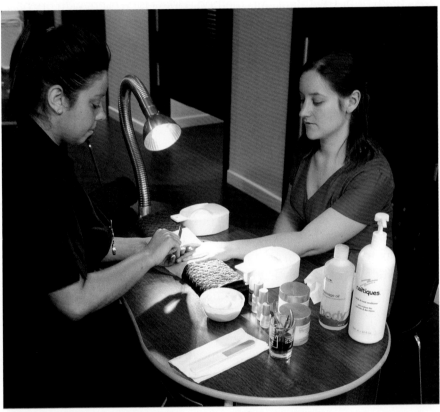

Filing the nails

HANDY HINTS

You could use a nail strengthener instead of buffing the nails.

HANDY HINTS

The coarseness of files and buffers is measured in grit size. The higher the number, the smaller the grit size and the finer the file. The lower the number, the coarser the file. You must never use a file or buffer on the natural nail with a grit size lower than 240. Anything coarser than this will damage the nail and cause peeling and splitting.

WHY DON'T YOU...

Collect a range of files or go to your local wholesaler and try to guess the grit size of the files. Find ones that are suitable for use on the natural nail.

HANDY HINTS

Don't use a glossing buffer if there's any oil on the nail. This will damage the surface of the buffer.

BUFFING THE NAIL

If your client wants their nails buffed to a shine, you can do it now before you soften the nails with water or cream.

Using a two- or three-sided buffer, gently move one side over the surface of the nail. You won't need much buffing here, as too much could thin the nail plate. If there are ridges in the nail, smoothe them lightly, but don't try to remove them. Use the final sides of the buffer to bring each nail to a high shine.

If you have a male client, ask if he wants his nails smooth or shiny.

SOFTENING THE CUTICLE (MANICURE)

There are two main ways to soften the cuticle for easy removal. However, these are not the only ways – your college might teach you a slightly different routine.

1 A water-based treatment: this is suitable for a client with normal nails and cuticles. Prepare a finger bowl with warm water and a few drops of water softener or a branded nail soak product. Place the fingers in the water for a few minutes to soften the cuticle layer on the nail plate. Remove your client's fingers from the bowl and dry on a clean towel. Place the other hand in the water while you use a cuticle knife on the hand that's been soaked. Apply a water-based cuticle remover on the cuticle area, using a hoof stick or a cotton wool-tipped orange wood stick. This will quickly soften the dead skin. Remember to wash the remover off with water; if you leave it on, it will soften the nail plate.

2 A cream or oil treatment: this method is ideal for a client with dry nails and/or cuticles. It will soften the cuticles and improve their condition. Massaging a cream or oil into the cuticles will soften and moisturise them, and the massage movements will improve blood flow to the area. Place just enough oil in a small bowl to cover the nails. Place this bowl in a larger bowl of warm water. Ask your client to put their fingers in this bowl for a few minutes. Remove their hand and dry the fingers with a disposable tissue.

A heat treatment using thermal mitts or similar will also soften the cuticle. If this is part of the agreed manicure service, massage the cuticle cream or oil into the area and apply the appropriate hand cream. Wrap the hands in a disposable plastic bag or cling film, place them into the inner liner and then into the heated mitts. Leave them in place for 5–15 minutes, depending on the manufacturer's instructions and the time limitations of the manicure. Remove and carry out the cuticle work. Use the remaining hand cream as a massage medium.

REMOVING THE CUTICLE

When you've softened the cuticle, remove it with a clean cuticle knife of your choice; there are several available. The knives can be sharp so take care not to damage the nail plate.

It should be easy to remove a softened cuticle. Find the edge of the cuticle on the nail plate and gently scrape it off towards the base of the nail. When you reach the eponychium, gently lift the edge and remove the cuticle. The dead skin should come away quite easily. If it doesn't, use a clean and sharp pair of cuticle nippers and cut it. Don't cut the skin of the nail fold/eponychium; this is living skin and will grow back thicker.

After you've removed the cuticle, use your nippers to take off any hang nails that you might find in the side walls. Clean under the free edge with an orange stick with some cotton wool wrapped around the end to remove any debris.

HAND TREATMENTS

When all the nail work is finished, it's time to treat the skin. The method you choose will depend on the type of manicure service you've

HANDY HINTS

When you're using cuticle nippers, make sure they're sharp. Grip the area, squeeze, release and remove. Don't squeeze and pull as this will tear the skin.

provided. After the cuticle work, apply a hand cream that is suitable for your client's skin type.

If the service is a luxury manicure, there are several steps that come next. If your client chose a heat treatment, you'll have already conditioned the skin. If they choose a full skin treatment, proceed with the following steps.

Paraffin wax

Most beauty therapists/nail technicians like to do this treatment before the massage, but others prefer to do it after the massage, when the client is relaxed. It's a simple and effective service that is ideal for treating dry skin, and is particularly soothing for those who suffer from arthritis.

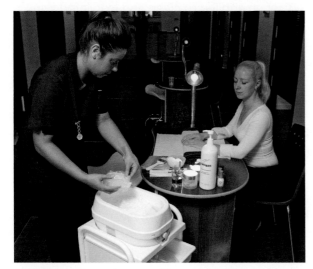

STEP 1 – Pour the paraffin wax into a smaller bowl and prepare a wax brush, some plastic film or foil and some towels.

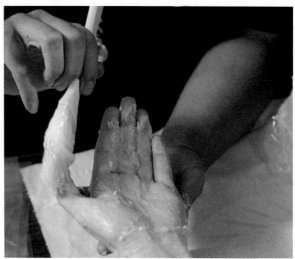

STEP 2 – Position your client's hand over the foil or a disposable tissue. Dip the brush into the melted wax and coat the hands, back and front, with a layer of wax. Repeat this three times to make sure you've applied a good layer of wax.

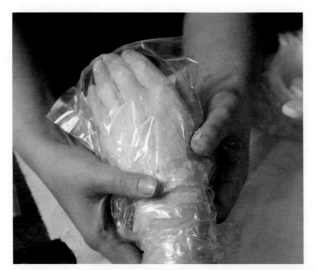

STEP 3 – To keep the heat in, wrap the hand in foil or plastic film.

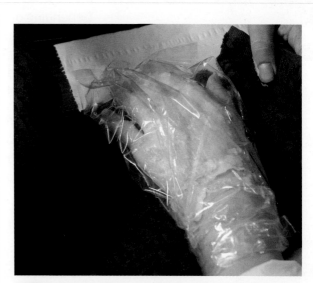

STEP 4 – Finally wrap the hand in a towel.

HANDY HINTS

See Unit B4 for how to apply a mask to the hands and feet – the technique is the same.

HANDY HINTS

Remember, if you're treating a male client, hairy arms might cause friction when you're massaging.

WHY DON'T YOU...

Read through SmartScreen handout 14 for further details on the massage movements and the benefits of massage.

 SmartScreen N2 handout 14

Repeat the above process with the other hand and leave for about ten minutes. Unwrap one hand and peel away the hardened wax into the plastic film or foil. Wrap up the plastic film or foil and throw away. Repeat this with the other hand.

Exfoliators and hand masks

Exfoliators are products that contain either small particles or specific chemicals to remove dead skin. This will brighten the skin and allow moisturising products to penetrate deeper into the skin. Massage briefly into the skin and remove with water or a towel.

A hand mask gives a 'facial' to the hands, as it uses similar products to cleanse, remove dead skin and remoisturise. A mask penetrates and moisturises the skin and, when applied to clean and exfoliated skin, makes it more plump. Some masks are particularly suitable for ageing skin as they stimulate the production of collagen and elastin and reduce age spots. Some masks dry on the skin, while others stay wet. Like exfoliators, you should remove masks with water or a towel and always follow the manufacturer's instructions.

A typical hand routine might be:

- apply exfoliator and massage
- remove exfoliator
- apply mask
- place the hands in heated mitts and leave for a few minutes
- remove mask
- apply hand cream and massage.

MASSAGE

The massage is most likely the last stage of the manicure before you paint the nails. A good massage will encourage blood flow and desquamation. It's also a relaxing and enjoyable experience for your client.

Depending on the products you're using and the agreed service plan, you can use a hand cream or lotion, a massage cream or a massage oil. The drier your client's skin, the more moisturising products you'll need. Massage products don't absorb into the skin too quickly and allow for an effective massage routine.

When you're measuring out the product into your hand, think about how it will spread over the hand. You'll need enough to cover the area, but not so much that the skin ends up too greasy. Remove any excess product with a towel at the end of the massage.

When you're providing a hand and arm massage for a male client, you might need to use more product to avoid pulling the hair on their arms.

Massage techniques

The time you spend massaging can vary according to the type of manicure and the time allocated to the service. Typically, the massage should last several minutes for each hand and arm. Ask your client to roll up their sleeves, as the massage will include the lower arm.

There are three main massage movements commonly used for the hand and lower arm:

1 Effleurage: use a light, stroking movement at the beginning of the routine to spread the massage medium, and at the end of the routine to indicate you've finished. It should be relaxing, calming and warming. Use effleurage to move your hands from one area to another so you don't lose contact with the skin.

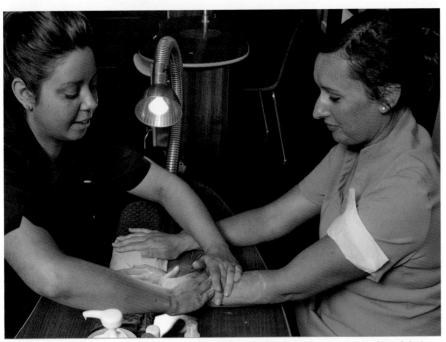

You may want to protect your client's clothes by securing a tissue around the edge of their sleeves.

2 Petrissage: this is a slightly deeper movement to massage the underlying structures. Always make sure your client is happy with the amount of pressure you're using. Use your fingers or knuckles for firm pressure or use your fingers gently to knead the arm. This provides a toning effect to the skin and muscles, and increases blood and lymphatic circulation.

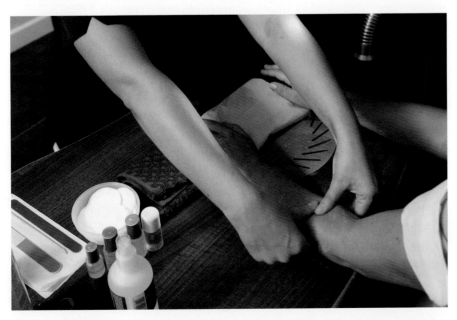

3 Vibrations or frictions: use the fingertips or thumbs in small circular movements to provide a targeted massage to smaller areas. This can help release tension on the backs of the hands and along the muscles of the arm.

Remove any oils from the nail plate.

Apply a base coat.

Be careful if your client has excessive erythema. This is a redness that occurs if the small blood vessels near the skin's surface are widened, due to friction or stimulation. If there's excessive erythema in areas that you've hardly touched, this could indicate irritation. Stop the massage and remove the cream or oil.

If you've used the correct amount of massage medium, the skin should absorb all the product and be moisturised but grease free. If you've used too much, take a towel and blot away the excess.

PAINTING THE NAILS

If the agreed service includes painting the nails, let your client choose a colour. Provide several alternatives and help them choose if they ask.

1 Clean the nail: the nail plate will be covered with oil from an earlier part of the manicure. Nail polish will not bond with the oil so you must clean the nail before you paint it. Soak a cotton pad in conditioner-free nail polish remover and wipe over each nail. Make sure you clean down the side walls and around the cuticle area, until you've removed all the oil. If there's any oil left behind, it will lift and chip the nail polish.

2 Apply a base coat: this is an essential part of the painting process. A base coat is usually thinner in consistency and is designed to bond with a clean nail plate. This will help prevent the nail polish getting chipped and stop the nail getting stained from the coloured pigment in the polish. If you have a choice of base coats for different nail conditions, choose one that best suits your client. Holding the bottle in the same hand that is holding your client's finger, remove the brush from the bottle and wipe off the excess product on the neck. Carefully paint the base coat on to each finger, starting with the little finger. Leave a small margin around the edges of the nail to avoid touching the skin.

3 Apply colour: apply two thin layers of colour, making sure that the edges are neat and close to the skin.

4 Apply a top coat: always use a top coat, as this will make the polish last longer and provide a glossy finish.

5 Finish: make sure the nails have a smooth and even finish and there's no polish on the skin. Check that your client likes the results and tell them they need to wait at least 15 minutes for their nails to be touch dry.

Nail finishes

Dark colour

Dark nail polish needs particular care; if you make a mistake, it's immediately obvious. A high gloss and perfect finish are essential with dark colours.

French manicure

This is where the nail is painted with a white polish on the free edge and a sheer or semi-sheer polish over the rest of the nail. Depending on your client's preferences, the white can be hard and bright and needs a sharp **smile line**, or it can be soft with a more natural appearance.

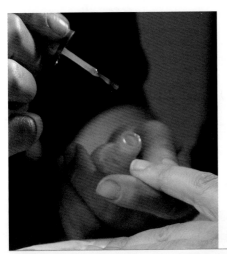
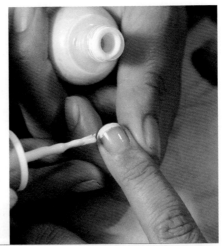

Apply a base coat before the white to the free edge.

The sequence for a French manicure is as follows:

- Apply a base coat.
- Apply the chosen white to the free edge and create a curve.
- Apply one or two layers of the chosen sheer colour depending on the effect your client prefers.
- Apply a top coat.

Buffed

Not every client wants to wear nail polish. They might prefer to have a natural and buffed finish. If you buff a nail to a high gloss, it will keep its shine for several weeks.

Apply colour polish to the nails.

HANDY HINTS

Have an orange stick ready in case you touch the skin with the nail polish, and use this to remove it before it dries.

Smile line

The line that naturally occurs at the hyponychium – where the nail plate leaves the nail bed. It's called the smile line because it curves upwards like a smile.

HANDY HINTS

There's an easy rule you can follow to create a perfect French manicure: make sure the white area is no more than one-third of the entire length of the nail.

HANDY HINTS

When you're removing nail polish, soak the centre of the pad in remover, start with the little finger/toe and move across to the thumb/big toe. If your client is wearing a dark colour, you might need three pads for each hand or foot, otherwise two should be enough. By starting at the little finger/toe, the polish you've removed will cover only a small area of the cotton pad and is less likely to transfer to the skin on the next finger.

HANDY HINTS

Always have a small, flat art brush handy. Dip this into nail polish remover to tidy up the smile line.

PEDICURE

This section shows the steps to take when you're providing a pedicure treatment. It shows them in sequence and explains what you should do, and how and why you should do it.

CLEANING AND DRYING THE FEET

The first stage of a pedicure, even before the consultation, is to clean your client's feet. If you're using a foot soak, have a towel ready to wrap up the foot you've taken out of the bowl and repeat on the other foot.

FILING NAILS CORRECTLY

Keep toenails short as long nails can cause problems with shoes rubbing. During the summer months, the big toenail can be left slightly longer, but not if your client wears trainers for sport or exercise on a regular basis.

File toenails in the same way as fingernails and follow your client's wishes. If you leave a sharp corner below the level of the skin, this could lead to an ingrowing nail. Use a gentle abrasive when you're filing natural nails and choose a grit size of no lower than 240. File the nails from the sides to the middle rather than backwards and forwards as this traumatises the free edge.

If you need to cut or clip the nails if they're too long, use sharp scissors or clippers. Cut small sections of the nail rather than the whole nail all at once as this distorts the natural nail shape. Cut to slightly longer than the required finished length and remove the remaining length with a file. This will stop the nail from splitting and peeling. Wear safety glasses when you're cutting nails to prevent clippings springing into your eye and causing damage.

File toenails straight across to avoid ingrowing toenails.

SOFTENING THE CUTICLE (PEDICURE)

There are two main ways to soften the cuticle for easy removal. Remember, your college might teach you a slightly different routine:

1 A water-based treatment: these are suitable for a client with normal nails and cuticles. Prepare a bowl of warm water and add a few drops of water softener or a branded nail soak product. Place the first foot in the water for a few minutes. This will soften the cuticle layer on the nail plate so you can remove it with a cuticle knife. Take your client's foot out of the bowl and dry it on a clean towel. Soak the other foot while you work on the cuticles of the foot that's been soaked.

   You can also add a water-based cuticle remover to the cuticle area, using a hoof stick or cotton wool-tipped orange wood stick. This will quickly soften the dead skin. Remember to wash off the remover with water; if you leave it on, it will soften the nail plate.

2 A cream or oil treatment: these methods are ideal for a client with dry nails and/or cuticles. Massage a cream or oil into the cuticles to soften and moisturise them. The massage movements will improve blood flow to the area.

   Use a nail oil or cream to soften the cuticle. For a warm oil treatment, place just enough oil in a small bowl to cover the nails. Place this bowl in a larger bowl of warm water. Ask your client to place their feet in this bowl for a few minutes, then remove and dry.

   A heat treatment using heated boots or similar will also soften the cuticle. If this is part of the agreed pedicure service, massage in the cuticle cream or oil and apply the appropriate moisturising cream to the feet. Wrap the feet in a disposable plastic bag or cling film, place them into the inner liner and then into the heated boots. Leave for 5–15 minutes, depending on the manufacturer's instructions and the time limitations of the pedicure. Remove and carry out the cuticle work. Use the remaining cream as a massage medium.

REMOVING THE CUTICLE

When you've softened the cuticle, it's safe to remove it with a clean cuticle knife of your choice; there are several available. The knives can be sharp so take care not to damage the nail plate.

A softened cuticle shouldn't take much effort to remove. Find the edge of the cuticle on the nail plate and gently scrape it off towards the base of the nail. When you reach the eponychium, use gentle pressure to slightly lift the edge and remove the cuticle. The dead skin of the cuticle should come away easily at this stage. If it doesn't, use a clean and sharp pair of cuticle nippers and cut it. Make sure you don't cut the skin of the nail fold/eponychium; this is living skin and will grow back thicker.

When you're using cuticle nippers, make sure they're sharp. Grip the area, squeeze, release and remove. Don't squeeze and pull as this will tear the skin. Take an orange stick with some cotton wool wrapped around the end and clean under the free edge of the nail to remove any debris.

Be very careful when you're using a cuticle knife.

BUFFING THE NAIL

If you've agreed with your client to buff the nails to a shine, take a two- or three-sided buffer and use one side over the surface of the nail. You won't need to buff much here, just enough to dull the shine. If you buff too much, you'll thin the nail plate. If there are ridges in the nail, smoothe them lightly but don't try to remove them. Use the other side of the buffer to bring each nail to a high shine. Ask your client to put their foot back in the water and repeat on the other side. Don't forget if you have a male client to ask him if he wants his nails smooth or shiny.

REMOVING HARD SKIN

After a soak in the foot bath, you need to remove any hard skin with a foot file or foot rasp. A rasp is made from metal and is rougher and more effective on hard skin. A foot file is gentler and is suitable for minor hard skin.

Ask your client to remove their foot from the bath and dry it with a towel. Use your fingers to find the hard skin. This is normally found on the base and sides of the heel, on the ball of the foot and sometimes on the side of the big toe. Use the rasp to buff away the worst of the hard skin. Keep feeling to check you are removing only the hard skin and not the soft, living skin underneath.

When you can feel you've removed most of the skin, use the softer side of the foot file or a buffer to smoothe the area. If you don't smoothe the skin, it will be rough when it dries out. The feet don't need to go back in the bowl anymore, so wrap the finished foot in a towel and place it on the floor. When you've done the second foot, move the bowl out of the way.

FOOT TREATMENTS

When you've finished the nail work and removed the hard skin, it's time to treat the rest of the skin. How you do this will depend on the type of pedicure service your client has chosen. If they've chosen a basic pedicure, apply a foot cream that is suitable for your client's skin condition. There are moisturising creams for dry skin; creams that will help dry and cracked heels; creams that stimulate cold feet; anti-inflammatory creams; and antiseptic creams to help control foot odour.

If your client's chosen a luxury pedicure, there are several steps that come next. If they want a heat treatment, you'll have already conditioned the skin. If they want a full skin treatment, proceed with the following steps.

Paraffin wax bath

This treatment follows the nail, cuticle and hard skin work. Most beauty therapists/nail technicians like to do this before the massage. Others like to do it after the massage when their client is relaxed. It's a simple and effective treatment that is ideal for dry skin and those who suffer from arthritis.

Prepare the paraffin wax bath and position it somewhere safe. Make sure you have a wax brush and foil ready, together with some towels. Remember to test the temperature of the wax on your wrist before you apply it to your client's foot.

HANDY HINTS

If you're using a colour polish or a strengthener, you don't always need to buff.

HANDY HINTS

Feet shouldn't be totally wet when you're using a hard skin removing tool.

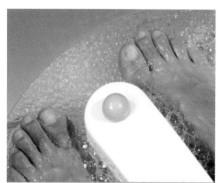

Your client should soak their feet in a foot bath before you remove hard skin.

Position your client's foot over the foil or a paper towel and place it on your (protected) lap or the foot rest. Dip the brush into the melted wax and coat the top and sole of the foot. Repeat three times so there's a good layer of wax. Wrap the foot in the foil or cling film and finally a towel to keep the heat in. Repeat this with the other foot and leave for about ten minutes.

Cover the foot with an even layer of paraffin wax.

Unwrap one foot, peel away the hardened wax, place it in the foil and throw away. Repeat for the other foot.

Exfoliators and foot masks

This is a 'facial' for the feet as it uses similar products to face masks and gives the feet a thorough cleanse to remove dead skin and remoisturises them.

Exfoliators are products that have either small particles or specific chemicals to remove dead skin from the surface. This will brighten the skin and help the moisturising products penetrate more deeply. Massage briefly into the skin and remove with water or a towel.

A mask is a product that cleans and exfoliates the skin and contains penetrating and moisturising properties to plump the skin. Some masks are particularly suitable for ageing skin as they stimulate the production of collagen and elastin and reduce age spots. Some masks dry on the skin and others stay wet. Always follow the manufacturer's instructions and remove with a towel or water.

A typical foot treatment routine might be:
- apply exfoliator and massage
- remove exfoliator by washing the feet in the bath
- apply mask
- place the feet in heated boots and leave for up to 15 minutes
- remove mask by washing
- apply foot cream and massage.

Heated boots

This is an intense treatment for the skin and it can be performed after the nail, cuticle and hard skin work. Prepare the boots and check they're not too hot. Apply a suitable moisturising cream all over the foot and wrap in a disposable plastic bag or cling film. Place the foot in the heated boot liner and then into the boot. Repeat for the second foot. Leave your client to relax for 5–10 minutes (or as long as the manufacturer's instructions suggest).

Remove one foot from the boot, the liner and the disposable plastic bag and begin your massage. Leave the second foot in the boot to keep it warm.

MASSAGE

The massage is often the last stage of the pedicure before you paint the nails. It's relaxing and enjoyable for your client and will improve blood flow and encourage desquamation. When you're massaging the legs, press harder when you're working towards the heart and release the pressure when you're returning to the feet. This is because veins have valves in them to control the direction of blood flow.

Depending on the products you've chosen and the agreed service plan, use a foot cream or lotion, a massage cream or a massage oil. The drier your client's feet, the more moisturising product you should use. Products designed for massage shouldn't absorb too quickly into the skin to allow for an effective massage routine.

When you're measuring out the product in your hand, think about how well it will spread over the area you're massaging. You'll need enough to cover the area but too much will leave the skin greasy at the end. If your client is male, you might need more product so you're not pulling the hair on their skin.

Massage techniques

The time you spend on massage will vary depending on the service plan but should usually last several minutes for each foot and lower leg. The massage will include the lower leg to just below the knee.

There are three main massage movements that are commonly used for the foot and lower leg:

1 Effleurage: this is a light, stroking movement used at the beginning of the routine to spread the massage medium and at the end of the routine to show you've finished. It should be relaxing, calming and warming. Use effleurage to move your hands from one area to another so you don't lose contact with the skin.

2 Petrissage: this is a slightly deeper movement to massage the underlying structures. Always check with your client that you're not pressing too hard. Use your fingers or knuckles for firmer pressure on the appropriate areas, or use your finger gently to knead the muscles on the leg or feet. This provides a toning effect to the skin and muscles and increases blood and lymphatic circulation.

3 Vibrations or frictions: use small circular movements with your fingertips or thumbs on smaller areas to release tension on the feet and the muscles.

Avoid touching any bruises on the legs. Legs are particularly susceptible to bruises, especially over the shin bone. Skim over this area and always check with your client that you're not hurting them.

You should also look to see if your client has developed excessive erythema. This is a redness of the skin when the small blood vessels near the surface widen because of friction or stimulation. If you find excessive erythema in areas you've hardly touched, it could indicate irritation. Stop the massage and remove the cream or oil.

If you've used the correct amount of massage medium, it should all be absorbed into the skin, leaving it moisturised but grease free. If you've used too much, use a paper towel and blot away the excess.

HANDY HINTS

Tapotement can be used on the calf muscles to help stimulate circulation. You may have been shown this movement.

ACTIVITY

Research a variety of pedicure products and brands and compare the features (ie size, price, etc) and benefits (ie formulation, ingredients, etc).

PAINTING THE NAILS

If your client would like their nails painted, follow the steps below:

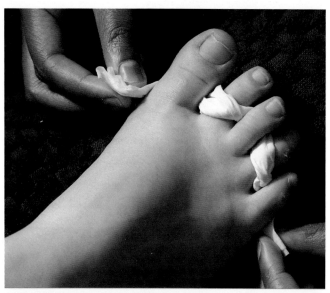

Separate the toes with toe separators or a clean tissue.

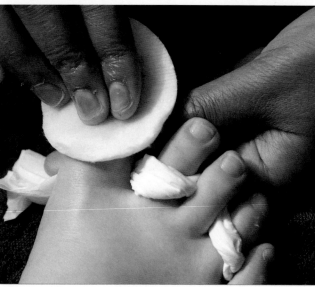

Clean the nails before you paint them.

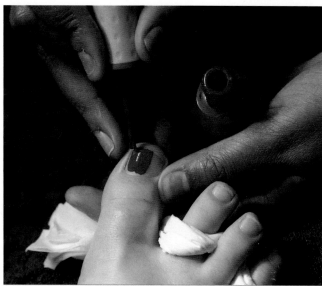

Make sure you apply a base coat before painting the nails.

1 **Separate the toes:** to paint toes and let them dry, you need to separate your client's toes as they can curve over on each other. There are several toe separators available or you can make your own with a clean tissue by twisting it into a rope. If you use re-usable separators, make sure they're clean and disinfected.

2 **Clean the nails:** the nail plate will be covered with oil at this stage and polish will not bond to the nail. Soak a cotton pad in conditioner-free nail polish remover and wipe over each nail. Make sure you clean down the side walls and around the cuticle area. You might need to add more remover to make sure you've removed all the oil. Any oil that is left on the nail plate will make the nail polish lift and chip.

3 **Apply a base coat:** this is normally thinner in consistency and is designed to bond with a clean nail plate. This will help prevent the polish from chipping and stop the coloured pigment in the polish from staining the nails. If you have a choice of base coats for different nail conditions, choose the one that best suits your client and follows the service plan. Remove the brush and wipe off the excess product on the neck of the bottle. Carefully paint the base coat onto each toenail, starting at the little toe. Leave a small margin around the edges of the nail to avoid touching the skin.

4 **Apply colour:** paint two thin coats of your client's chosen colour. Use the brush to create an even and smooth line at the cuticle area. Use your orange stick to remove any polish on the skin. Sweep the brush around the edge of the nail to stop the polish from chipping.

5 **Apply a top coat:** every colour must be finished with a top coat. This has a slightly different formulation that is tougher and keeps its shine. The top coat seals the edge of the nail and stops the polish from chipping.

6 **Finish:** make sure the nails have a smooth and even finish. Check there isn't any polish on the skin and your client likes the results. Tell them to wait at least 15 minutes for their nails to be touch dry.

HANDY HINTS

Conditioner-free nail polish remover doesn't contain moisturising conditioners. Use this type of remover to help the nail polish stick to the nails.

THE CITY & GUILDS TEXTBOOK

Nail finishes

Dark colour

Be careful with dark nail polishes; any mistakes you make are immediately obvious. Make sure you create a high gloss and a perfect finish.

French pedicure

This is where the nails are painted with white on the free edge and a sheer or semi-sheer polish on the rest of the nail. Depending on your client's preferences, the white can be hard and bright with a sharp smile line. Or it can be soft and more natural. A French pedicure needs to have a narrow white band to look attractive.

The sequence for a French pedicure is as follows:

- Apply a base coat.
- Apply the chosen white to the free edge and create a curve.
- Apply one or two layers of the chosen sheer colour depending on the effect your client prefers.
- Apply a top coat.

HANDY HINTS

When you're removing polish, hold the cotton pad between your fingers, not with your fingertips. This will prevent you from removing your own polish. Place the wet pad on the nail and hold it in place for a couple of seconds to melt the polish. Pull the pad down off the free edge to stop any polish transferring on to the skin. If you rub the polish off, it will spread around the skin and take longer to clean off. It also destroys the pad. Move on to the next finger or toe and add more remover to the pad if necessary.

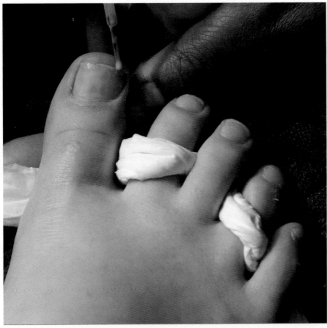
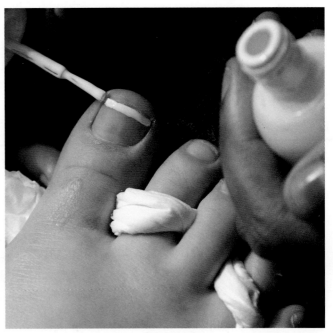

As in manicure, add a base coat before the white to the free edge

AT THE END OF THE SERVICE

After every nail service, clean the area thoroughly to avoid cross-infection.

Clean or disinfect all tools and equipment immediately or place them in a container and deal with them later. They shouldn't be left in the work area.

Clean and replace every product ready for the next service. Make sure you've got enough time to prepare your work area before each new client.

HANDY HINTS

Polish actually takes several hours to dry properly so putting tights/socks and shoes back on is always a problem. Your client might have brought some sandals to avoid this problem. If not, there's a trick that can work very well. Smother the nails in nail oil and wrap the toes in cling film. The oil will stop the polish becoming tacky and the cling film will keep the oil in place and help protect the polish.

SmartScreen N3 handout 14

SmartScreen N2 handout 18

It's an essential part of the manicure and pedicure service that your client understands what you've done to their nails and skin. As you perform each stage, explain what you're doing and why. This will not only demonstrate your expertise but help your client understand why they might have problems and how to avoid them. Aftercare advice helps them build on their treatments and make the benefits last as long as possible.

GIVING ADVICE AND RECOMMENDATIONS

There are several ways that a client can help improve the condition of their skin and nails and avoid potential problems. Your home care advice should be specific to each client and fit in with their skin and nail conditions.

SUITABLE AFTERCARE TOOLS AND PRODUCTS AND THEIR USE

1 Recommend (and explain during the service) that they should use a gentle nail file to avoid any trauma and delamination.
2 Suggest they avoid using cuticle nippers at home in case they go too far and remove living skin.
3 Reapply a protective top coat every 2–3 days to keep a gloss finish and prolong the life of the colour.

After manicures only:

1 Recommened they apply nail oil and/or cuticle cream daily by massaging it into the cuticle area. This will make a big difference to the condition of both the skin and nails. Apply several times a day if possible, but last thing at night is essential.
2 Apply hand cream several times a day and recommend a barrier cream for clients who have their hands in water on a regular basis. Suggest a cream with an SPF for mature skin.
3 Tell clients to wear gloves when they're using cleaning products, as the chemicals can cause severe damage to skin and nails.

After pedicures only:

1 Always recommend a moisturising foot cream. It will help keep dry skin conditions soft and stop the heels from cracking.
2 Use a foot file to remove hard skin after a bath.

CONTRA-ACTIONS

A contra-action is when a reaction occurs at any time during a service. You must identify the contra-action, stop the service and remove the product that could be causing the reaction. This could be swelling, irritation or excessive erythema.

Advise your client on how to recognise a possible allergic reaction if it happens after they've left the salon. You should also explain the things that can cause problems, such as wearing tight-fitting shoes or washing up without gloves.

FOLLOWING THE SERVICE PLAN

During your consultation, you'll have discussed a service plan. As part of this plan, you'll provide recommendations for further services. For example, if your client has a severe problem with their skin or nails, recommend they come weekly to begin with followed by longer intervals. Or if your client is just coming for a treat, suggest they come for their the next service in a month's time.

Try to give your client a routine to follow at home, particularly after a manicure. For example, tell them to use hand cream 3–4 times a day after they've washed their hands; massage nail oil into the cuticle area morning and night; remove the edge of the nails once a week with a gentle nail file; and wear gloves when they're using detergents or other cleaning materials. This type of advice will have more effect than simply suggesting they use a cream or oil.

END OF UNIT SUMMARY

Now you've reached the end of the unit, you should feel confident in the theory and practical aspects of all areas of manicure and pedicure services. Use the checklist below to see if there are any areas you feel you need to recap before beginning the end of unit assessment:

- maintain safe and effective methods of working when providing manicure and pedicure services
- consult, plan and prepare for manicure and pedicure services
- carry out manicure and pedicure services
- provide aftercare advice.

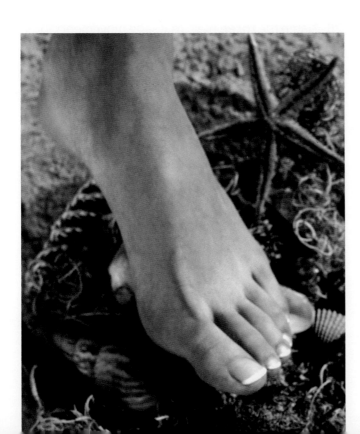

Using the questions below, test your knowledge of Units N2/N3 to see how much information you've retained. These questions will help you to revise what you've learnt in this chapter.

Turn to pages 409–411 for the answers.

1 Who is responsible for the health and safety of everyone in the salon?

2 Why is it important not to discriminate against clients?

3 What types of personal protective equipment (PPE) should you be provided with and why?

4 What is contact dermatitis and how can you avoid it?

5 What methods should you use to clean and disinfect tools and equipment?

6 How do you keep tools and materials in a hygienic condition?

7 Why is it important to disinfect your hands?

8 Why is it important to maintain standards of hygiene?

9 Why is it important to position tools and equipment safely?

10 How can you avoid injury to yourself and your clients by correct positioning?

11 During a pedicure, when and why should you wear safety glasses?

12 How should you leave the work area?

13 Why are accurate records important and how does the Data Protection Act affect them?

14 Name **four** consultation techniques and how they help.

15 Name **two** questioning techniques and how you can use them during a consultation.

16 Can you provide a manicure or pedicure service to anyone under 16 years?

17 Name **four** contra-indications to a manicure and describe them.

18 What does a condition that might restrict the service mean?

19 Why should you encourage your client to ask questions?

20 Can you diagnose specific contra-indications?

21 Name **four** treatable conditions that affect the nail or the skin around the nail.

22 What is a service plan?

23 Why should you keep toenails short?

24 What are the benefits of using cuticle products during a manicure treatment?

25 Name the **three** main massage movements for a manicure or pedicure service.

26 Why do you need to clean the nail plate before you paint the nails?

27 Why do you need to use a base and top coat?

28 Why is it important to keep to service times?

29 Why is aftercare advice important?

30 What is a contra-action? Give **two** examples.

WHY DON'T YOU...
Test your knowledge further by logging into SmartScreen and completing the revision activities before attempting the sample GOLA revision questions.

N4
CARRY OUT NAIL ART SERVICES

Nail art is a popular service and fun to do. It's also easy when you know how! It's a professional service so all the important aspects of nail services apply. However, this chapter will give you product information and ideas on how to create your own designs for your clients.

Even if you're not artistic, there are many simple techniques that you can master. Your clients will love your bespoke nail designs on their fingers and toes.

In this chapter you'll learn how to:

- maintain safe and effective methods of working when providing nail art services
- consult, plan and prepare for nail art services
- carry out nail art services
- provide aftercare advice.

When you're providing a nail art service, it's important to use the skills you've learnt in the following units:

Unit G20	Ensure responsibility for actions to reduce risks to health and safety
Unit G18	Promote additional services or products to clients
Unit G8	Develop and maintain your effectiveness at work
Unit N2/N3	Provide manicure and pedicure services.

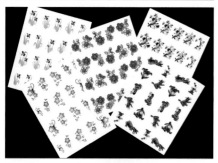

Transfers come in many fun designs!

Use glitter to add shimmer to your client's nails.

Make sure you use the correct side of your foils.

Flatstones and rhinestones can make your client's nails stand out from the crowd.

MAINTAIN SAFE AND EFFECTIVE METHODS OF WORKING WHEN PROVIDING NAIL ART SERVICES

Most of the information in this section is contained in Unit N2/N3. Please refer to the manicure section of that unit.

TOOLS AND EQUIPMENT

Look at all the hygiene methods in Unit N2/N3 for your tools and equipment. Make sure you have all your tools, products and equipment on your desk or in the drawers. It's disconcerting for your client if you keep jumping up to fetch things during the service.

ADDITIONAL TOOLS AND EQUIPMENT FOR NAIL ART SERVICES

Make sure you have a wide range of polish colours and effects, such as shimmers, iridescents, metallics, etc. You will also need:

1 Transfers: these are ready-made designs that you peel off a backing paper and apply to painted nails. Sometimes you'll need water to release them from the backing paper. Cut out the chosen design and drop it in water. Leave for a few seconds and lift out with tweezers. Slide the transfer off the paper and directly on to the painted nail.

2 Glitters: these can come already mixed in a clear polish or they can be loose in a pot. Paint on the ready mixed versions just like nail polish. For loose glitters, pick them up with a brush that you've dipped in clear polish or glitter mixer or sprinkle them over wet polish. They'll only stick to wet polish, so draw your shapes with the polish first and quickly add the glitter. Another alternative is to dip the nail into the pot, or maybe just the tip. When you're using loose glitter, remember to work over a clean sheet of paper so you can collect excess glitter and return it to the pot.

3 Foil: foiling is a quick and easy nail art technique. You'll need a special foil adhesive and a variety of foil designs. Apply an even, thin layer of the adhesive to the area of the painted nail that you want to foil. The adhesive will look milky at first and turn clear when it's ready. When the adhesive is clear, place the foil (the design side must face upwards) on the nail and gently press with your finger. Pull the foil strip off and this will leave the foil where you painted the adhesive. If you can't see any foil, you've used the wrong side of the strip. If there are any patches, reapply the adhesive and follow the same steps. You can make shapes, stripes and even a French tip depending on where you paint the adhesive.

4 Flatstones/rhinestones: there's a wide variety of tiny stones that you can use to decorate the nail. They come in all colours and shapes and you can use them singly or place several on one nail. The most important characteristic is that they have a flat back so they sit on the nail. The easiest way to apply them is to place a small amount of Blu-Tack® on the end of an orange stick and shape it to a point. Use it to pick up a single stone and place it on the painted nail. Remember to

press firmly into the wet top coat to hold it in place. If necessary, add a tiny spot of nail adhesive on the stone to help it stick to the nail.

5 Marbling and dotting tool: there's a specific marbling/dotting tool that has a spherical shape at either end, but a small brush or an orange stick will also work. Marbling is a quick technique that mixes several nail polishes or water-based acrylic paint colours together on the nail to create a random pattern. Or you can drag a few colours through each other to create a 'Bakewell tart' effect. Dotting is creating dots of different sizes to create a pattern or, for example, the detail in flowers.

6 Striping tape: small rolls of striping tape are available in a variety of colours and effects. These have a sticky back so you can place it accurately on the painted nail and trim to size.

7 A selection of water-based acrylic paints: these are available from nail art suppliers and dry quickly. There are lots of colours to choose from and you can mix them together to create more colours.

8 Nail art sealer: all of the techniques need sealing to make sure they stay in place. There are top coat/sealers specifically designed for this job. Some other top coats can affect the nail art by moving it or removing the colour.

9 Free-hand painting brushes: these can be made from man-made fibre or natural hairs. Natural hairs are more precise and accurate but are usually more expensive. The types of brushes include:

- small pointed brushes for detailing
- two sizes of square-ended flat brushes
- long thin striping brushes
- a fan brush
- a glitter dust brush.

Other tools and equipment you might need are:
- a small pair of sharp scissors
- tweezers, both flat and pointed
- orange sticks
- a small mixing palette for the paints
- Blu-Tack® or similar.

Cleaning and storage

Make sure you keep all your nail art tools and products together. Put them in a covered box to keep them clean and away from dust. Tools for nail art services don't need special disinfecting because they don't come into contact with the skin. Wash any tool that has been used to apply acrylic paints in soapy water and rinse. Clean anything that has been in contact with nail polish and top coats or sealers (for example a glitter dust brush) with nail polish remover.

SERVICE TIMES

When you're providing a nail art service, it's important you make it commercially viable. You need to create designs that don't take too much time otherwise you'll have to charge more money and this will discourage your client from coming back another time.

This tool is useful for marbling and dotting.

Water-based acrylics can be mixed together to create many fantastic colours!

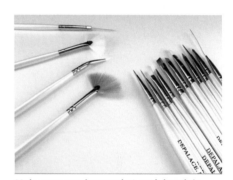
Make sure you know what each brush is used for.

A mixing palette might also be useful for nail art services.

WHY DON'T YOU...
Make a list of what you would like to have in your nail art kit. Look at products from the Internet, trade magazines and professional suppliers and compare prices. Try to discover some additional tools and products that you could introduce into your collection.

Nail art isn't that expensive and can really make your client's nails look distinctive.

HANDY HINTS

To give clients more choice, keep simple designs that use a couple of diamantés at a fixed price. If clients want to have more, charge a little more per stone. The price you charge will depend on the type and quality of stone.

The recommended time for nail art is 30 minutes, depending on how complex the design is. During this time, you might need to paint and decorate all ten fingers. Most designs need a base coat and there are some techniques that need the top colour to be almost dry, such as striping tape, foiling and transfers. These methods can easily disturb wet polish and make dents and smudges.

As an average pricing guide, 30 minutes for nail art should cost between £15–30 depending on where in the country your salon is located. Over time prices will also rise. Some of the most expensive products used in nail art are diamantés and other flatstones, especially Swarovski crystals, a high-quality diamanté with amazing effects. They can, however, be the quickest and easiest method to brighten up a nail. Take into account the cost of these products when you're deciding how much to charge your client.

CONSULT, PLAN AND PREPARE FOR NAIL ART SERVICES

Before you begin the nail art service, you must carry out a full consultation. Please refer to N2/N3 for all the information you need for this.

Make sure you note down the consultation results on the client record card. All the contra-indications and restrictions that apply to nail art services are the same as for Unit N2/N3.

When you're deciding on the right nail art service for your client, you'll need to ask questions and encourage your client to answer them as fully as possible. When you have all the information you need, discuss the possibilities with your client. There are some nail shapes, lengths and conditions that can limit the type of nail art.

For example:
- Short nails aren't suitable for designs that are too complicated because the detail will be lost.
- Bitten nails are difficult to decorate but it might encourage your client to stop biting them.
- Ridged nails might have a surface that isn't suitable for some products or techniques, such as transfers and diamantés.
- Nails with severe delamination can cause the designs to chip very quickly.
- Some toenails might be too small for designs. If so, decorate the big toe and paint the other toes with a matching colour.

If your client would like nail art designs for a special occasion, ask what they're wearing and the colours and design of the outfit. If they want to have their toes decorated to match a specific pair of sandals, ask them to bring the sandals with them. You also need to find out what types of designs and colour combinations your client likes.

ACTIVITY

It's difficult describing nail art designs in words. The best way to discuss the possibilities with your client is to show them some examples of your own work. When you've practised a specific technique or design, make a nail tip for display. Also, when you've painted a set of nail art designs, ask that client if you can take a picture of the nails. Use these to create a portfolio that you can show during a consultation.

Make sure you understand exactly what your client wants. You could even make a sketch of the agreed design on the record card so both you and your client are clear on the end result. When you've agreed on a design, make sure you and your client sign the record card.

CARRY OUT NAIL ART SERVICES

PREPARING THE NAILS

You will often provide a nail art service after a manicure, pedicure or nail enhancement service. If your client has just booked in for nail art, you'll need to provide a mini manicure or pedicure:

1 Wash and sanitise the hands or feet (as in Unit N2/N3).

2 Remove any existing nail polish.

3 Shape the nails according to the agreed length and shape.

4 Remove any cuticle on the nail plate by gently using a cuticle knife. You can use a cuticle remover if necessary but make sure you remove all traces of the cuticle and remover. Wash the nails or wipe them with a cotton pad dampened with an alcohol-based nail cleanser.

5 Clean the nail plate, removing any debris and oils.

6 Apply a base coat.

7 Apply the base colour.

You're now ready to start the nail art service.

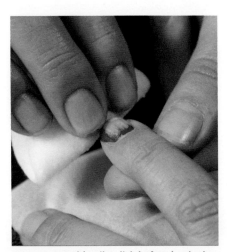

Remove any old nail polish before beginning the nail art service.

NAIL ART TECHNIQUES

It's important that you practise all the techniques and build a variety of designs that you can apply quickly and effectively. For example, you can use several techniques on one nail. It's also worth looking at websites, such as **www.salongeek.com** and magazines, such as *Scratch* magazine (**www.scratchmagazine.co.uk**) to get some ideas. There are many sites that have hundreds of ideas. You might also find inspiration by looking at fashion, celebrities and the media.

ACTIVITY

Prepare a number of nail tips by placing them on to the ends of orange sticks using Blu-Tack® (or similar). Hold each orange stick while you paint the tip. Apply a base coat to each tip so you achieve a good base colour. Paint the tips in a variety of base colours using nail polish. When you're happy with your designs, keep the tips and use them in your display.

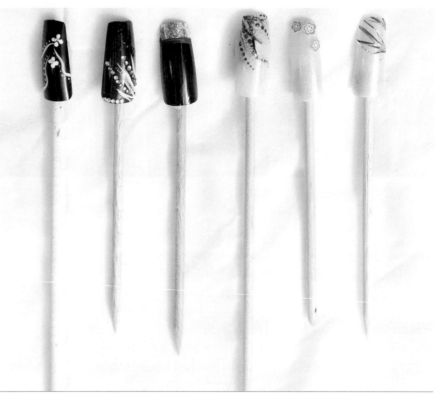

Nail tips attached to orange sticks with Blu-Tack®

NAIL ART DESIGNS

Nail art almost always needs a base colour of nail polish. Paint your prepared tips with a variety of colours in preparation for practising various techniques.

Transfers

1 Choose your transfer and soak it if necessary. Take a pair of pointed tweezers and pick up the transfer by its edge.

2 Place the transfer carefully on to the prepared nail.

3 All nail art needs sealing to keep it in place. Sealers aren't always very glossy so you can apply a top coat over the sealer to make the designs stand out.

There are many transfers you can choose from for nail art designs.

HANDY HINTS

Remember to keep the designs you like the most and start your design display.

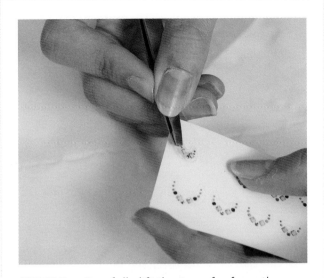

STEP 1 – Carefully lift the transfer from the backing sheet.

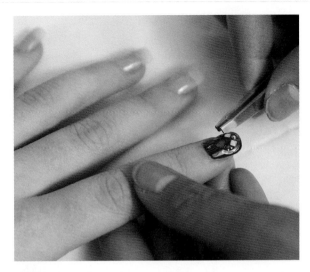

STEP 2 – Place the transfer on the prepared nail.

STEP 3 – Seal the design.

Some other examples of using nail transfers.

N4 NAIL ART

Glitter dusts

You can use glitter dusts in a variety of ways.

STEP 1 – Paint the nails with a base coat or a colour. While still wet, dip the tip into the glitter.

STEP 2 – Very gently seal the glitter with top coat.

The easiest way is to dip the edge of a nail into the glitter. It will stick to wet polish and you can brush off any that gets on the skin. You can dip the nail straight in or at an angle.

Another way to use glitter is to pick it up with a wet top coat brush or use a glitter dust brush.

STEP 3 – Dip a clean brush into the top coat or glitter mixer to pick up the glitter.

STEP 4 – Apply the glitter to the nail.

STEP 5 – Seal with top coat.

You can then place it in a specific pattern on the nail.

Place several colours on to one nail to make an interesting design.

You can use glitter to create lots of different designs!

Foils

There are a large number of foil designs you can use in nail art designs. They might not work over the whole nail as they tend to crease over the curves in the nail. They are effective if you use them in specific areas.

HANDY HINTS

You can use a striping brush and a contrasting colour or stones to hide an untidy edge.

1 The foil will stick only to the adhesive. When the base polish colour is dry, apply a thin and even layer of adhesive to the areas you want to put the foil. Wait until the adhesive is transparent. The foil won't stick to the adhesive if it's still wet.

STEP 1 – Apply adhesive to the nail.

2 With your chosen foil, gently press the foil (with the pattern facing upwards) on to the nail with your thumbs or a hoof stick. Make sure you've pressed it over all the adhesive. Pull the foil off quickly but gently. The foil should come off the backing sheet and stay on the adhesive. If you've missed any areas, reapply the adhesive and repeat.

STEP 2 – Place the foil on the nail.

3 You'll need to seal the foil. Use a sealer that's specifically recommended for nail art as other top coats can affect the foil and make it shrivel. Apply a top coat over the sealer if necessary. Be careful though: excessive brushing can damage the wrap.

STEP 3 – Seal the foil.

HANDY HINTS

Always check you have removed any backing when you're working with foils.

With a bit of imagination, you can use foils to create lots of quick designs.

Flatstones/rhinestones

Like all nail art products, there are hundreds of stones to choose from. Many are diamantés, others are coloured stones or pearls, and all come in many varieties and sizes. Avoid stones that are too big as they won't sit flat on the nail because of its curves.

STEP 1 – Apply top coat to the nail.

STEP 2 – Pick up the stone.

STEP 3 – Place the stone precisely on the nail and gently press it into the top coat.

STEP 4 – Seal with top coat.

Stones need a layer of wet polish to stick to. Paint one nail at a time so the polish is still wet.

One of the easiest methods of picking up stones is to use a piece of Blu-Tack® shaped to a point on the end of an orange stick. This will pick up the tiniest stone. When the Blu-Tack® loses its stick, just reshape it.

If you seal the stones, they'll last longer but it can dull them slightly. If you've pressed the stone into a thick top coat, they'll last quite well.

Using stones singly or in a pattern can brighten up any polish colour quickly and easily.

Marbling

Marbling can use nail polish or nail art paints and can be an effective technique. The colour combinations are key to creating an effective design, so you'll need to practise and experiment.

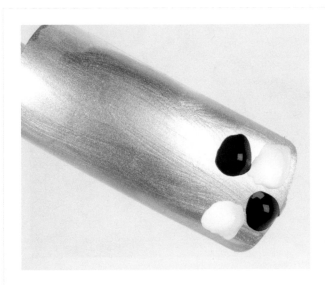

STEP 1 – Apply blobs of contrasting colours on the nail. These can be at the base of the nail, in one corner or in the centre.

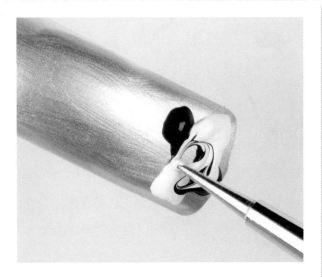

STEP 2 – Use the marbling/dotting tool and swirl the colours together. Marbling/dotting tools are available in a variety of sizes.

STEP 3 – If the nail polish you've used doesn't need sealing, enhance the effect with a quick-drying, glossy top coat.

You can achieve lots of different effects with this technique.

Dotting

Use the same tool as for marbling for this technique. You can use dots on their own or to enhance other designs.

STEP 1 – Choose your marbling/dotting tool and dip the end into the chosen colour of paint. You can use polish for this technique but it needs to be one that has a lot of dense pigment.

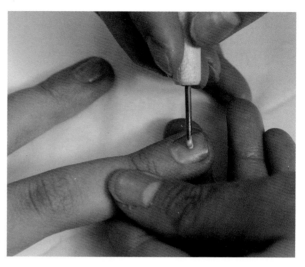

STEP 2 – Carefully place the paint on the nail.

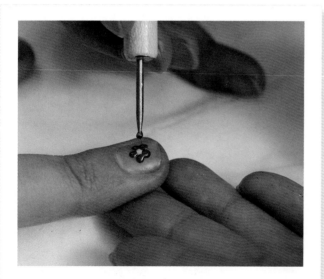

STEP 3 – You can also use the dotting tool to drag dots of colour to create leaves and flower petals.

This is a simple technique that can create lots of quick designs.

Striping tape

Striping tape is available in all colours, metallics and patterns. You can use it to create tartans or simple and easy designs.

STEP 1 – Position the tape on dry polish in the place you want it. Use tweezers if you find this easier. The tape is self adhesive so will stay in place on its own.

STEP 2 – Use scissors (or an old pair of nippers) to cut the tape just short of the free edge or the edge of the nail plate. By cutting it just short, you can seal the end and stop it lifting.

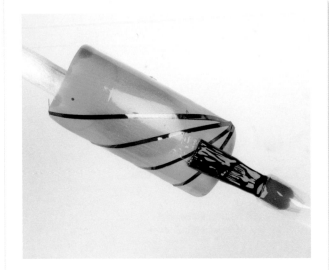

STEP 3 – Seal the finished design. Make sure you've sealed the ends of the tape.

Here are some ideas for using striping tape.

Flicks can create an effective nail art design.

Nail art paints for free-hand painting and other decorations

Some water-based and highly pigmented paints are ideal for hand painted designs and let you use your imagination and artistic skills to the full. Some nail artists can paint the most intricate designs, but you can create some effective designs even if you're not quite so artistic. Using different brushes will create different designs.

Use a palette to put a selection of colours on. This makes it easier for you to use the nail art brushes and you can mix the colours on the palette to create more shades.

Colour mixing

Don't forget you can have a small number of nail art paints but you can mix them together to create many more. Choose primary colours as you can use these to make almost every other colour. Black and white are useful as you can use them to lighten or darken any colour.

The primary colours are:

- red
- yellow
- blue.

Some nail art paints are iridescent. Add a colourless nail paint to plain colours to give them more depth.

Try mixing nail art paints together for lots of fun combinations!

ACTIVITY

Use the three primary colours, plus white and black, and mix some colours together to see what you get.

For a simple design, take a small detailing brush and flick a contrasting colour over the base polish colour. You can also use this brush to paint a variety of animal prints. For those with good artistic skills, use this small brush to create more detailed paintings.

A long thin striper brush can create straight, thin lines on the nail or the outline for a French manicure.

Lay the brush on the nail or pull the brush across the nail.

Hold the brush upright and use a zigzag and swirling movement to create a petal of a flower, for example.

Remember all nail art paints need sealing for protection!

When you've practised and experimented with the various techniques on nail tips, it's time to work on real nails. You'll find it harder working on the actual fingernail to begin with, because it will be harder for you to position someone's hands the way you want them.

N4 NAIL ART

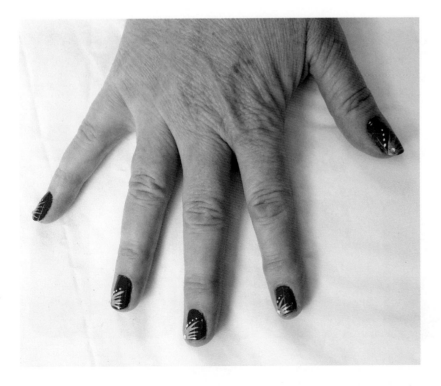

Here are some designs that combine some of the techniques. They're all quick and easy and you should be able to do each of them in around 30 minutes.

PROVIDE AFTERCARE ADVICE

Like all nail services, make sure you give your client aftercare advice that is specific to their individual needs. The aftercare advice is the same for a manicure:

- Don't use your nails as tools, eg don't use them to open a can of fizzy drink.
- Apply nail oil to the cuticle area daily.
- Use hand cream frequently during the day.
- Use gloves when you're working with water and chemicals.
- Apply a clear top coat every 2–3 days to keep the nail art in place and help the nails stay glossy.
- Remove all nail art with nail polish remover.
- If your client wants to keep their designs for a long time, advise them to make another appointment in 1–2 weeks' time.
- If your client follows this advice, the nail art should last a long time, or your client can remove it with nail polish remover at any time.

POSSIBLE CONTRA-ACTIONS

Refer to Unit N2/N3 for the possible contra-actions to nail services. These can include irritation and excessive erythema. If your client experiences any of these conditions at home, tell them to come back to the salon for further consultation.

After the nail art service your client might find their flatstones/rhinestones get knocked off. Advise your client to reapply a top coat every 2–3 days to stop this happening.

Striping tape can also start to lift from the nail edges. Suggest your client either snips off the end with a pair of small sharp scissors or uses a spot of nail adhesive or a clear top coat to seal the edge back in place.

> **HANDY HINTS**
>
> Some other things your client needs to be aware could happen:
>
> - discolouration of nail
> - peeling and chipping
> - smudging and smearing
> - flaking, cracking and crumbling of art.

END OF UNIT SUMMARY

Now you've reached the end of the unit, you should feel confident in the theory and practical aspects of all areas of nail art services. Use the checklist below to see if there are any areas you feel you need to recap before starting the end of unit assessment:

- maintain safe and effective methods of working when providing nail art services
- consult, plan and prepare for nail art services
- carry out nail art services
- provide aftercare advice.

Use the questions below to test your knowledge of Unit N4 to see how much information you've retained. These questions will help you revise what you've learnt in this chapter.

Turn to pages 411–412 for the answers.

1 Why might your client want a nail art service?

2 Name **five** useful nail art products.

3 Name **four** essential nail art tools.

4 Why should you keep your nail art tools in a box?

5 What is the recommended time for a nail art service?

6 Explain why you should use a nail art sealer.

7 What is the difference between a nail art sealer and a top coat?

8 What do you need to find out from your client during the consultation?

9 Why is it important to have a display of your nail art designs?

10 What should you remember when you're applying foil adhesive?

11 What are the **three** primary colours?

12 Why is it useful to include black and white in your collection of nail art paints?

13 What is the easiest method of applying flatstones/rhinestones?

14 How are these methods of nail art removed?

15 List **four** pieces of aftercare advice.

16 List **four** possible contra-actions.

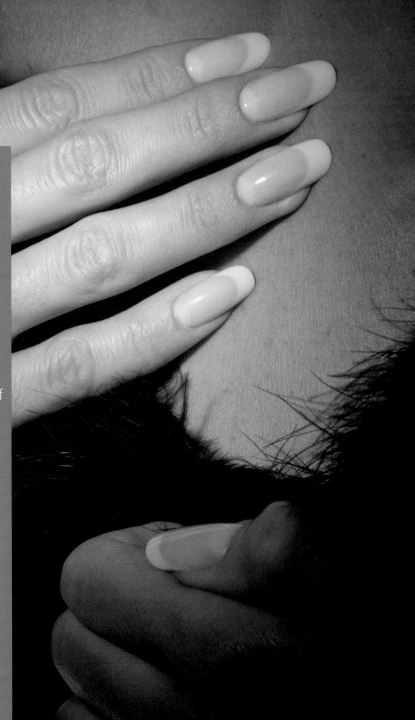

N5

APPLY AND MAINTAIN NAIL ENHANCEMENTS TO CREATE A NATURAL FINISH

Not everyone has the nails they want. A series of manicures might achieve your client's goal but this will take time. Sometimes the best solution is to recommend nail enhancements. Your client can wear their enhanced nails over a long period of time or temporarily until the natural nails are the desired length.

There are three main systems of nail enhancements: liquid and powder, UV gel and wraps. You need to learn one of them.

In this chapter you'll learn how to:

- maintain safe and effective methods of working when enhancing, maintaining and removing nail enhancements
- consult, plan and prepare for nail enhancement services
- apply natural nail overlays
- apply a tip and overlay
- maintain nail enhancements
- remove nail enhancements
- provide aftercare advice.

When you're performing a nail enhancement service, it's important to use the skills you've learnt in the following units:

Unit G20	Ensure responsibility for actions to reduce risks to health and safety
Unit G18	Promote additional services or products to clients
Unit G8	Develop and maintain your effectiveness at work
Unit N2/N3	Provide manicure and pedicure services.

Solvents
Liquids that dissolve other solids.

Ventilation

Extraction

An example of a nail station with ventilation and extraction

MAINTAIN SAFE AND EFFECTIVE METHODS OF WORKING WHEN ENHANCING, MAINTAINING AND REMOVING NAIL ENHANCEMENTS

Maintaining safe and effective working methods, good hygiene and anatomy and physiology have the same basic principles as outlined in Unit N2/N3. Please refer to this unit for guidance.

The following information applies specifically to nail enhancements.

HEALTH AND SAFETY
You must follow all the necessary health and safety requirements that are listed in Unit N2/N3.

Nail enhancement services have some additional health and safety issues that you must know about and make sure your salon is prepared for.

The main potential hazards that you need to understand and deal with to create a safe working environment are:

1 effective ventilation

2 effective dust control

3 using **solvents** and other nail products.

Nail polish remover is used in nail polish to keep it in liquid form and, when it's applied to the nails, it evaporates and leaves behind the solid and dry polish. Nail polish remover dissolves the nail polish when you're removing it from the nails. The solvents are volatile meaning they have a high tendency to evaporate into the air. This means that molecules of the solvent are in the air (called a vapour, NOT an odour nor fumes). A high level of these vapours in the air creates an unhealthy environment.

HOW TO MANAGE VAPOURS
Effective ventilation and extraction will remove unwanted vapours from the environment. Air in the salon must be clean and fresh. Too many unwanted vapours can result in headaches, dizziness, fatigue and nausea. However, if you use the correct working procedures, you'll minimise the amount of vapours and the risk of side effects.

Effective ventilation
There should be an efficient ventilation system that changes the air in the salon several times an hour. The type of unit will depend on the size of the salon and your salon might seek professional advice to make sure the correct method is installed. As vapours from the products are heavier than air, you might find that the unit is placed down low.

Effective extraction
A good nail desk or nail station should have an extraction system. This will include a specialist filter that extracts the chemicals from the air. Filters might need changing regularly as they can become saturated quickly.

EFFECTIVE DUST CONTROL

During your training, you should learn how to minimise dust. That is, when you're applying a nail overlay, try to create the finished shape without having to file lots of the nail away at the end. Not only is this time consuming but it also creates a large amount of dust.

However, in every nail enhancement service, there will be some amount of dust and, like vapours, the dust can be controlled by ventilation, extraction and correct working practices. Dust in the atmosphere is a health hazard and can cause respiratory problems.

- Dust extraction: it's easier to remove dust from as close to the source as possible, that is, right under where you're filing. An efficient extraction unit will catch most of the dust before it enters the environment.
- A nail desk should have a dust extractor fitted into it. You can cover the extractor with a towel at other times but uncover it when you're filing and buffing. The dust is collected in a catchment area that you'll need to empty at the end of every day. Towels should be regularly changed during the filing/buffing process.
- Good working practices: minimising the amount of dust you create is the most important method but you cannot completely avoid creating dust.

A nail enhancement service

USING SOLVENTS AND OTHER NAIL PRODUCTS

Good general working practices

It's relatively easy to minimise the amount of vapour and dust in the air by working cleanly and tidily. There are several ways to do this:

1 Have a metal waste bin with a lid: metal doesn't absorb vapours and the lid will keep them contained. Line the bin with a disposable waste bag that you should remove at the end of the day or when it's full. Tie the bag up and place it in the general rubbish.

2 Keep all containers closed except when you're using them.

3 Avoid overuse of sprays.

4 If you're using a liquid and powder system, have lint-free pads on your desk. Use these to wipe your **L&P** brush during the service and change it on a regular basis.

5 Cover the towel that is on the desk with two or three layers of paper towels and change them on a regular basis to remove any dust.

6 Keep all application brushes in a closed container.

7 Keep used files and buffers in a closed container until you clean them to avoid spreading dust.

ACTIVITY

Carry out your own risk assessment using a risk assessment form from the Habia health and safety pack for nail technicians or beauty therapists. Choose a selection of products (eg polish remover, liquid monomer, resin activator, acetone), collect the Material Safety Data Sheets (MSDS) from the supplier and complete the form.

OTHER HEALTH RISKS

Information on the use of personal protective equipment (PPE) is explained in Unit N2/N3. Make sure you read this and understand the importance of your employer providing the right equipment.

Several nail products used for enhancements are known allergens, that is they can cause an allergic reaction. It's important you know what they are and how to minimise the risk.

Controlling vapours and dust will help to keep the environment safe. When you're working with any product, you need to avoid unnecessary contact with the skin.

Overexposure is one of the most common problems when you're working with nail products but it's easy to minimise the risk by following good working practices and the general health and safety information in this unit.

Be careful not to get solvents into the eyes

Some nail technicians are advised not to wear contact lenses if they're working with volatile solvents all day. This is because solvents can permeate the lense and get trapped next to the eye. Ask your salon what their practice is.

Good working practices are essential. In addition to those described above:

- Avoid getting any liquid monomer on your skin, eg don't touch your L&P brush with your fingers.
- Avoid touching the skin around your client's nails with your L&P brush.
- Don't rest your arm in the dust on any paper towel. Throw the towel away and replace it with a clean one until you've finished the stages that create dust.
- Only wipe your L&P on the lint pad, NOT on the paper towel.
- Take particular care when you're removing the sticky layer of UV gel.

CONTACT DERMATITIS

Dermatitis is a condition that causes inflammation of the skin. There are several types of dermatitis. Atopic dermatitis is often hereditary and it's linked to other conditions, such as asthma and hay fever.

Contact dermatitis occurs when your body comes into contact with a particular substance, which causes your skin to become inflamed. There are two types of contact dermatitis, allergic and irritant. See Unit N2/N3 for more details.

Contact dermatitis

HANDY HINTS

Remember to follow the manufacturer's instructions when you're using any disinfectant. Make up a fresh solution every day and remember to wear PPE when you're handling undiluted disinfectant as it's an irritant.

Overlay

The covering placed on the natural nail or a natural nail with a tip in either L&P, gel or wrap systems.

HANDY HINTS

The edges of files and buffers are often quite sharp and you could cut the skin at the side or the base of the nail. When you're using a new file, use another file to smoothe the edges and take off the sharp edges.

A dappen dish

YOUR TOOLS AND EQUIPMENT

Follow all the hygiene methods that are described in Unit N2/N3 for your basic tools and equipment. The information below is relevant to nail enhancements only and applies to the three systems: liquid and powder, UV gel and wrap.

ADDITIONAL TOOLS AND EQUIPMENT

The following is a list of additional tools and equipment for nail enhancement services:

1 Several types of files and buffers:
   - a 240 grit file for shaping the natural nail and blending the tip (if recommended by the manufacturer)
   - a cushioned file or buffer no lower than 240 grit for removing the shine on the natural nail and removing any scratches on the overlay
   - a file for shaping the **overlay**. This could be a combined 180/240 grit where the 180 grit side shapes the overlay and the 240 refines it. (Don't use lower than 180 as it will disturb the overlay.)
   - a three-way buffer for creating a glossy finish (except for UV gel because that has a glossy top coat already)
   - soft sponge files, white block or similar to refine the surface of the overlay.

After you've finished using them, place all files and buffers in a covered container until you can clean them. This will contain the dust. If the files are disposable, throw them away after one use. If the files are washable follow these instructions:

   - Using a stiff brush, clean away all the dust from the file under running water.
   - Rinse the file and place it in the disinfectant for the time recommended by the manufacturer.
   - Remove the file, rinse and blot dry.
   - When dry, keep in a closed container ready for use.

2 A covered dish for liquid monomer (often called a dappen dish): this is for the L&P system. Have a small bottle of the monomer by your desk and remove a small amount using a pipette. Soak up any liquid left after the service with a paper towel and place it in the lidded waste bin.

3 A sable brush for L&P: keep this flat and in a covered container to avoid contamination and vapours escaping into the atmosphere. Clean the brush with monomer and NOT a brush cleaner. At the end of your application, dip the brush in the monomer to remove any remaining powder, wipe it on the side of the dish and shape it into a sharp point on a lint-free pad. Discard the pad in the waste bin and store the brush in its container.

4 A nylon or sable gel brush for the UV gel system: you should also store this in a covered container. When you've finished with it, wipe it with an alcohol-based cleaner, such as the product you've used to remove the sticky layer from the UV gel after **curing**.

Curing

The name used to describe the polymerisation process or the hardening of the acrylic, ie a cured nail is an overlay that has hardened.

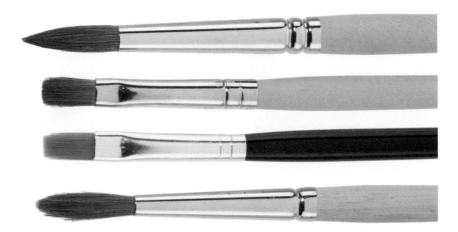

5 Tip cutters or clippers: you'll need these to cut the excess length from the tip. They only need occasional cleaning as they don't come into contact with your client's skin or nails.

Some beauty therapists and nail technicians like to keep a jar of disinfectant on their desks. You can place tools, such as nippers and cuticle knives, in here but remember you MUST scrub and wash them with detergent before you disinfect them.

If you drop any tools or equipment on the floor, don't use them again until you've cleaned them.

WHY DON'T YOU...
Collect a range of files or go to your local wholesaler and try to guess the grit size. Find the ones that are suitable for use on the natural nail and a nail enhancement.

HANDY HINTS
Have two containers with lids on your desk. One container is to store clean tools. The other container is for storing tools ready for cleaning later.

PREPARING THE NAIL STATION

Before your client arrives, make sure your nail desk is ready. For nail enhancements, you'll need:

- disposable towels
- lint-free pads
- nail polish remover
- nail dehydrator
- primer (if required)
- a box of tips
- nail adhesive
- a variety of files and buffers
- a cuticle knife
- tip cutters
- a cuticle remover (if the service requires one)
- overlay products
- hand cleanser
- Barbicide
- disinfectant spray or gel

- for L&P:
  - liquid monomer
  - clear or pink powder
  - a dappen dish
  - a pipette
  - an L&P brush
- for the UV gel system:
  - a stable UV lamp
  - a base gel or primer
  - a clear UV gel
  - a top coat gel (if used in system)
  - a gel brush
  - a sticky layer remover
- for the fibre system:
  - resin
  - an activator (spray or brush on)
  - fibre in a closed container or bag
  - fibre scissors
  - extra nozzles
- nail oil
- a base coat
- a top coat
- hand cream.

SERVICE TIMES

It's important that you know and keep to the industry accepted times. This might not be possible when you're learning as every stage will take much longer. However, if you practise, you'll find your times will be reduced. The service times below are for a newly qualified nail professional. You should be able to reduce these times when you're more experienced to make the service more cost effective.

At the beginning, focus on completing each stage and trying not to damage the natural nail. Also, focus on creating a natural-looking nail enhancement that suits the fingers and wishes of your client. These times exclude consultation.

The prices of these services are probably the widest ranging of all beauty services. A full set of tips with overlay can range from £18 up to £120! This will depend on the type of salon, the geographical area and the quality of products. Prices also vary over time.

As a general average, services could fall into the following ranges:
- natural nail overlay – £20–40
- tips with overlay – £30–60
- maintenance – £20–40
- removal – £10–30

Treatment	Times
Natural nail overlay	75 minutes
Tips with overlay	120 minutes
Maintenance	90 minutes
Removal	60 minutes

HAND WASHING

You: It's essential that you wash your hands before and after every client to avoid cross-infection. It's good practice to use a disinfecting spray or antibacterial gel, but remember to wash your hands first to remove debris and dust.

Your client: Ask your client to wash their hands with soap and water, paying particular attention to their nails. You shouldn't be expected to clean dirt out from under their nails. Make sure they have access to a sink with hot and cold water, liquid soap, a good supply of disposable (or clean) towels and a waste bin.

After you've washed your hands and your client has washed theirs, it's good practice for you both to use an antibacterial gel or spray at the nail desk. This demonstrates good hygiene.

During a nail service, it's important not to touch your face or eyes as you might transfer product from your hands. If you have a cold, sneeze into a paper tissue, blow your nose and throw the tissue into a lidded waste bin. Wash your hands with soap and water and use a sanitising spray or gel before resuming the service. If you've got a bad cold or it's in its early stages, you could wear a face mask to avoid cross-infection. Make sure you wash your hands after the nail service.

Don't forget to wash your hands before and after every service.

CONSULT, PLAN AND PREPARE FOR NAIL ENHANCEMENT SERVICES

Please refer to Unit N2/N3 for the necessary consultation information.

CONTRA-INDICATIONS

The contra-indications listed in Unit N2/N3 also apply to nail enhancements. However, there are specific conditions that will also affect nail enhancements.

CONDITIONS THAT RESTRICT THE SERVICE

The conditions that restrict a manicure will apply here. They're all conditions that can weaken the nail plate and make the skin sensitive and delicate.

Minor nail separation

You shouldn't work on nails with severe separation but you can work on nails with minor separation, eg when only a small part of the nail has separated from the nail bed. You shouldn't proceed if you think that the separation has been caused by a fungal infection.

Any separation means that the nail is weaker than it should be so you must take care not to place any unnecessary pressure on the nail. Nor should you apply tips with overlays that are long as they will cause the nail to lift even more.

Minor eczema, psoriasis and dermatitis

If these conditions are on the hands, take extra care not to get any nail product near the affected areas as it could make the condition worse or start an allergic reaction. If your client has dermatitis that has been possibly caused by a previous nail enhancement service, then you cannot proceed. If the nails are affected, they will be delicate so you must treat them gently and avoid long enhancements.

Severely bitten nails

It's possible to apply tips with overlays to bitten nails but it's a difficult service and you should wait until you've had plenty of time to practise enhancements. The enhanced nails shouldn't be longer than the finger as the nail won't be strong enough and your client won't be used to having long nails. Make sure your client understands that they need to return on a weekly basis as the nails and the shape of the finger will change quite dramatically in the first few weeks.

Severely damaged nails

Nail enhancements can improve the appearance of damaged nails, eg severe nail separation, trauma, bruising, or a nail that has been ripped off. However, if it's recent damage, it's advisable to wait until any pain and swelling has gone. Don't apply any enhancement to a nail that has any inflammation surrounding it.

Unknown swelling and redness

If there's any swelling and/or redness around the nail, avoid the area associated with it.

BACTERIAL INFECTION

There's a bacterial infection that is associated with nail enhancements, sometimes referred to as pseudomonas. This occurs when the overlay has lifted, usually at the base or side of the nail. This creates the ideal environment for infection, ie warm, moist and lacking oxygen. The infection will look pale yellow and darken to green if left untreated. The discolouration is not actually the bacteria but a by-product of the organism that stains the nail plate. You can continue the service if you follow this advice:

- Remove the nail enhancement and, as a precaution, throw away the files you've used on the nail.
- Reapply a new nail enhancement because you've removed the environment that supported the growth of the bacteria. An overlay shouldn't be reapplied if bacteria is in advanced stages.
- Don't try to buff off the staining as this will thin the nail plate. The staining will grow out with the nail.

Pseudomonas can only occur where there's **lifting** that has been present for a period of time. Make sure your nail preparation is accurate and meticulous and also make sure your client understands that they should return if they notice any further lifting or discolouration.

Lifting is caused by inaccurate preparation of the nail plate (ie cuticle or oil left on the nail plate), the wrong ratio of L&P, insufficient curing of UV gel, overactivation of resin, the overlay touching the skin around the nail, or the overlay being too thick or too thin at the base of the nail (Zone 3).

HANDY HINTS

The client might need a manicure a few days prior to a nail enhancement service to help soften hard, forward-growing cuticles.

Lifting

When the overlay lifts from the nail plate. It can be seen as a whitish area usually at the base of the nail in the cuticle area. It weakens the nail enhancement but, more importantly, allows bacteria to enter the space under the overlay. This is an ideal environment for bacteria to grow as it's warm and moist. After a few days, a yellow stain will appear. This, if left unchecked, will darken to almost black. This is sometimes known as pseudomonas.

HANDY HINTS

When you're applying overlays, think of the nail in zones. The free edge of the nail is Zone 1 (Z1) where the overlay needs to be very thin; the middle of the nail is Zone 2 (Z2) where the overlay needs to be slightly thicker as this is where you need extra strength to prevent breakages; the base of the nail is Zone 3 (Z3) where the overlay should be thin and tapered down to the nail plate so there's no unsightly ridge. This will create a natural-looking and balanced nail.

CONSULTATION

In addition to the standard consultation information in Unit N2/N3, you must find out from your client:

1 The reason why they want nail enhancements, eg to reinforce their own nails, to stop biting them, to have long nails immediately, or to grow their own with the help of enhancements.

2 If they've had enhancements before and what their experience was.

3 If they understand any restrictions that might apply to them, eg a nail biter cannot have long enhancements because their nails won't be strong enough; if they've had an allergy to enhancements before, they will still be allergic. There are certain natural nail shapes that dictate the length of the nail enhancement. For example, fan shaped or hooked nails cannot usually have long enhancements as the nail will be either unstable or unbalanced.

4 If they understand and agree to the maintenance they'll need to do at home.

As with all consultations, you must write the information on the record card. Let your client read and agree on the treatment plan before both of you sign the card.

APPLY NATURAL NAIL OVERLAYS

Natural nail overlays (NNOs) are useful to repair broken, split or peeling nails, strengthen nails, prevent biting and provide a base that stops polish from chipping.

This section covers the application of all three systems: liquid and powder (L&P), UV gel and wraps. During your unit, you will learn one of these systems.

A UV gel system

A fibre system

An L&P system

KEY DIFFERENCES BETWEEN THE SYSTEMS

There are three main systems used for nail enhancements:

1 Liquid and powder (L&P): this system uses a liquid **monomer** and powder **polymer** that, when mixed together, form a solid **acrylic** plastic. This is applied using a brush that is dipped in the liquid monomer to pick up a bead of powder which is put on the nail and shaped. Mixing the two components with their **initiator** and **catalyst** starts the **polymerisation** process and heat from the finger speeds it up. This is usually accepted as the strongest of the three systems and can be used as a natural nail overlay, over a **tip**. There are several colours of powder available, from clear through to opaque colours.

You need a high level of skill to create strong and natural-looking enhancements. The system uses volatile products that some clients object to because of the liquid's strong smell. However, good working practices can minimise this problem.

Over time, you can minimise the odours associated with the liquid and powder system.

2 UV gel: this system uses a semi-solid gel and needs a UV light to initiate the polymerisation process to turn it into a solid. Apply the gel to the nail with a brush and cure it under a UV lamp. This system is strong and slightly more flexible that L&P. There are two distinct types of UV gel: one is resistant to solvents and can only be removed by buffing; the other can be soaked off in acetone. Like L&P, the gels are available in a wide range of colours.

Vapours with this system are lower. You also need a high level of skill for this technique and you need to take extra care when you're removing buff-off versions otherwise you could damage the nail plate.

Monomer

Used in some nail enhancements. The liquid must polymerise to become a solid.

Polymer

A substance (eg a plastic) that is formed from many repeating units.

Acrylic

A type of plastic. All nail enhancements are acrylic and made of polymers.

Initiator

An additive that starts a chemical process.

Catalyst

An additive that works with the initiator and controls the speed of the chemical reaction.

Polymerisation

The chemical process that turns a liquid (or semi-solid) into a solid.

Tip

A plastic nail shape that is available in various shapes and sizes. It's applied to a natural nail and buffed to provide the length for the nail enhancement.

> **HANDY HINTS**
>
> UV gel is considered an odourless system, but precautions should be taken as vapours are present. Dust is finer and stays airborne for longer.

3 Wrap system: this system uses a cyanoacrylate resin, a fabric to provide some extra strength and an activator that cures the resin. Of the systems, this is the weakest so it's not recommended for clients who use their hands for heavy work. There aren't any colours used in this system and it cannot be used for sculpted nails. It's excellent for natural nail overlays and suitable for tips with an overlay. The technique is relatively easy to learn and quick and easy to remove.

HANDY HINTS

There are two types of fabric generally available. A fibreglass fabric and a silk fabric, each with a sticky back to make it easier to apply to the nail. The fibreglass version is slightly stronger but can be more difficult to soak with the resin so it becomes transparent. The silk is much easier to soak but is not quite as strong as fibreglass.

PREPARING THE NAIL

The preparation of the nail is the same for all systems and also for tips with overlays and natural nail overlays.

Nail preparation is an essential stage of all enhancement services. If you don't do this correctly, the enhancement will lift from the nail plate. You need to prepare the surface of the nail so it will bond properly with the overlay.

Enhancement products don't bond with skin so you need to remove every trace of cuticle from the nail. Also, the products won't stick to the nail if there's any oil, moisture or debris on the surface. You must be accurate in this process to achieve a successful nail service.

To prepare the nail:

1 Wash your hands and ask your client to do the same. Remove any polish from the nails and if you find any traces of previous enhancements, gently buff with a 240 grit buffer.

HANDY HINTS

Nails must be dehydrated before buffing at stage 1.

N5 NAIL ENHANCEMENTS

2 Remove the cuticle: this is where your accuracy is important. It's easy to leave a trace of cuticle on the nail and this will cause lifting. The method you use will depend on the manufacturer's instructions but there are two main methods:

- Wet method: this uses a cuticle remover to soften the cuticle before removing it with a cuticle knife. If you use this method, remember to remove all traces of remover and dry the nail thoroughly.
- Dry method: use a cuticle knife to remove any cuticle on the nail. This is quick and efficient but take care not to damage the nail plate.

Make sure you pay attention to the side walls during this stage as this is another area that will lift if there's any skin or debris left over. Only use your nippers on the remaining cuticle and make sure you don't cut into living skin. This will thicken the cuticle and possibly lead to infection.

Shape the nail.

Remove the shine.

3 Shape the nail: depending on the nail service you're providing, you need to shape the nail at this stage. If you're providing a natural nail overlay, you must shape the client's natural nail according to your client's preferences. For tips with overlay, shape the tip's free edge with a 240 grit file so it fits snugly against the tip's 'stop point'.

4 Remove the surface shine from the nail plate: overlays don't bond to a shiny surface. However, it's only the shine you want to remove, NOT any nail layers. Use a fine cushioned buffer for this at 240 grit or higher. Use gentle strokes in the direction of the nail growth (from base to tip), taking care to go down the side walls.

5 Dehydrate the nail: remove any oil, moisture and other debris from the nail plate. The nail bed continually moisturises the nail plate but you need the surface to be moisture free for a good bond.

Now the nails are prepared for the next steps. Make sure neither you nor your client touches the nails, eg make sure your client doesn't touch her face as this will put oil on the nail.

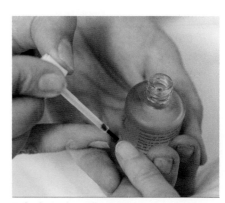

Dehydrate the nail.

HANDY HINTS

Even the finest grit file can be damaging in the wrong hands. Use the correct file for the job, hold it gently between your fingers and use a light stroke on the nail (or tip or overlay). Keep the file moving and do NOT file in the same place for too long. The nail is not flat. Keep in mind the curves of the nail and keep the file moving around those curves.

APPLYING A NATURAL NAIL OVERLAY

There are three main systems to choose from. Each system is described below.

LIQUID AND POWDER

It's essential that you use products from the same brand and make sure you don't mix brands. This avoids an ineffective service, as products from different brands don't always mix together. It's also important you follow the manufacturer's instructions for health and safety reasons.

If you've never used L&P before, there are some things you can do to help you understand how to use the product:

1 Have ready a dappen dish of monomer, a small tub of powder, a clean brush and some lint-free pads. Dip your brush into the liquid and wipe the excess on the side of the dish. Dip only the end of the brush tip in the powder and draw a short line. Look at the bead that you've picked up: it should be round and glossy rather than dry or dripping off the brush. If it's not right, wipe the bead onto the pad and try again. Keep going until you get a round glossy bead. Throw the lint-free pads into a lidded waste bin.

2 Repeat this process but this time look at the size of the bead you've picked up. The size will depend on the amount of liquid on the brush. You need to learn to pick up beads of different sizes. It's important that you're able to do this because different nails need different-sized beads.

3 Find a piece of plastic. Pick up a small bead and place it on the plastic. It should start to melt after the count of three. If it melts sooner, the **mix ratio** is wrong and it's too wet; if it takes longer, the mix ratio is again wrong and it's too dry. The wrong consistency can lead to overexposure, lifting, brittleness and loss of strength in the enhancement. Keep practising until you get the right consistency.

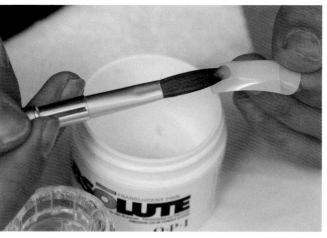

Mix ratio
The ratio of liquid to powder in the bead.

4 Take a tip and place a bead near to the end. Let it just start to melt then press down with your brush, taking some of the bead to one side and the rest to the other side, and smoothe it over with a few gentle strokes of your brush. Look at it from all angles to see if you've created an even, smooth finish. Place another bead just behind the first and repeat. Blend the two areas together with a few strokes of your brush. Keep practising until you've got reasonable control of the overlay.

When you're happy with the results, you're ready to apply a natural nail overlay.

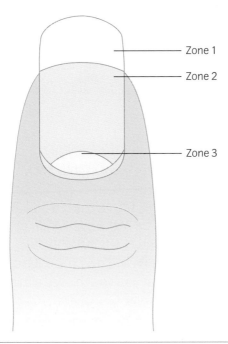

Zone 1

Zone 2

Zone 3

Zones of the nail

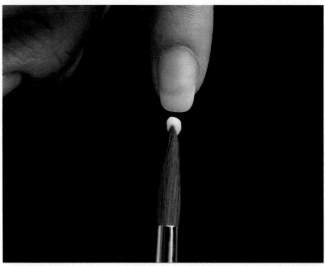

A perfect bead

Primer

Some L&P and UV gel systems use a primer. This is a product that prepares the surface of the nail to create a better bond with the overlay. Some of them use methacrylic acid so take care when you're using this as it's an irritant. Apply sparingly and always follow the manufacturer's instructions. Many modern and good quality systems don't need a primer and some UV gel systems have a specially formulated base layer instead of a primer.

Application

1 Have one hand of prepared nails ready.

2 If the brand you're using requires you to use a **primer**, now is the time to apply it. Just touch the brush on the base of the nail (Zone 3) and the primer will spread out. Apply to each finger and wait for it to dry.

3 Now apply the overlay. As you'll be using only clear (or transparent pink) powder, you can apply the overlay in either two or three zones depending on the size of the nail, ie you can apply the overlay on a smaller nail in two zones and on a large nail in three zones.

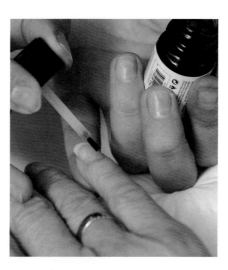 

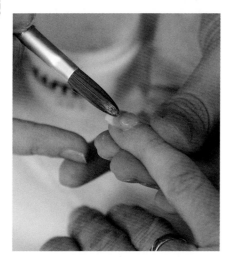

4 Assuming you're applying three zones:

- Pick up a bead of an appropriate size (not too small and not too big) and place it in the centre of the free edge but slightly back from the edge of the nail. Wait three seconds for it to melt. PRESS (don't push or pat) one side of the bead out to one side of the nail and then the other side of the bead to the other side of the nail. Take care not to touch the skin and make sure the overlay is thin at the sides. Lightly brush over the surface bringing it down and over the edge of the nail. Check from all sides to make sure that you've achieved a thin and even coverage.

- Pick up a bead and place it just behind Z2. Repeat as above and blend Z1 and Z2 together. Check from all angles to ensure an even overlay.

- Pick up a smaller bead and place in Z3. Press from side to side then angle the tip of the brush into the nail and press the edge of the overlay to create a thin and even coverage a millimetre away from the skin. Don't touch the skin; you could cause an allergic reaction. To avoid this, leave a small margin around the edge of the overlay. Blend it into Z2.

- You should now have a smooth and even overlay that is thin around the edges and slightly thicker in the centre to give it strength.

- Test to see if the overlay is cured by tapping it with the handle of your brush. It should make a clicking noise when it's cured. Repeat this process on each nail.

- Clean your brush in the monomer, shape it to a point on the damp pad and place it in its covered container.

Finishing the nail

When you've added the overlay to all the nails, you're ready to refine the shape and buff them.

STEP 1 – To shape the overlay, use the 180 grit side of your file. Make sure the edges of the overlay are even and smoothe (the small margin will help to smoothe the edges without touching the skin). Look down the nail and file the free edge so that it's about the thickness of a credit card and follows the natural curve of the nail.

STEP 2 – Buff over the whole surface of the overlay. Remove any lumps, bumps and thickness. The centre of the nail should be the thickness of about two credit cards. Check from the side to make sure there's a smooth and even curve from Z3 to Z1.

STEP 3 – Using the 240 grit file, refine the surface and gently blend the edge of the overlay in Z3. Take care not to buff the natural nail. Follow this process for all nails.

STEP 4 – When you're happy with the shape, use your block or cushioned buffer and further refine the surface. Then use a high-shine buffer and use each side in turn to buff the nails to a high shine.

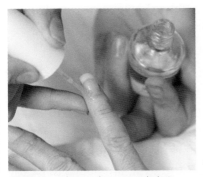

STEP 5 – Ask your client to wash their hands to remove any dust. Massage nail oil into the nails and surrounding skin.

STEP 6 – Check your client is happy with the result.

UV GEL

There are many brands of UV gel on the market. The main distinction is whether they're soak-off or buff-off. But, within these two types, there are different application methods. Some have just one component, ie one type of gel that you paint on. Others have several components, eg bonder, builder and top coat gels. A builder gel is one that holds its shape when it's applied so you can create the structure and thickness in the right areas.

The most important rule to keep to is to follow the manufacturer's instructions. It's also important to use a recommended UV lamp. UV lamps have many variables: number, wattage and output of the UV tubes, reflectors, and the distance from the nails. Each of these factors has an influence on how the gel cures. UV tubes have a certain number of hours that they can efficiently cure the gel. After this time, they won't cure the gel properly. You should keep a check on how much you've used each tube and change it regularly. Failure to do this will result in a poor service and problems with the overlays for your clients.

These instructions assume that you're using an advanced gel system that has three components.

Application

1 Have your gels ready together with a clean gel brush. Plug in your UV lamp and place it safely on your desk.

2 With a UV gel application, you need to prepare both your client's hands as you'll work on both of them at the same time.

3 The type of lamp you use will depend on the order in which you do things. Some lamps can accommodate five fingers; the manufacturer's instructions will tell you this but don't assume that it does. This means you can apply the gel to one hand, place this hand under the lamp and apply the gel to the other hand in the meantime. Some lamps can only accommodate four fingers so you need to apply gel to the fingers and cure them BEFORE you apply gel to the thumbs. These instructions are for a four-finger lamp.

4 Apply the bonder gel (or primer) to the first four fingers. This is usually a thin gel that is formulated to bond to the natural nail. Apply a thin layer and make sure you cover the whole surface of the nail plate without touching the skin. Place the fingers under the lamp and cure for the recommended time.

5 Repeat on the four fingers of the other hand.

6 Apply the bonder gel to the thumb of the first hand and place under the lamp.

7 Apply the bonder to the second thumb and place under the lamp.

8 Apply a thin layer of the builder gel to the four fingers of the first hand. This is a thicker gel that is formulated to create a structure on the nail to provide strength. Like L&P, the structure needs to be thin in Z1 and Z3 and slightly thicker in Z2. It takes practice to place the gel correctly. Run the brush around the free edge of the nail to cap it and prevent any lifting. You can also do this at step 4.

9 Place the fingers under the lamp and repeat on the second hand.

HANDY HINTS

Make sure reflectors are cleaned regularly to ensure complete curing.

HANDY HINTS

Some gels, especially thick layers, cure very quickly and create a **heat spike**. If this happens, remove your client's fingers from the lamp and the heat will subside. Replace the fingers under the lamp. Applying thinner layers of gel will help avoid this.

Heat spike

The chemical process of polymerisation is exothermic, ie it releases heat. This problem often occurs during the curing of UV gel. It happens when the polymerisation process occurs too fast under the UV lamp. It's a sudden and painful heat sensation on the nail plate and is alarming for clients. It only lasts a few seconds at the most but it's unpleasant. Modern UV gels have their cure time matched to their recommended UV lamp so it's unlikely to happen. Gels that don't have a dedicated lamp often exhibit this. The way to overcome this is to apply thin layers of gel as thicker layers are more likely to get a heat spike and less likely to cure fully.

HANDY HINTS

Some builder gels lose their structure as they settle on the nail. If this is the case, it might be necessary to apply gel to two fingers only.

Cure the first four fingers.

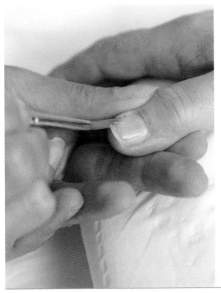

Apply bonder gel to the thumbs and cure in the UV lamp.

10 Repeat on both thumbs.

11 When you've applied and cured the builder gel, the hands are ready for finishing.

Finishing the nail

STEP 1 – You must remove the **inhibition layer** first. Soak a lint-free pad in the cleanser supplied with the gel and wipe the nails from the base up to the free edge. Start with the little finger as this will stop you getting gel on the skin.

STEP 2 – Choose a 240 grit file because the gel is very soft. Refine the shape of the overlay to make it thin and smoothe and create neat and even edges and a thin free edge.

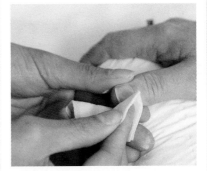

STEP 3 – When you're happy with the shape, remove the dust with a lint-free pad and cleanser.

STEP 4 – Apply a thin layer of gel top coat in the same sequence as before. Make sure you cap the free edge and place the hand under the UV lamp for the recommended time.

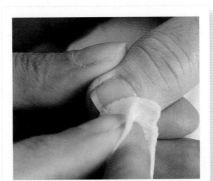

STEP 5 – Remove the inhibition layer as before, and massage nail oil into the nails and skin.

Inhibition layer

The surface of the UV gel doesn't cure under the lamp as oxygen prevents this. When the nails are removed from the lamp, there's a sticky surface. You need to remove this carefully with an alcohol-based cleanser. Uncured gel is a common allergen so take care not to get it on the skin.

WRAP SYSTEM

This system can be used as a natural nail overlay, for repairing breaks in the nail and as nail enhancements for clients who aren't too heavy on their hands.

There are three components for this system: resin, activator and fibre.

1 Resin: this is a cyanoacrylate **adhesive** similar to the nail tip adhesives. It's slightly thicker so it can create more strength. It's easier to use if you put a disposable nozzle on it. Some brands also have a brush-on version to create thin layers of resin.

2 Activator: this is usually available in a spray or a brush-on. If you're using a spray, use as little as possible and spray from a distance of around 10–12 inches (25–30 cm). A light mist on the nails should be enough. First, you don't want to have too much of the activator in the atmosphere. Second, you only need a tiny amount on the resin to cure it. If you use too much, your client will feel a sudden burning of a heat spike. You can avoid this problem by using a brush-on activator because the concentration of the activator is lower.

3 Fibre: fibreglass or silk is available for this system. There's little to choose between them but fibreglass is slightly stronger but more difficult to cover; silk is not quite as strong but much easier to soak with the resin. You'll need a pair of sharp, fine-pointed scissors to cut the fibre.

Application

1 Prepare the nails.

2 Layer the nail with resin. You need to put the fibre in the centre of the nail where it will give it some strength. Take the fibre and cut a piece that is approximately the width of the nail. Take care not to touch the fibre as oils from your fingers will affect it. Use the backing strip to hold it while you place it on the nail plate and press into place.

Press the fibre into place.

3 Trim the fibre if it's too wide using fine scissors.

4 Trim the length so the fibre is just shorter than the nail. (The edge needs to be sealed with the resin to prevent it lifting.) You can add an additional strip to the **stress area** on long nails to give extra strength.

Trim the fibre.

5 Repeat for all fingers on one hand.

6 When the fibre is in place, apply a small amount of resin and gently spread it with the side of the nozzle. Make sure you've soaked the fibre so it's not visible. Allow this layer to dry naturally. Do not activate.

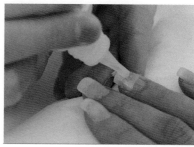

Soak the fibre with resin.

Adhesive

A cyanoacrylate adhesive that is safe to use on the skin and bonds the tip to the nail. It's often incorrectly called glue.

Stress area (or apex)

This is the area of Zone 2 where the apex of two curves meet (the curve from side to side of the nail and the curve from the base to the tip). The structure of the nail needs to be at its strongest here as this is where it could break if there's any accidental damage. NB: This can affect any nail system.

7 Repeat for all fingers on one hand.

8 Apply the resin for strength.

- If you're using a spray activator, apply a small amount of resin down the centre of the nail. Use the nozzle to spread it evenly over the nail but without touching the skin. Repeat this on each finger (not the thumb). When you've applied the resin to all the fingers, spray a small amount of activator about 12 inches (30 cm) above the fingers (any closer could cause a heat spike). Wait until you see the surface of the resin change. Don't be impatient and use the spray again. Repeat on the thumb.

- If you're using a brush-on activator, apply a small amount of resin down the centre of the nail. Take the activator brush and spread the resin evenly over the nail but without touching the skin. This will mix the activator with the resin at the same time. Repeat for all fingers on one hand.

9 Depending on how much strength the nail needs, you can add more layers of resin in the same way.

10 Repeat the process on the other hand.

The spray activator must be used about 12 inches above the fingers.

Finishing the nail

This system is quite delicate and shouldn't need much buffing. If you've applied the resin evenly, it will just need a white block or 240 grit file to smoothe the surface.

If you're using a brush-on activator, apply the resin evenly to the nail.

STEP 1 – Shape the nails to create a natural shape from all angles.

STEP 2 – Smoothe the surface of the nails with a soft buffer, eg 240 grit cushioned buffer or white block.

STEP 3 – Use a three-way buffer to bring the nails to a high shine.

STEP 4 – Ask your client to wash their hands to remove any dust. Massage nail oil into the nails and surounding skin.

This is a nail service that gives the nails length. When you discussed this at the consultation stage, you should have checked your client understands the process, has reasonable expectations of the service (eg doesn't want nails that are too long for her nail shape and lifestyle) and knows that regular maintenance appointments are essential.

Although you'll have already discussed length and shape, it's important you communicate with your client throughout the process.

TIPS

Apply tips to the nails before the overlay to give the length and shape that you've already agreed with your client. There are many different shapes and types of tip available. Which brand you use is more down to personal choice than anything else. However, which shape you use is dictated by the shape of your client's nails.

'C' curve

The natural curve of the nail from side wall to side wall. You need to look down the finger from the end to see the 'C' curve.

HANDY HINTS

The weakest part of the nail is just above the hyponychium. This is where it usually bends when accidentally knocked. An overlay needs to be at its thickest here to give it strength. As the nail grows, this area will grow with it and end up over the free edge. This puts the nail out of balance and more liable to breakage. When you apply an overlay over the tips, you must structure it in the zones that have been described to create a balanced nail.

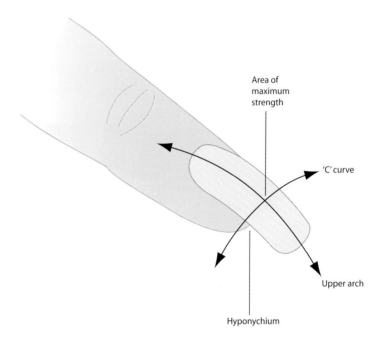

Area of maximum strength

'C' curve

Upper arch

Hyponychium

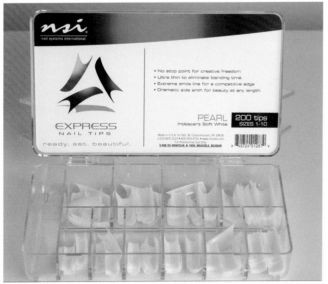

A selection of nail tips

You need to look at the **'C' curve** of your client's nails and see what shape of tip to use. You must use the one that matches this curve as much as possible. If you use one that is flatter or more curved, it will put pressure on the nail bed and pull the nail plate into its shape. It will also make the nail enhancements weaker and might not adhere correctly. Sometimes, the wrong-shaped tip can cause discomfort and make the nail throb.

Most tips (with the exception of French tips) have a contact area or well. This is a thinner part of the tip that comes into contact with the nail plate. You need to blend this to the nail during application to make it invisible.

Where the contact area becomes the main part of the tip, there's a ridge. This ridge, or stop point, needs to fit snugly around the free edge of the natural nail. Make sure you shape the nail so it fits this shape. This will look better on the finished nail, protect the nail plate and prevent debris from getting trapped.

The tips you use might have a small contact area. Other tips have a large contact area and you need to remove most of this to leave just a small amount behind. This will make the tip easier to apply. Make sure you don't get any air bubbles trapped under the tip. Remove the contact area using a file or a pair of curved scissors.

There's no real strength in the tip; it's just there to provide a platform for the overlay. The strongest bond in the nail enhancement structure is between the nail plate and the overlay. Therefore, the tip shouldn't cover much of the nail plate and you should place it close to the end of the nail.

HANDY HINTS

The majority of the free edge should be removed.

Tip application

If you're doing an L&P or wrap overlay, apply the tips to one hand at a time and apply the overlay. This way, your client has a free hand. If you're working on both hands, make sure the nail plate is clean and oil free. With UV gels, get both hands ready as you'll alternate them under the UV lamp to cure them.

1 Prep and shape the free edge.

2 Choose the shape of tip that fits your client's nails.

3 Start with the little finger and choose a tip that is the exact width of your client's nail at the free edge. Remember you'll be removing the unnecessary contact area. Make sure you choose the right size. If the nail is in between sizes, choose the larger tip and file the side walls so the tip fits snugly.

4 If necessary, remove the contact area so the tip sits between 35 and 50 per cent on the nail. Use a 180 grit file or a pair of curved scissors and follow the line of the stop point.

HANDY HINTS

When you're holding the tip on the nail, push the finger up rather than the nail down. This will stop you from lifting the tip at the wrong angle.

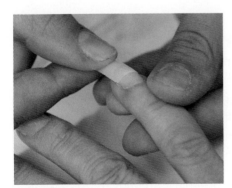
Choose the correct size tip.

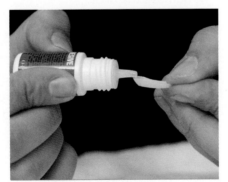
Apply adhesive to the contact area.

Apply the tip to the nail.

4 Apply a small amount of adhesive onto the contact area.

5 Hold the tip at a downward angle, fit the nail into the stop point and lift the tip upwards so it gradually comes into contact with the nail plate. This will ensure there aren't any air bubbles under the tip. Hold this in place for a few seconds until the adhesive holds the tip on to the nail.

6 Repeat this on all the fingers on the first hand (continue with the second hand if you're applying UV gel).

N5 NAIL ENHANCEMENTS

7 Using tip cutters, cut the tips to the length you've agreed with your client.

8 Use a 180–240 grit file to blend the tip:

- File the sides of the tip so they're in line with the side walls of the nail plate.
- Roughly shape the free edge of the tip to the agreed length and shape.
- Start at the end of the tip and remove the shine.
- Work backwards on the tip until you reach the contact area over the nail plate.

- Blend the contact area into the nail and take care not to file the nail plate. Keep the file moving across the contact area, using the full length of the file. Otherwise you could cause a friction burn. Keep the file flat and don't tilt it into the nail plate. The contact area should disappear and the tip shouldn't create a visible line (join) or shadow over the nail.
- Go back to the free edge and refine the shape so the tip looks natural on the nail and is the correct shape and length (check with your client).
- Repeat this for all tips.
- Remove the dust.

Upper arch

The curve of the nail from the base to the tip. A perfectly shaped nail has a gentle curve. Some people have flat nails, others have nails that can tilt upwards. These tend to be weaker than those with an upper arch curve.

APPLYING THE OVERLAY

Applying an overlay is exactly the same as applying a natural nail overlay. Remember that a tip with overlay needs some extra strength in Zone 2 to allow for the added length of the enhancement. Check your overlay from all angles while you're finishing it. Every nail should look the same as the others in shape and relative length. Check the 'C' curve of each nail and the **upper arch**. Every nail should look natural.

Check under the free edge and make sure there isn't any debris. Like a natural nail overlay, remove the dust and massage in nail oil. Always give your client aftercare advice and book their maintenance visit.

MAINTAIN NAIL ENHANCEMENTS

It's essential that every nail enhancement client returns for a maintenance visit. Like having your hair coloured and the roots showing, nails grow and the enhancement grows with them. Unlike hair that takes several weeks for the growth to show, nails grow much faster and need maintenance at least two weeks after the first application. Recommend that nail biters return after one week.

There are several reasons for a maintenance visit:

1 To make sure there isn't an allergic reaction to the products. This will mean a contra-action, ie removal.
2 To make sure there aren't any problems with the enhancements, eg lifting, breakages, length too long for your client, etc.
3 To infill the gap that has appeared at the base of the nail.
4 To rebalance the shape of the nail so that the stress area is in the correct place and not over the free edge.

There are two general types of maintenance services:

1 an infill in the growth area if the nail doesn't need rebalancing
2 a rebalance if the stress area needs to be replaced in the correct area of the enhancement.

PREPARING THE ENHANCEMENTS FOR MAINTENANCE

The most important part of a maintenance visit, especially the first appointment, is to look for any problems.

LIFTING

The most common problem is the overlay lifting from the nail plate, usually in Z3. Lifting appears as a white area of overlay where it's detached from the nail plate. Hopefully, if there is lifting, there won't be any evidence of a bacterial infection. If there is any lifting, you need to work out what has caused it. There are several possibilities:

1 Inaccurate nail preparation: there was cuticle left on the nail or traces of oil or moisture.
2 Primer (or bonding layer in UV gel) wasn't applied correctly: the bonder needs to be placed accurately.
3 The overlay is too thick: in Z3, the overlay needs to be quite thin. If it's too thick, it will not be as flexible as the nail plate and will pull away.
4 The overlay is too thin: the overlay has been applied or buffed too thin. This will not be able to hold on to the nail plate and will crack away from it.
5 With L&P, the consistency could be wrong: if it's too wet or too dry, the bond won't be strong enough.
6 Touching the skin: if the overlay touches the skin anywhere around the nail plate, it will lift from the nail as the skin moves.
7 Client interference: some clients like to pick at their enhancements. You must look at all the other reasons first as it's easy to blame your client.
8 Product contamination.

HANDY HINTS

Sometimes it's difficult to buff off lifting as more of the overlay keeps lifting. To avoid this, buff the area of overlay just behind the lifted area. This will cause the loose area to flake away.

BREAKAGES

If a nail is missing or broken, there could be several reasons:

- If the enhancement is completely missing and there's no trace of the enhancement left on the nail plate and the nail plate is undamaged, then the enhancement didn't bond properly. The reasons for this are the same as for lifting.
- If the enhancement is missing but there's some overlay left on the nail plate, the enhancement has broken off. This might be because the nail was too long for your client to cope with, was not balanced correctly or it might have been an accident.
- If the enhancement is missing but there's some damage on the nail plate, the overlay has been forced off. This could've been caused by an accident or breakage but is more likely due to your client picking it off or a poor tip fit application.

You'll need to talk to your client to discover the reason for the problem and how to rectify it. You might need to make changes to your application. The nails could be too long and need to be shorter, or you might need to educate your client on how to take better care of their nails.

When you've done this, you're ready to prepare the nails for maintenance. If the nails haven't grown too much and the stress area is still in roughly the right place, all your client will need is an infill. If the nails have grown and the stress area is over the free edge, you'll need to rebalance the nails. Both alternatives should take roughly the same time, but there are minor differences to the preparation and the application.

On any fingers where the nails are missing, you need to prepare the nails as you would for a new application.

General preparation for an infill:

1 Clean the hands and the nail plate. Prep the cuticle and regrowth.
2 Blend the overlay in Zone 3 with a suitable file. Take care not to file the new nail plate.
3 Quickly buff the entire overlay.
4 Quickly refine the free edge shape.
5 Use your cuticle knife to remove any new cuticle from the new growth.

For a rebalance, the procedure is the same for an infill with the additional step of buffing the entire overlay so it's even and thin. You need to take away the thickness of the stress area so you can replace it in the correct position.

APPLYING AN INFILL

When you've prepared the nails, you're ready to apply an infill.

L&P

1 If required by the brand manufacturer, apply a small amount of primer to the new nail growth and allow to dry.

2 Pick up a small bead of powder and place on Z3.

3 Wait for the bead to start melting and press with your brush.

4 Blend the bead over Z2 so there isn't any ridge.

5 Repeat on each finger on the first hand.

6 Use a 180–240 grit file to smoothe and blend the new application into the whole enhancement for each finger.

7 Buff the whole enhancement with a sponge buffer or white block.

8 Use a three-way buffer and bring the overlay to a high shine.

9 If there's any sign of a ridge, go back and refine with a cushioned buffer.

10 When the nails are refined and shiny, wash your hands and then massage nail oil into the nail and surrounding skin.

UV GEL

As for the original application, this is assuming you're using a three-component system:

1 Apply the bonder layer to the new nail growth for each finger and cure under the UV lamp.

2 Repeat on the other hand, curing the thumbs separately if necessary.

3 Apply a small amount of the builder gel to the new growth area and blend over the enhancement on each finger and cure as before.

4 Remove the inhibition layer with the cleanser.

5 Use a 180–240 grit file and refine the new application, blending it into the existing overlay.

6 Remove all traces of dust.

7 Apply a top coat UV gel over the whole enhancement on each finger and cure.

8 When you've cured the nails, remove the inhibition layer as recommended.

WRAPS

1 On the prepared nail, apply a small amount of resin to the new growth.

2 If you're using a spray activator, spread over the area and blend into the enhancement with the nozzle on each finger on the first hand. Apply separately to the thumbs.

3 Spray the activator briefly from 12 inches (30 cm).

4 If you're using a brush-on activator, use the activator brush to spread and blend on each finger individually.

5 When the first hand is complete, use a sponge buffer or white block to refine the surface.

6 Use a three-way buffer and bring each nail to a high shine without any ridges.

7 Remove all traces of dust.

8 Wash your hands and massage nail oil into the nails and surrounding skin.

APPLYING A REBALANCE

As for an infill, you need to prepare the nails in exactly the same way but you need to buff the existing overlay to a thin and even layer ready for a new complete overlay with its correctly placed stress area.

ALL SYSTEMS

Rebalancing enhancements is exactly like the original application in that you must create a structure with a stress area. The only thing you need to remember is that there's a thin overlay on the nail already where you've buffed down the original overlay.

The new overlay needs to be slightly thinner to take this into account.

Finish the new overlay as before.

REMOVE NAIL ENHANCEMENTS

You must remove nail enhancements if there's any suggestion of an allergic reaction. If you have any concern that there could be a reaction to the products, you should discuss this with your client but recommend that they have all the enhancements removed.

If your client wants to have their enhancements removed, this might be because their natural nails have grown or because they want to have a new set of enhancements.

It's important that you remove nail enhancements correctly. You must strongly advise your clients that they shouldn't try to remove the nails themselves or pick at them to remove them. If the enhancement is applied correctly, it will have a strong bond to the natural nail. If it's pulled off, it will remove several layers of the nail and result in a thin nail plate. A thinned nail plate can result in lifting from the nail bed which opens it up to possible infection.

REMOVING L&P, SOAK-OFF UV GELS AND WRAP SYSTEMS

There are two methods of removing L&P, soak-off UV gels and wrap systems.

SOAKING METHOD

Acetone is the solvent you should use to remove these enhancements. Acetone doesn't actually melt the enhancements. What it does do is break the bonds and soften them sufficiently to remove them.

You'll need:

- a small solvent-resistant bowl that can fit all the fingers of both hands. Put some acetone in this of sufficient depth to cover the nails but no more
- a larger bowl that the small bowl can sit in. Put in this some hot water that is at a level that will not spill over when the small bowl containing acetone is placed in it (this will speed up the process)
- a clean towel
- a few orange sticks
- a cushioned buffer
- a three-way buffer
- nail oil.

Process:

1 Place the bowls on a desk where they cannot be easily knocked over.

2 Ask your client to place the fingers of both hands in the bowl with the acetone.

3 Cover your client's hands and the bowls with a clean towel so the vapours don't escape.

4 Leave your clients in place for ten minutes for wraps and 15–20 minutes for UV gel and L&P.

5 After that time, check your client's nails. If you can easily scrape off the enhancements with an orange stick, remove most of the soft enhancement into the solvent.

6 Remove the hand where you've removed most of the enhancement and dry.

7 Leave the other hand in the solvent.

8 Use a 240 grit file or a cushioned buffer to remove all remaining product from each finger.

9 After you've removed all the product, either provide a hand soak or ask your client to wash their hands.

10 If you're not reapplying an enhancement, use a three-way buffer and bring the natural nail to a high shine.

11 Massage nail oil into the nail and surrounding skin.

12 OR proceed to a reapplication service.

13 When you've finished with the acetone, soak it up in paper towels and place in the lidded waste bin.

HANDY HINTS

If your client's skin is a bit dry or they don't like the feel of a solvent, you can apply some nail oil to the skin around the nails to form a barrier to the solvent.

HANDY HINTS

If you remove your client's hands without removing the soft enhancements, the remaining product will harden. Leave the fingers in the solvent until you're ready.

FOIL METHOD

This is an alternative to the soaking method.

You'll need:

- aluminium foil cut into squares of approximately 4 inches (10 cm)
- lint-free pads
- acetone
- a cushioned buffer
- a three-way buffer
- nail oil.

Process:

1 Place one of the foil squares on the desk and ask your client to place their finger on it.
2 Soak a folded lint-free pad with acetone and place it on the nail.
3 Fold the foil over the nail and wrap to keep the pad in place.
4 Repeat for all fingers.
5 Leave the foil wraps on for ten minutes for the wrap system and 15–20 minutes for L&P and UV gel.
6 Check inside one of the wraps to see if the enhancements are ready to come off after this time.
7 When they're ready, twist the foil wraps off the nails, squeezing them to take off as much of the softened product as possible.
8 Use the cushioned buffer to remove any remaining product.
9 If you're not reapplying enhancements, use the three-way buffer to bring the natural nails to a high shine.
10 Wash your hands.
11 Massage nail oil into the nails and surrounding skin.

REMOVING BUFF-OFF UV GEL

Buff-off UV gels are resistant to solvents. The only way to remove these is to buff them off.

You'll need:

- a 180/240 grit file
- a cushioned buffer
- a three-way buffer
- nail oil.

Process:

1 Using your 180 grit file, carefully remove the majority of the UV gel overlay from each finger. Don't file near the new growth of the natural nail.
2 Don't take all the overlay off. Use the 240 grit to refine the surface. If the overlay hasn't lifted, leave a thin layer of gel on the nail plate as this will protect the nail plate.
3 When there's a thin layer that has no lifting on each nail, use a three-way buffer to bring the nails to a high shine.
4 Wash your hands.
5 Massage nail oil into the nails and surrounding skin.

PROVIDE AFTERCARE ADVICE

After every nail service, you must give suitable, understandable and effective aftercare advice. There are several recommendations you should make to enhancement clients, especially with regards to contra-actions:

- Maintenance visits are essential: generally at two-week intervals but every week for nail biters. It might be slightly longer for some clients after the first few visits if they have slow-growing nails.

- You must impress on your clients that they must look out for any discolouration on the nail and show you as soon as possible. Lifting will appear as a discolouration and this can encourage a bacterial infection. The start of an infection will show as a pale yellow colour.

- Any itching of the skin around the nails, swelling or other irritation anywhere on the body could be a sign of an allergic reaction. If this is suspected, they must return to have the enhancements removed as soon as possible.

- Explain to your client that they should not use their nail as tools, eg they shouldn't use them to open a can of fizzy drink!

- Nail oil massaged into the nails and surrounding skin every day will help keep the enhancements and natural nail flexible and moisturised, and the skin nourished and healthy. This is an ideal retail opportunity.

- Suggest that your client wears gloves when they're doing work that involves detergents and other cleaning products, such as gardening.

- If your client finds that the nail enhancements are too long for their lifestyle, suggest they return for you to make them shorter otherwise they have a good chance of breaking and possibly damaging their own nails.

- Clients should always return to the salon for removals.

END OF UNIT SUMMARY

Now you've reached the end of the unit, you should feel confident in the theory and practical aspects of all areas of nail enhancements. Use the checklist below to see if there are any areas you feel you need to recap before beginning the end of unit assessment:

- maintain safe and effective methods of working when enhancing, maintaining and removing nail enhancements
- consult, plan and prepare for nail enhancement services
- apply natural nail overlays
- apply a tip and overlay
- maintain nail enhancements
- remove nail enhancements
- provide aftercare advice.

Using the questions below, test your knowledge of Unit N5 to see just how much information you've retained. These questions will help you revise what you've learnt in this chapter.

Turn to pages 412–413 for the answers.

1 Why is it important to minimise the production of dust and remove it from the atmosphere?

2 Where is the best place to extract dust from the air?

3 List **four** working practices that will reduce vapours in the salon.

4 List **three** working practices that will reduce dust.

5 List **four** working practices that will reduce the risk of overexposure.

6 What is the minimum grit size that you should use on a natural nail and why?

7 List **five** conditions that restrict the service.

8 List **three** circumstances where you would recommend a natural nail overlay.

9 List **two** benefits and **two** negatives of the liquid and powder system.

10 List **two** benefits and **two** negatives of the UV gel system.

11 List **two** benefits and **two** negatives of the wrap system.

12 List **three** reasons why it's important to prepare the nail properly.

13 What are the **three** zones of the nail?

For the L&P system:

14 How do you know if the overlay is sufficiently cured?

15 How do you clean and store your L&P brush?

16 How do you remove L&P overlays?

For the UV gel system:

17 How do you know how long to cure the gel under the UV lamp?

18 What is the inhibition layer and how should you deal with it?

19 How do you remove UV gels?

For the wrap system:

20 How do you use a spray activator?

21 What is a heat spike and how do you avoid it?

22 How do you remove wraps?

For all systems:

23 What is the 'C' curve?

24 Give **three** reasons why it's useful to remove most of the contact area of a tip.

25 What is the difference between an infill and a rebalance?

26 List **four** possible causes of lifting.

27 What is the main cause of nail enhancements breaking and leaving overlay on the nail?

28 When applying a tip and overlay to a bitten nail, how long should it be?

29 What would you do if there was a yellow/green discolouration under the overlay where it's lifted?

30 List **four** important pieces of aftercare advice.

B8
PROVIDE MAKE-UP SERVICES

Make-up is a very creative service you can offer to your clientele as it allows you to show off your artistic flair. Many beauty therapists are afraid of providing make-up services for this reason, thinking the client might not like the finished result. But don't worry if your client isn't sure about it – all you need to do is adapt the make-up and start again! In this unit, you'll learn how to use relevant tools and equipment, as well as the effects make-up can create. As a result, you'll have the knowledge and skills to produce a variety of different looks, ranging from day and evening to special occasion make-up. This unit will give you the power to make your clients feel like a million dollars when they leave with their new look!

In this chapter you'll learn how to:

- maintain safe and effective methods of working when providing make-up services
- consult, plan and prepare for make-up services
- apply make-up products
- provide aftercare advice.

Primer

A product that is applied instead of moisturiser, when it's unavailable, to provide a velvety texture to the skin so make-up application is smooth and even.

MAINTAIN SAFE AND EFFECTIVE METHODS OF WORKING WHEN PROVIDING MAKE-UP SERVICES

As with all beauty treatments, it's important you understand and adhere to the relevant health and safety legislation throughout to ensure you perform a safe and enjoyable treatment for your client. The main legislation affecting make-up services is:

- Data Protection Act (DPA)
- Control of Substances Hazardous to Health (COSHH)
- Provision and Use of Work Equipment Regulations (PUWER).

Each of these Acts is described fully in Unit G20 along with all other health and safety legislation.

SALON ENVIRONMENT

Before beginning a treatment, it's important that you've set up your work area properly. To reduce the risk of cross-infection, sterilise any metal implements and disinfect all non-metal implements and work surfaces; check Unit G20 for further assistance with this. Start with the trolley and disinfect the surfaces with an appropriate solution. Protect the trolley with couch roll and place the following items on the top shelf:

- face wipes
- a selection of cleansers
- a selection of toners
- a selection of moisturisers
- a small bowl for damp and dry cotton pads
- disposable spatulas
- tissues
- make-up range:
  - a **primer**
  - a selection of concealers and colour correctors
  - a selection of foundations
  - a highlighter and shader
  - a selection of powders
  - a selection of blushers and bronzers
  - a selection of eyeshadows
  - a selection of eyeliners
  - a selection of mascaras
  - a selection of lip products
- a selection of good-quality make-up brushes
- foundation sponges
- disposable make-up brushes:
  - mascara wands
  - eyeshadow applicators
  - lip brushes

M·A·C PRO LONGWEAR FOUNDATION

A long-wear foundation that gives up to 15 hours of wear in any environmental condition. Lightweight and creamy, applies smoothly to provide sheer to medium coverage. Provides everyday SPF protection.

- eyeliner brushes
- a pencil sharpener
- eyelash curlers.

On the second shelf you'll need the following:
- a small towel
- a square of couch roll
- a hand-held mirror
- make-up brush cleaner spray
- a small bowl lined with tissue.

On the bottom shelf you should have the client record card and any aftercare advice leaflets you want to give your client before they leave. Check you have a lined pedal bin next to the treatment couch for waste.

Additional equipment you'll need:
- a magnifying lamp.

A trolley set up for make-up services

HANDY HINTS

Wash your make-up brushes after every use with warm water and a good quality shampoo. Leave them to dry on a flat surface and place them in a UV cabinet. When you need to disinfect brushes quickly, use a good-quality brush spray before blotting on a paper towel.

WHY DON'T YOU...
Read through SmartScreen handout 1 for more suggestions for work area set-up.

SmartScreen B8 handout 1

Before you use the magnifying lamp, make sure it's been disinfected and is in safe working order. Check it has passed a PAT test in the last 12 months.

Place a protective sheet on the treatment couch and use two small towels to cover the head and foot of the couch. Place couch roll on top to protect the sheet. Always keep a pillow or rolled-up towel to hand in case your client requires extra back or neck support.

If you have a make-up chair, make sure it offers enough support for your client's back and keep a pillow or rolled-up towel to hand just in case.

HANDY HINTS

Take care not to be wasteful with your consumables; don't use too many cotton pads or too much product as it will make the treatment less cost effective. Remember, you can always add more.

When you're happy with the work area, remember to check your own comfort as you'll be standing for the duration of this treatment. If you're using a treatment couch, ensure it's height adjustable to prevent unnecessary stretching that could lead to fatigue and injury. If you're using a make-up chair, adjust it to a suitable height to prevent any overstretching.

Make sure the area where you're applying the make-up is well lit.

WHY DON'T YOU...
Read through SmartScreen handout 11 to find out how different lighting affects the appearance of make-up.

 SmartScreen B8 handout 11

Natural daylight

Ideal for day make-up or bridal make-up application.

HANDY HINTS

Other types of lighting include:

Fluorescent light – intensifies darker tones and softens blues and greys

Incandescent light – enhances frosted tones as well as silvers and golds making it ideal for evening make-up.

HANDY HINTS

When you're considering pricing structures for different make-up services, remember to think about including the cost of a trial run for special occasion make-up. Consider also the time you've allocated to each make-up look and the resources you've used.

The environment you create should be relaxing and provide suitable lighting so you can see what you're doing. Refer to Unit G20 for details on how to create the right environment and focus on lighting, temperature and general comfort. **Natural daylight** is the best possible lighting for any make-up treatment. If possible, use a treatment area with plenty of natural light. If this isn't possible, avoid placing your client under any down lighting as this will create shadows; white light is a good option when natural daylight is unavailable.

Before beginning the consultation, make sure you're aware of the industry accepted times for make-up services. These times exclude consultation.

Treatment	Times
Day make-up	30 minutes
Evening make-up	45 minutes
Special occasion make-up, eg bridal	45 minutes
Make-up lesson	75 minutes

B8 MAKE-UP SERVICES

CONSULT, PLAN AND PREPARE FOR MAKE-UP SERVICES

You should always perform a consultation and obtain your client's signature before beginning any treatment to safeguard yourself and the salon. However, with make-up services, you'll need to gather some additional information to devise a suitable plan and choose the right product to suit your client's skin condition. The information you'll need includes:

- contra-indications
- age group
- occasion
- skin colour
- skin type and condition
- eye colour
- face shape
- nose shape
- eye shape.

A therapist performing a consultation prior to the make-up service

CONTRA-INDICATIONS TO MAKE-UP SERVICES

As part of the consultation, you also need to identify whether or not your client has any contra-indications that could prevent or restrict this service. However, you might not become aware of this until you perform the visual consultation as part of the superficial cleanse and skin analysis. The following list indicates the contra-indications that require medical referral and, as a result, prevent make-up services:

- bacterial infections, such as impetigo, conjunctivitis and boils: risk of cross-infection and further skin damage
- viral infections, such as herpes simplex and warts: risk of cross-infection

- fungal infections, such as ringworm: risk of cross-infection
- parasitic infections, such as scabies and pediculosis: risk of cross-infection
- systemic medical conditions: risk of injury and skin damage
- severe skin conditions, such as acne: the condition could worsen or result in a reaction
- eye infections: risk of cross-infection.

If you identify one of the above contra-indications, explain to your client that the treatment cannot go ahead but don't name the condition in case you're wrong. Instead, tell your client you've identified a contra-indication and that to perform the service could make it worse. Advise them to see their GP for a proper diagnosis.

The following list indicates the contra-indications that restrict the application of make-up and require you to modify the service.

- Recent scar tissue: the skin is fragile and tender to touch, so work around the area.
- Eczema: if the skin is open and weeping, the treatment shouldn't go ahead. If it's not open and weeping, then treatment is fine as long as you use cream-based products and regularly check for a reaction. Remember to always communicate with your client.
- Psoriasis: treat in the same way you would eczema to prevent aggravating the condition and choose products with a higher moisture content.
- Hyper-keratosis: choose products with a higher moisture content as it will create a smoothing effect and diminish any unevenness in the skin's texture. Avoid frosted products and shimmers as this will draw attention to any rough areas.
- Skin allergies: talk to your client and check the skin reaction throughout. If your client is allergic to any of the ingredients, avoid using them and replace with an alternative.
- Bruising: the skin will be tender to touch, so work around the area to avoid further tissue damage.
- Styes: if there are several styes, you might want to advise your client to see their GP and offer them another treatment. However, if there's only one, simply work around it.
- Watery eyes: if your client suffers with watery eyes, choose waterproof make-up, as well as products that are designed for sensitive eyes. Place tissues around the eyes to prevent the make-up from running.

AGE GROUP

Your client is likely to fall into one of three age groups: 16–30, 31–50 and 50+. It's important you identify which of these categories your client falls into so you can choose products that will flatter and complement them as a person, enhance their natural features and suit the occasion for which the make-up is intended.

Make sure the final make-up look suits your client, no matter what their age.

Avoid darker colours and smoky eyes for a more mature client as dark colours recede and might have a draining effect on the complexion. Instead, use more subtle colours to create the same effect, such as golden tones and browns.

Younger clients might be able to get away with almost any look depending on their skin tone and personality. Remember to keep up with current trends and fashion so you have the most up-to-date shades available.

CLIENT PREPARATION

When you've completed the initial consultation and identified any contra-indications, you need to prepare your client. Inform them that a round-necked top is ideal for make-up application when your client books their treatment, then when they arrive, all you need to do is protect their top with some couch roll. Position your client comfortably and provide adequate support at all times. Lay your client supine on the treatment couch to prepare their skin, but transfer to an upright or semi-reclined position for the make-up application. Provide additional pillows or rolled-up towels to maintain your client's comfort.

When you're ready, wrap your client's hair in the small towel and tuck two tissues in to protect the towel. Start with a superficial cleanse (see Unit B4 for more information on this) to remove all traces of make-up before performing a thorough skin analysis to determine your client's skin type and condition. Then perform a deep cleanse to clean and free the skin from dirt and make-up. Tone and blot before moisturising to finish.

SKIN COLOUR/TONE

Make sure you have a good selection of foundation colours so that you can offer make-up services to people with all possible skin shades to avoid discrimination. Remember that skin colour will also affect the other colours you choose: intense colours tend to suit Afro-Caribbean skin, as well as glitter and frosted shades; matte tones may look better on Caucasion skin; and a **dewy** look often suits olive complexions as it enhances their natural tan.

Dewy

A popular summer look that provides a shimmer to the skin, enhancing natural features with frosted highlighters and tints. Use cream, liquid and gel products rather than powders. This look is particularly suited for those going on beach holidays and those with blemish-free complexions.

WHY DON'T YOU...
Refer to Unit B4 to remind yourself of the factors that affect the skin's ageing process, and how environmental and lifestyle factors affect the skin's condition.

SKIN TYPE AND CONDITION

During the skin analysis, you'll need to identify your client's skin type and condition to ensure you choose the most suitable products. Refer to Unit B4 to remind yourself of the different skin types and conditions, and the characteristics that will help you identify them.

Now you've prepared the skin, bring your client into an upright, or semi-reclined position and perform an analysis of the face, nose and eye shapes to determine how to apply your make-up.

EYE COLOUR

Take note of your client's eye colour as you want to draw attention to the eyes rather than the make-up itself.

FACE SHAPE

A person's face shape will affect how you apply the make-up as you might want to enhance or diminish certain features. The face shapes you're likely come across are described below.

OVAL FACE SHAPE

This is seen as the perfect face shape as it's neither too wide nor too long and is in proportion. You don't need any corrections here but you can use highlighter and shader to enhance natural features.

LONG FACE SHAPE

As the face is longer than it is wide, the idea is to rebalance the face by reducing the length and increasing the width. This is achieved by applying shader at the forehead and chin and then highlighter at the sides of the face.

SQUARE FACE SHAPE

The jawline will be prominent here and the widest parts of the face are the temples and jaw. To rebalance this face shape, apply shader to the widest points. Avoid highlighter so you don't draw attention to the angular features.

HEART FACE SHAPE

Here the forehead is considerably wider than the jawline. To rebalance, apply shader at the temples to reduce the width and highlighter along the jawline to increase the width.

ROUND FACE SHAPE

Round face shapes appear slightly wider. To rebalance and give the appearance of a longer face, apply highlighter down the forehead to the tip of the nose and shader to the sides of the face.

DIAMOND FACE SHAPE

This face shape is quite angular so to rebalance, apply shader to the forehead and chin to reduce the length. To diminish any angles, apply shader to the centre point at the sides of the face. Add highlighter above and beneath these centre points at the sides of the face to create width where the face is at its most narrow.

NOSE SHAPE

It's important to rebalance the shape of the nose if necessary so that the overall look is well balanced. You might come across three types of nose shapes.

LONG NOSE

If your client has a long nose, apply shader to the length of it at the outer edges to create width.

SHORT NOSE

To increase length, apply highlighter down the centre with shader at the tip.

UNEVEN NOSE

If the nose is uneven, apply shader and highlighter strategically to hide any irregularities and use the tips highlighted above.

WHY DON'T YOU...
Read through SmartScreen handout 13 for further advice on face shape corrections.

SmartScreen B8 handout 13

EYE SHAPE

A person's eye shape will greatly affect how you apply make-up and certain corrections might be necessary. There are a variety of eye shapes so it's important you know how to apply make-up to suit each shape.

DOWNWARD SLANTING EYES

These are otherwise known as drooping eyes because the eyes droop, or slant, downwards at the outer corners. To rebalance the eyes, apply eyeshadow upwards and outwards especially at the outer corners. Add eyeliner to help lift the eyes.

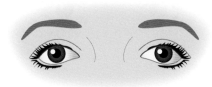

Downward slanting eyes

OVERHANGING EYELIDS

These are also known as hooded eyes because the lower halves of the upper eyelids are difficult to see when the eyes are open. Apply highlighter in the centre of the upper eyelid to create width and use a darker shade nearer the inner corner of the eye to create the illusion of a distinguished upper eyelid.

Overhanging eyelids

SMALL EYES

To make these eyes appear bigger, use a highlighter on the brow bone to open up the eye area and use lighter shades of eyeshadow. Apply eyeliner on the upper eyelids but avoid using it on the inner rim of the lower lashline as this will make the eyes appear even smaller. Curl the lashes before applying mascara to open up the eyes.

Small eyes

Prominent eyes

Almond eyes

Deep-set eyes

Wide-set eyes

Close-set eyes

PROMINENT EYES

Prominent eyes can sometimes be referred to as bulging eyes because they bulge out of the eye socket. To diminish this appearance, use a medium/dark eyeshadow in the centre of the upper eyelid, with a darker shade at the outer corner and blend in an upwards direction. Finish with highlighter on the brow bone.

ALMOND EYES

These are seen as the ideal eye shape so you don't need to make any corrections here. However, you might want to use a highlighter on the brow bone to enhance the brows and open up the eye area.

DEEP-SET EYES

This is where the eyes are set deep into the eye socket and have naturally occurring shadows surrounding them. To bring out the eyes, use a good quality light-reflecting concealer to diminish the shadows.

Use light shades on the upper eyelid and eyeliner along the upper lashline, with a wider line at the outer corners.

WIDE-SET EYES

This is where the eyes are more than one eye distance apart. Use darker shades at the inner corners and lighter shades at the outer corners to bring the eyes closer together. This will create the illusion of evenly set eyes.

CLOSE-SET EYES

This is where the eyes are less than one eye distance apart. Apply darker shades at the outer corners with lighter shades at the inner corners to take the eyes further apart. Add highlighter at the inner corner of the eyes to enhance this further.

WHY DON'T YOU...
Read through SmartScreen handout 15 to discover more tips on eye shape corrections.

SmartScreen B8 handout 15

LIP SHAPE

Look at your client's lip shape to see if there are any irregularities, and ask them if they're happy with their lip shape; even though they might have full lips, they might not particularly like them.

THICK LIPS

To create a thinner lip line, apply foundation to the lips and set with powder. Take a dark lip liner and apply just inside the natural line and fill with a matching shade of lipstick. Avoid gloss as it will enhance the fullness of your client's lips. Remember, the darker the lipstick, the thinner the lips will appear.

THIN LIPS

Conceal the natural lip line with foundation and powder and apply a pale pink lip liner just outside the natural lip line. Fill the lips with a matching shade of lipstick before applying gloss. Remember, the lighter the shade of lipstick, the fuller the lips will appear.

UNEVEN LIPS

If your client has uneven lips, conceal them with foundation and powder and create your own lip line with your chosen colour. Fill the lips with lipstick and apply gloss if necessary.

When you've determined all of these factors, plan which products you'll use. It's important to agree these ideas with your client so they'll be happy with the finished result.

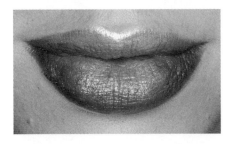

WHY DON'T YOU...
Read through SmartScreen handout 16 to discover more tips on lip shape corrections.

SmartScreen B8 handout 16

APPLY MAKE-UP PRODUCTS

Now you're ready to apply the make-up, select the right products for your client, the occasion and their personality based on your findings at the initial consultation, skin analysis and facial analysis. Below is a detailed guide on the products available and how they will enhance your client's features.

COLOUR CORRECTION

Make-up application always begins with colour correction as it evens out your client's skin tone and colouring. Below are the types of colour corrector and concealer you're likely to use and, while they often come as a stick, there are liquid and cream varieties available as well.

GREEN CORRECTOR

Green neutralises red so apply it to areas of redness, such as the cheeks and nose where your client might have dilated capillaries or their skin might be naturally rosy.

HANDY HINTS
When you're applying make-up, remember to decant the product on to a palette or the back of your hand. Make sure you've thoroughly washed your hands to ensure there's no risk of cross-infection.

M·A·C STUDIO FINISH SPF 35 CONCEALER

A lightweight, creamy, discreetly opaque concealer. Provides a smooth, long-wearing, invisible coverage for all skin blemishes.

HANDY HINTS

Stick concealer: useful on combination and oily skin as it provides thicker coverage. Apply using a damp sponge.

Liquid concealer: ideal for a blemish-free complexion as it provides a light coverage. Apply with clean fingers.

Cream concealer: beneficial for a dry, dehydrated or mature skin as it contains a high moisture content. Apply with clean fingers or a dry sponge for even application.

LILAC CORRECTOR

Lilac is recommended for a sallow complexion and dark circles under the eyes as it diminishes any dullness from the skin.

PEACH/YELLOW CORRECTOR

Peach or yellow neutralises blue so is ideal for areas where blue veins are quite noticeable.

CONCEALER

These come in a variety of colours ranging from fair to dark and can be used on imperfections that don't require colour correction.

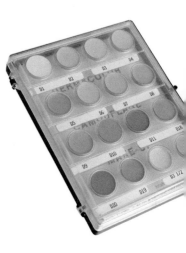

FOUNDATION

Apply foundation after colour correction and concealer to provide an even finish to the skin tone and a base for the rest of the make-up. There are many types of foundation available for many different complexions; each is described below with advice on application techniques and what skin types and conditions they benefit the most. Always test foundation on the jawline; the shade that blends into the natural skin tone is the one you want.

LIQUID

Liquid foundation contains a high water-to-oil ratio, similar to a liquid cleanser. It's ideal for a blemish-free complexion as it provides a light coverage. Apply with clean fingers, blending upwards and outwards towards the hairline.

CREAM

This is similar to a cream cleanser as it contains a high oil-to-water ratio. This foundation is perfect for drier and mature complexions as it provides medium coverage for a smooth finish, without drawing attention to any fine lines and wrinkles. Apply with clean fingers or a dry sponge, blending towards the hairline.

COMPACT

This type of foundation contains some powder and comes in a semi-solid form. It will provide thick coverage for an oily or problem skin type. Apply with a damp sponge and blend into the hairline.

STICK

This is similar to a compact foundation except in stick form. As it's semi-solid, it provides thicker coverage so is ideal for the more congested skin conditions.

MINERAL

These types of foundations are becoming more and more popular among consumers who want a make-up range to complement their skin care routine. Mineral foundations contain two common

Always blend foundation down on to the neck so you don't get any tide marks along the jawline and your client's face isn't a different colour from their neck.

ingredients: **titanium dioxide** and **zinc oxide**. Both these organic minerals allow the skin to breathe and prevent congestion caused by clogged pores. Apply with clean fingers for an even finish.

TINTED MOISTURISERS

These are the lightest of all foundations as they're basically a moisturiser with a hint of colour added. Best suited for clients who prefer to wear little make-up or don't like the feeling of being made-up.

POWDER

Apply powder after the foundation to set it and ensure it lasts much longer. There are different powders available, and each one is applied slightly differently.

LOOSE

This is the most popular choice amongst make-up artists as it's the easiest to apply. Decant a small amount into a small bowl lined with tissue. Take a dry cotton pad and use it to roll the powder on to the entire face and neck. Blend downwards in the direction of hair growth using a large **sable** brush.

COMPACT

This powder is set into a compact to make it solid. Take a large sable brush and apply it all over the face in an outwards direction.

MINERAL

These often come loose and should be decanted in the same way as a loose powder. However, application is different. Take a large sable brush to pick up the powder and tap off any excess. Apply to the entire face and neck using a buffing motion for an even application.

BLOT

This type of foundation provides a matte finish and should be used throughout the day to reduce high shine. This product can come as a loose or compact powder and so application will vary depending on this. Blot powder is ideal for oily or greasy complexions, or those that require mattefying.

LIGHT-REFLECTING

This can come loose or as a solid and so application will vary depending on this. Light-reflecting powder is designed to draw attention away from any flaws as it contains light-reflecting ingredients. This results in a brighter complexion and makes it ideal for sallow skin.

SHIMMER

This powder contains shimmer and makes it suitable for an evening look as it will draw attention to the face. Avoid using on mature or drier complexions as it will instantly draw attention to any fine lines and wrinkles. Apply to the areas you want to enhance, such as the brow bone, the inner corner of the eyes, down the centre of the nose, the cheekbones and the collar bones.

Titanium dioxide
A white mineral that provides a natural sun protection factor (SPF) to the skin.

Zinc oxide
A white mineral with a more opaque tone that provides light-reflecting qualities.

Sable
Horse hair.

EYESHADOW

There are a variety of eyeshadows available in many different colours and consistencies, so what you choose depends on the occasion, your client and their skin.

POWDER

This is the most popular type of eyeshadow and comes in a wide range of colours and shades. Apply powder eyeshadow with a thick sable brush to allow for easy blending between the different shades. Don't apply more than three shades of the same colour to the eyes.

CREAM

These products are becoming more and more popular as they require less precision during application. However, it's a good idea to use a powder eyeshadow as a base to allow for longer-lasting colour. Apply with your fingers or a synthetic brush.

MINERAL

Similar in consistency to mineral powder, this powder contains the same ingredients but here **mica** is used to create colour. Apply in the same way as powder eyeshadow for even blending.

PIGMENT

This is a versatile product that is popular amongst make-up artists and make-up lovers alike because it can be mixed with glosses, creams and tints to achieve vivid shades on the eyes, lips and cheeks. It contains more pigment colour than any other eyeshadow on the market so it lasts much longer. The colours achieved are so vivid and create high impact effects so you'll only need a small amount. Apply and blend with a thick sable brush and remember to protect the skin with tissues as this usually comes loose.

EYELINER

There are many types of eyeliner available. The one you choose should reflect the look you're aiming to achieve and complement your client's age range and personality.

LIQUID

Liquid eyeliner is popular for an evening look or creating a high glamour look. Apply with a disposable eyeliner brush along the upper lashline and make sure the line becomes thicker at the outer corners.

GEL

This product is similar to a liquid eyeliner but different in consistency and application. It contains a gel base and is thicker than a liquid foundation so is best applied with a flat synthetic brush along the upper lashline.

KOHL PENCIL

This creates a dramatic and intense colour that can be applied along the upper and lower lashline and can be smudged to create a smoky eye effect. Remember to sharpen the pencil between clients.

Light pinks can create a baby doll look.

Mica
Describes the natural colour used in mineral eyeshadows.

M·A·C PIGMENT
Pigment is a highly concentrated loose colour powder and comes in an excellent range of colours.

Ask your client to look up when you're applying eyeliner.

B8 MAKE-UP SERVICES

PENCIL

This is similar to a kohl pencil but the colours are less intense. Apply in the same way as a kohl pencil and make sure you sharpen it for each new client.

CAKE

This type of eyeliner is used in the same way as liquids and gels to create a dramatic, high-glamour look. However, application is slightly different. Take a disposable eyeliner brush and dampen in cool water. Coat the brush with the cake eyeliner and apply along the upper lashline in the same way as a liquid and gel liner.

MASCARA

There are many types of mascara available to thicken and lengthen the lashes and provide high-impact effects. Mascara comes in a wide range of different colours; the one you choose will depend on the occasion and your client's age. To make sure each lash is evenly coated, ask your client to look straight ahead and then to the right. Apply mascara with a disposable wand to the upper lashes of the left eye in a downwards motion. Work your way towards the inner corner as your client brings their eyes to the left. Then ask them to look down and right as you apply mascara to the outer corners of the upper lashes in an upwards direction. Work towards the inner corners as your client brings the eyes to the left. Repeat on the right eye then apply a second coat to both eyes. When the mascara on the upper lashes has dried, ask your client to look up and, using the tip of the mascara wand, gently skim over the lower lashes by moving the wand from left to right.

Alway use a disposable wand to apply mascara

WATERPROOF

Waterproof mascara will not run if it comes into contact with tears, rain, sweat or the water of a swimming pool. A variety of colours are available but it can only be removed with an oil-based eye make-up remover that's gentle enough for delicate skin but tough enough to clean off the most stubborn make-up.

NON-WATERPROOF

Non-waterproof mascara is only suitable for a day or evening look where your client will not come into contact with water. This type of mascara is easily removed with a gentle facial cleanser or face wash.

Some new mascaras on the market evenly coat all the lashes. This is achieved with an oscillating wand that vibrates when applied to the lashes.

> **HANDY HINTS**
>
> If you get mascara on the surrounding skin, use a dry cotton swab to wipe it away before it dries. If you're using waterproof mascara, apply a little eye make-up remover to the cotton swab to remove it, before re-applying a small amount of foundation and powder to the area to conceal.

WHY DON'T YOU...
Read through SmartScreen handout 15 to find out more about the different eye products available.

 SmartScreen B8 handout 15

WHY DON'T YOU...
Read through SmartScreen handout 13 for more advice on the different blushers available.

 SmartScreen B8 handout 13

Blushers can give your client a warm, rosy glow

EYEBROW PRODUCTS

These are applied to enhance the brows or to even them out to frame the eyes and create balance to the facial features. Use a pencil that has been slightly blunted on a paper towel. Apply with short strokes along the eyebrow to create the illusion of natural hair then blend with an eyebrow brush.

CHEEK PRODUCTS

There are plenty of products available for the cheeks and the product you choose will depend on the look you want to achieve and your client's complexion.

CREAM

Cream blusher creates a dewy glow and suits a cream foundation base. Apply with clean fingers to the cheekbones and blend quickly before it sets on the skin. Cream blusher is also ideal for mature and drier skins as it will provide a smooth and even finish. These clients should avoid any cream that contains shimmer, as it will highlight any flaws.

POWDER

Use powder blusher on any foundation base that has been set with powder. Apply using a medium sable brush and ask your client to suck in their cheeks. This will make sure you apply the product only to the cheekbones. Then ask your client to give a cheesy smile and apply to the apples of the cheeks to balance the features.

TINTS

Tints usually come with a synthetic brush and are suited to blemish-free complexions that require a hint of colour to the cheeks. Apply in a criss-cross motion to the cheeks before blending with clean fingers.

MINERAL

Mineral blushers come loose or as a solid and should be applied in the same way as a powder blusher with a medium sable brush. Mineral blushers contain the same ingredients as mineral powders and mineral eyeshadows.

BRONZER

Use bronzer to create a natural glow to the skin and enhance your client's tan. Apply to the areas that are affected most by the sun's rays, including the cheeks, forehead, nose and collarbone.

POWDER

This should also be applied with a medium sable brush to the areas of the face that have been affected by the sun.

GEL

This type of bronzer provides a medium coverage and should be applied with clean fingers to any areas affected by the sun. It complements a cream base and cream blushers to enhance a dewy glow.

LIQUID

A liquid bronzer provides a light coverage so is perfect for blemish-free complexions. Apply on top of a cream foundation base with clean fingers to the parts most affected by the sun's rays.

LIP PRODUCTS

There are many shades of lipstick and gloss available and you should choose the colour that best suits your client's features. Even if your client doesn't normally wear a lip colour, you should never leave them bare as the finished look will seem unbalanced and incomplete.

LIP LINER

Use this to create a new lip shape or even out the existing shape of the lips. This will prevent the lipstick and/or gloss from bleeding on to the skin. Sharpen the liner before each new client, and blunt on a paper towel. This will create a natural line rather than a sharp one.

LIPSTICK

When you've applied lip liner, use lipstick to fill the lips. Take a disposable spatula and remove some colour from the lipstick and apply to the lips with a disposable lip brush. Blot with a tissue and reapply to make the colour last much longer. Lipstick is popular amongst more mature clients – it was the only lip product available for a long time. Originally, lipstick provided a matte finish but now it can have a glossy or creamy finish.

Apply lipstick with a lip brush.

LIP GLOSS

Apply gloss on top of lipstick to create depth and intensity. It can be used on its own and doesn't require lip liner. Take a small amount of gloss and apply with a disposable brush. Blot with tissue and reapply to make the colour last longer. Gloss is popular among younger women and teenagers as it's quick and easy to apply.

LIP BALM

This is a must-have in every make-up artist's kit because not all clients have smooth and soft lips. Some suffer with dehydrated lips that crack easily; in which case apply lip balm before any lip product for a smooth, even finish.

Make sure you have a good assortment of make-up brushes. Most are made from synthetic fibres, sable or other animal hair, such as goat.

WHY DON'T YOU...
Read through SmartScreen handout 16 for more information on the different lip products available.

 SmartScreen B8 handout 16

MAKE-UP BRUSHES

It's important you know which make-up brushes are designed to apply each make-up product so you get a flawless and natural finish. Below are the different types of brushes on the market.

CONCEALER BRUSH

Made from synthetic fibres and oval in shape, this brush provides even coverage of imperfections
and blemishes and is best suited for blending colour correctors. Use in a light patting and pressing motion rather than stroking.

FOUNDATION BRUSH

Usually made from synthetic fibres, this brush gives an even coverage and a flawless make-
up base. The bristles are shaped in an oval similar to a concealer brush but are thicker and larger to allow you to cover a wider area. Apply foundation using light sweeping motions.

POWDER BRUSH

This brush can be made from either synthetic or natural bristles. However, some make-up artists feel natural bristles pick up and disperse just the right amount of product on to the skin. This brush is thick and will be the largest in your collection.

BLUSHER BRUSH

This will look similar to your powder brush but half the size. It's designed to apply powder blush to the cheeks and is made from sable or synthetic bristles.

FAN BRUSH

This brush is perfect for dusting on powder highlighters to the top of the cheekbones.

EYESHADOW BRUSH

This can also be made from sable or synthetic fibres and will be the largest of the eye brushes you use. These brushes are usually styled in a flat shape for blending in the eye area.

EYE CONTOUR BRUSH

This brush is much smaller than the eyeshadow brush and is designed to fit into the crease of the eye to add definition.

EYELINER BRUSH

This is a thin brush with a small number of bristles (usually synthetic) for the application of liquid eyeliner. These brushes can be long and thin or completely flat.

EYEBROW BRUSH

These are angled brushes that define the eyebrows.

LIP BRUSH

This brush is often made with sable bristles for even coverage and is designed to apply lipstick and gloss to the entire lips. It's small with a slightly rounded finish.

Now you know about the different make-up products and brushes, you need to know what type of client they would be suitable for and the type of occasion. Below are three examples of looks on three different clients.

In groups of three or four, discuss why the looks below suit the different clients.

CLIENT A

A day look on a mature client over 50 with Caucasian skin.

1. Apply the appropriate colour corrections and concealer.
2. Choose an appropriate foundation before setting with powder.
3. Apply corrections to face and nose shapes as required.
4. Take a light eyeshadow in a beige colour and apply to the entire upper eyelid up to the brow.
5. Take a light brown eyeshadow and apply to the upper eyelid to the crease.
6. Take a darker brown eyeshadow and add to the outer corner of the upper eyelid in a triangular motion and blend.
7. Take a dark brown eyeliner pencil and apply to the upper lashline to define the eyes.
8. Curl the lashes and apply mascara to the upper lashes and the centre of the lower lashes only.
9. Define the brows with an appropriate eyebrow pencil.
10. Apply a powder blusher to the cheekbones to complement your client's undertones.
11. Add powder highlighter to the brow bone and just above the blusher to enhance the bone structure.
12. Apply lip liner and fill the lips with a matching shade of lipstick.

CLIENT B

An evening look on a younger client between 16 and 30 with Afro-Caribbean skin.

1 Apply the appropriate colour corrections and concealer.
2 Choose an appropriate foundation before setting with powder.
3 Apply corrections to face and nose shapes as required.
4 Take a matte brown shade and apply to the entire eyelid.
5 Take a golden shimmer shade and apply to the outer edge of the upper eyelid, up to the crease. Bring this colour down to the lower lashline.
6 Finish by applying an ice blue shade to the inner edge of the upper eyelid, bringing it down to the lower lashline.
7 Take a black kohl pencil and apply to the upper lashline only and smudge with a sponge applicator brush. Use a sponge applicator brush to smudge the line and create a smoky effect.
8 Apply a set of strip lashes for added effect (see Unit B5 for how to do this).
9 Add rose blush to the cheeks followed by highlighter above and bronzer beneath the cheeks to create a 'chiselled' effect.
10 Define the brows with an appropriate eyebrow pencil.
11 Highlight the brows, centre of the nose and cupid's bow of the lips with a liquid highlighter.
12 Line the lips with a nude lip liner.
13 Apply two coats of a matching lipstick and blot in between.
14 Apply a coat of gloss in the same shade to complete the look.

CLIENT C

A bridal look on an Asian client.

1 Apply the appropriate colour corrections and concealer.
2 Choose an appropriate foundation before setting with powder.
3 Apply corrections to face and nose shapes as required.
4 Take a navy shade and apply to the upper eyelid up to the crease.
5 Apply a fushia shade above the crease.
6 Finish off with an earthy green to the bottom lashline.
7 Take a black liquid eyeliner and apply to the upper lashline to draw attention to the eyes.
8 Define the brows with an appropriate eyebrow pencil.
9 Curl the lashes and apply mascara to the upper lashes and the outer corner of the lower lashes.
10 Apply an appropriate blusher to the cheeks.
11 Highlight and shade the cheeks appropriately and apply any necessary products to the brow bone, centre of the nose and the cupid's bow.
12 Line the lips with a coral pink lip liner.
13 Fill the lips with a matching lipstick.

WHY DON'T YOU...
Read through SmartScreen handout 14 on bridal make-up for tips on the considerations you need to think about when you're providing this service.

 SmartScreen B8 handout 14

ADAPTING MAKE-UP FOR CLIENTS WHO WEAR GLASSES OR CONTACT LENSES

If a client wears glasses, you need to adapt your make-up application to keep the eyes balanced with the rest of the make-up. For example, if your client is short sighted, lenses can make their eyes appear much smaller; apply the make-up in a way that enhances the eyes and makes them appear bigger. However, if your client is long sighted, lenses will make their eyes appear much bigger; in this case, you need to draw attention away from them.

If your client wears contact lenses, they could have sensitive eyes so you should choose products that are hypo-allergenic.

When you've completed the make-up, remove all towels and tidy your client's hair. Step back and make sure everything is balanced, then let your client see the finished result in the mirror. Ask your client if they're happy with the application and, if not, remove and re-apply the areas they're unhappy with. When you're certain your client is happy, give them aftercare and home care advice.

PROVIDE AFTERCARE ADVICE

On completion of the treatment, you need to give the appropriate aftercare advice to help your client maintain the results. Aftercare advice will be the same for every client; however, home care advice will be more specific to each client's individual needs. This will include product recommendations, advice on removal and re-application techniques.

AFTERCARE ADVICE

The reason why aftercare advice is so important is because your client needs to know how to maintain the finished result, how to re-apply certain products and how to achieve this look for themselves. Your client also needs to know how to remove the make-up at the end of the day or when the occasion is over. This advice is:

- Avoid heat treatment, such as steam, sauna or hot tubs.
- Avoid swimming.
- Avoid UV treatments.
- Use an oil-based eye make-up remover for stubborn eye make-up and waterproof mascara.
- Remember to cleanse, tone and moisturise twice daily to maintain the skin condition.
- Exfoliate one to three times a week to brighten the complexion.
- Apply an appropriate mask after exfoliating to clear the skin and bring natural radiance.

WHY DON'T YOU...
Think about why it's important to follow the aftercare advice.

HOME CARE ADVICE

This is more client specific and will include product recommendations, tips for re-application and make-up removal techniques. Product recommendations depend on your client's skin type and condition as well as the look they want to achieve at home.

Re-application techniques depend mostly on the occasion. For example, a bride might want to keep lip liner, lipstick and gloss in her purse to re-apply throughout the day; a client who is going out for the evening might want to keep powder and blusher handy to maintain the base and add warmth to the skin.

Removal techniques depend on the type of make-up. With waterproof mascara, recommend an oil-based eye make-up remover that isn't too harsh on the skin. Advise your client on how to take off eye make-up; if they don't remove their make-up and rub their eyes, it could damage the skin and lead to premature wrinkles.

CONTRA-ACTIONS TO MAKE-UP SERVICES

The following contra-actions could occur during or after make-up application. Keep an eye out for such reactions so you know how to deal with them and what advice to give your client to reduce the effects. These can include:

- excessive perspiration
- adverse skin reactions
- watery eyes
- excessive erythema.

EXCESSIVE PERSPIRATION

If your client perspires during or after make-up application, use a mattefying powder to set the foundation and advise them to invest in one for home; your client can then re-apply the powder as often as required.

ADVERSE SKIN REACTIONS

This is usually caused by an allergic reaction to a product or an ingredient. If this occurs, treat in the same way as you would excessive erythema and give the same advice to calm and **dissipate** the reaction. If it doesn't go down after 24 hours, advise your client to seek GP assistance.

WATERY EYES

If your client's eyes water during a make-up service or when the application is complete, use a tissue gently to absorb the tears. Check your client is OK before continuing or re-applying the make-up. If this reaction persists, you must stop the treatment and remove all traces of the make-up. Keep your client in a semi-reclined position so that the product doesn't enter their eyes. Apply a cool compress to the eyes. Then advise them that the treatment cannot continue and recommend they see their GP for further advice.

WHY DON'T YOU...
Refer to the 'Apply make-up products' section to remind yourself which products benefit which skin types and conditions and then have a go at SmartScreen worksheet 3 to test your knowledge.

 SmartScreen B8 worksheet 3

Dissipate
To make disappear; disperse.

HANDY HINTS
Clients with watery eyes will benefit from the use of hypo-allergenic products and waterproof mascara.

EXCESSIVE ERYTHEMA

This is identified as redness and warmth in the skin and could mean your client is touch sensitive. You will notice this quickly so make sure you adjust your pressure when you're applying make-up to the face. If excessive erythema occurs during the treatment, stop immediately, remove the make-up and apply a cold compress to the area to reduce the heat. You could also apply a calamine mask made with a rose water toner to cool and soothe the skin. Advise your client to apply cool compresses over the next 24 hours, by which time the reaction should have gone. Recommend they seek GP assistance if it hasn't. Excessive erythema can also accompany an adverse skin reaction.

END OF UNIT SUMMARY

Now you've reached the end of the unit, you should feel confident in the theory and practical aspects of all areas of make-up services. Use the checklist below to see if there are any areas you feel you need to recap before beginning the end of unit assessment:

- maintain safe and effective methods of working when providing make-up services
- consult, plan and prepare for make-up services
- apply make-up products
- provide aftercare advice.

Using the questions below, test your knowledge of Unit B8 to see how much information you've retained. These questions will help you revise what you've learnt in this chapter.

Turn to pages 413–415 for the answers.

1 Why is it important to clean all make-up brushes before use?

2 What health and safety measures do you need to follow during make-up services?

3 Why is it important to maintain good posture during make-up services?

4 How long should a make-up lesson take?

5 Why should you establish your client's skin type and condition before you apply make-up?

6 List the contra-indications to make-up services that require medical referral and why.

7 How does lighting affect make-up application?

8 Explain how to prepare your client for make-up services.

9 Why is it important to analyse the face, nose, eye and lip shapes before you apply make-up?

10 What corrections should you apply to rebalance a heart face shape and why?

11 What corrections should you apply to prominent eyes and why?

12 How should you apply make-up to create a new lip line?

13 Why might you use colour correctors?

14 How do you know what foundation colour to use?

15 Why should you apply powder over foundation?

16 Why should you apply lip liner?

17 How should you use eyeliner to create a smoky effect?

18 Why shouldn't you use shimmers and cream eyeshadows on dry, dehydrated and mature skins?

19 What aftercare advice should you give to each client after make-up application?

20 What are the **four** possible contra-actions to make-up services and how should you deal with them?

WHY DON'T YOU...
Test your knowledge further by logging into and completing the revision activities before attempting the sample GOLA revision questions.

B9
INSTRUCT CLIENTS IN THE USE AND APPLICATION OF SKIN CARE PRODUCTS AND MAKE-UP

This unit will equip you with the skills you'll need to provide advice to clients on appropriate skin care routines, make-up and product recommendations. This advice can be given on a one-to-one basis or as part of a demonstration, seminar or presentation. If you use a model and an audience, you'll need to project your voice and speak clearly. You might use equipment, such as a microphone or diagrams and charts on a PowerPoint presentation and screen.

In this chapter you'll learn how to:
- maintain safe and effective methods of working when providing skin care and make-up instruction
- consult, plan and prepare for skin care and make-up instruction
- deliver skin care and make-up instruction
- evaluate the success of skin care and make-up instruction.

HANDY HINTS

When you're providing an instructional service on skin care and make-up, it's important to use the skills you've learnt in the following units:

Unit G20   Ensure responsibility for actions to reduce risks to health and safety

Unit G18   Promote additional services or products to clients

Unit B8   Provide make-up services

Unit G8   Develop and maintain your effectiveness at work

Unit B4   Provide facial skin care treatment.

WHY DON'T YOU...
Work through SmartScreen worksheet 7 to test your knowledge of consumer legislation affecting the promotion and retail of services and products.

 SmartScreen B9 worksheet 7

MAINTAIN SAFE AND EFFECTIVE METHODS OF WORKING WHEN PROVIDING SKIN CARE AND MAKE-UP INSTRUCTION

As with all beauty treatments, it's important you understand and adhere to the relevant health and safety legislation throughout to ensure you perform a safe and enjoyable treatment for your client. The main legislation affecting skin care and make-up instructional services includes:

- Data Protection Act (DPA)
- Disability Discrimination Act (DDA)
- Control of Substances Hazardous to Health (COSHH)
- Provision and Use of Work Equipment Regulations (PUWER).

Each of these Acts is described fully in Unit G20 along with the other health and safety legislation.

SALON ENVIRONMENT

When you're preparing the work area, make sure you include the following items:

- a selection of skin care products
- a selection of make-up products and samples
- make-up tools including brushes, sharpeners and lash curlers
- a suitable mirror (either free standing or hand held)
- a face chart – to record what make-up you use
- a colour wheel – to see which colours complement one another

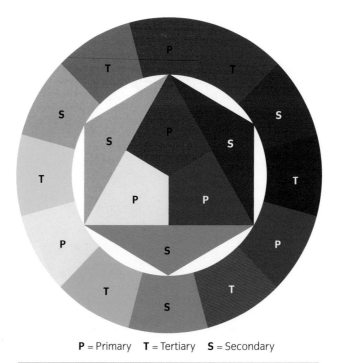

P = Primary   **T** = Tertiary   **S** = Secondary

The colour wheel

SKIN	
FACE	
EYES	
CHEEKS	
LIPS	
TIPS	

MAKEUP ARTIST _____

STORE _____

TELEPHONE _____

BOBBI BROWN ●●●● www.bobbibrown.com

Use a face chart to record the make-up you use on your client.

- promotional materials – to promote the products you've used and the other treatments you offer
- a treatment couch/make-up chair
- appropriate coverings, eg small/medium/large towels
- one square of couch roll.

When you're preparing the treatment area, make sure you set the lighting to an appropriate brightness and provide enough pillows and blankets so that your client or audience is comfortable at all times.

A mirror is a very important tool for make-up instruction.

Promotional materials are an important part of skin care and make-up instruction.

SmartScreen B8 handout 1

WHY DON'T YOU...
Refer to Unit B8 to remind yourself how to set up for make-up treatments, and read through SmartScreen handout 1 for additional suggestions.

Audience watching a demonstration at a seminar

WHY DON'T YOU...
Read through SmartScreen handout 11 to remind yourself how lighting affects the appearance of make-up or refer to Unit B8.

SmartScreen B8 handout 11

HANDY HINTS

Remember that natural daylight is ideal when you're applying make-up but other types of lighting will vary the way make-up appears:

- natural daylight – ideal for day make-up or bridal make-up application
- fluorescent light – intensifies darker tones and softens blues and greys
- incandescent light – enhances frosted tones as well as silvers and golds, making it ideal for evening make-up.

WHY DON'T YOU...
Check out Unit G20 for further assistance with sterilisation and disinfection techniques.

It 's important to sterilise or disinfect all your tools and equipment and, if possible, place them in the UV cabinet for ten minutes on each side. Make sure you've cleaned all work surfaces and non-metal implements with an appropriate disinfectant.

Before beginning the consultation, make sure you're aware of the industry accepted times for skin care treatments and make-up services. The times below are for the actual treatment, so you might want to use this as a guide, especially for a seminar. If you talk for too long, people will get bored. These times exclude consultation.

Treatment	Times
Basic facial	45 minutes
Facial	60 minutes
Specialised facial	75–90 minutes
Day make-up	30 minutes
Evening and special occasion make-up	45 minutes
Make-up lesson	75 minutes

Client receiving make-up application

WHY DON'T YOU...
Read through SmartScreen handout 5 to see what limitations a particular venue might have on the success of the event.

SmartScreen B9 handout 5

CONSULT, PLAN AND PREPARE FOR SKIN CARE AND MAKE-UP INSTRUCTION

It's always important to perform a consultation and obtain your client's signature before beginning any treatment to safeguard yourself and the salon. You'll also need to identify additional information depending on the instructional advice you're giving, whether it be skin care or make-up related, or both. This information should include:

- a client's colour preferences
- their expectations
- what they hope to learn
- do they have a skin care routine?
- do they wear make-up regularly?

WHY DON'T YOU...
Refer to Units B4 and B8 to remind yourself of other additional information you need to obtain from your clients regarding these treatments.

CONTRA-INDICATIONS

As part of the consultation, you also need to identify whether or not your client has any contra-indications that could prevent or restrict this service. However, you might not become aware of this until you perform the visual consultation as part of the superficial cleanse and skin analysis. The following list indicates what contra-indications require medical referral and, as a result, prevent make-up services:

- Bacterial infections, such as impetigo, conjunctivitis, boils and styes: risk of cross-infection or further skin damage.
- Viral infections, such as herpes simplex: risk of cross-infection.

B9 SKIN CARE AND MAKE-UP

- Fungal infections, such as ringworm: risk of cross-infection.
- Parasitic infections, such as scabies and pediculosis: risk of cross-infection.
- Systemic medical conditions: risk of injury or skin damage.
- Severe skin conditions: the condition could get worse or result in a reaction.
- Eye infections: risk of cross-infection.

If you identify one of the above contra-indications, explain to your client that the treatment cannot go ahead but don't name the condition in case you're wrong. Instead, tell your client you've identified a contra-indication and that to perform the service could make it worse. Advise them to see their GP for a proper diagnosis.

The following list indicates the contra-indications that restrict the application of make-up and require you to modify the service:

- Recent scar tissue: the skin is fragile and tender to touch, so work around the area.
- Eczema: if the skin is open and weeping, the treatment shouldn't go ahead. If it's not open and weeping, then treatment is fine as long as you use cream-based products and regularly check for a reaction. Remember to always communicate with your client.
- Psoriasis: treat in the same way you would eczema to prevent aggravating the condition and choose products with a higher moisture content.
- Hyper-keratosis: choose products with a higher moisture content as it will create a smoothing effect and diminish any unevenness in the skin's texture. Avoid frosted products and shimmers as this will draw attention to any rough areas. For skin care products, recommend a suitable exfoliator and mask that will even out the skin's texture.
- Skin allergies: talk to your client and check the skin reaction throughout. If they're allergic to any of the ingredients, avoid using them and replace with an alternative.
- Bruising: the skin will be tender to touch, so work around the area to avoid further tissue damage.
- Watery eyes: if your client suffers with watery eyes, choose waterproof make-up and products that are designed for sensitive eyes. Place tissues around the eyes to prevent the make-up from running. When you're performing skin care instructions, bring your client into a semi-reclined position to prevent any product getting into their eyes.

It's also important that you don't apply make-up to minors aged under 16 years unless you've written parental/guardian consent and a parent or guardian is present throughout the treatment. Habia has advised that you shouldn't use eyelash curlers on a minor for safety reasons.

When you've completed the initial consultation and identified any contra-indications, you need to prepare your client or audience. For a make-up lesson, instruct your client to remove their top and change into a gown that you have provided. Tuck a square of couch roll into the neckline of the gown to protect it. If your client is sitting on a treatment couch, bring them into a reclined position. Wrap their hair in a small

WHY DON'T YOU...
Work through SmartScreen worksheet 4 to test your knowledge on the contra-indications to instructional events.

SmartScreen B9 worksheet 4

WHY DON'T YOU...
Check out the restrictions on treating under 16s at **www.habia.org**.

B9 SKIN CARE AND MAKE-UP

towel or use a headband and cap and tuck in two tissues at the hairline to protect it. If your client is sitting in a make-up chair, use a headband to keep their hair off their face and tie their hair up with a clip if it's long. Check that your client is sitting opposite a mirror or give them a hand-held mirror so they can see what you're doing.

A make-up seminar

If you're providing a skin care seminar, tell each person to wear a round-necked top and to tie their hair back.

Example of a client ready for skin care instruction

WHY DON'T YOU...
Read through SmartScreen handout 4 to find out more about the skills needed for carrying out make-up demonstrations.

SmartScreen B9 handout 4

In this unit, you'll find guidelines on how to plan and provide a make-up lesson on a one-to-one basis or as part of a group skin care seminar.

As part of a make-up lesson, you must prepare the skin before you start. Begin with a superficial cleanse to remove all traces of make-up and carry out a thorough skin analysis to determine your client's skin type and condition. Next, perform a deep cleanse to make sure the skin is completely clean. Tone and blot before moisturising to finish. See Unit B4 for guidance.

WHY DON'T YOU...
Refer to Unit B4 to remind yourself of the different skin types and conditions you're likely to come across, as well as skin care routines and products.

As part of a skin care seminar, your audience will be doing this themselves so there's no need for you to prepare the skin beforehand.

It's also important you identify your client's age range. They're likely to fall into one of three age groups: 16–30, 31–50 and 50+. You need to identify which of these categories your client falls into so you can choose products that will flatter and complement them as a person, enhance their natural features and suit the occasion for which the make-up is intended.

It's also important to check whether your client wears glasses or contact lenses as you'll need to modify both the make-up and skin care application in this case.

For skin care application, ask your client to remove their glasses or contact lenses to prevent damage. If any product does get into the eye, it's easier to remove with an eyebath and stops it getting trapped under the lenses.

When you've made any necessary modifications, you need to form a plan in your mind. Make sure you agree your plan with your client so they understand the techniques you want to use and are happy with your decision. You also need to make sure you have everything you need for your plan, for example, check you have the appropriate skin care and make-up ranges to cater for your client's age, face shape and skin condition. Refer to Units B4 and B8 to remind yourself of the techniques that you can use.

DELIVER SKIN CARE AND MAKE-UP INSTRUCTION

WHY DON'T YOU...
Refer to Outcome 2, 'Consult, plan and prepare for skin care and make-up instruction', to check you have everything you need and you're prepared for every eventuality.

Below are step-by-step guides to planning a one-to-one make-up lesson with a client and a skin care seminar. Make sure you have all the products and equipment you'll need for both events, as well as additional promotional material.

MAKE-UP LESSON

When you've prepared the skin, sit your client in front of a mirror or give them a large mirror so they can see what you're doing. One approach is to apply the make-up to one side of the face and let your client try to recreate the look on the other side. This is an interactive method that keeps your client interested and makes them feel involved in the process. It will also help them feel confident in their own ability to recreate the same look at home. Below is a step-by-step guide to a make-up lesson on a client who is 31–50 years old and has Caucasian skin. This guide can be adapted and applied to any make-up look. Remember to explain what you're doing throughout the lesson to avoid any confusion and make a note of all the products you use on a face chart.

STEP 1 – Apply the appropriate colour correction, such as green, lilac or yellow concealer to hide any redness, a sallow complexion, dark circles, or any obvious blue veins. Choose the right concealer and add to any blemishes and imperfections that don't require colour correction.

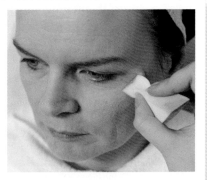

STEP 2 – Choose an appropriate foundation. Test it on the jawline and then blend over the face and on to the neck, remembering to avoid any tide marks along the jawline. Apply with clean fingers or a foundation sponge.

STEP 3 – To set the foundation, apply powder and stand back to check that the base looks as natural as possible. You can use a brush or sponge here.

STEP 4 – Move to the eye area and check the colours you've chosen complement your client's skin colour, eye colour, personality, age and preferences. Begin with the lightest shade and apply to the entire upper eyelid. The client pictured here has Caucasian skin, so choose rosy pinks to bring warmth to paler complexions.

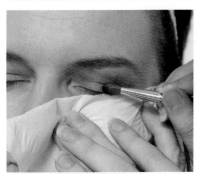

STEP 5 – Take the medium shade and apply up to the crease of the upper eyelid and blend with the base shade.

STEP 6 – Apply the darkest shade to the outer corners of the upper eyelid and blend just along the crease to give a natural light-to-dark effect. Apply along the lower lashline with a smaller eyeshadow brush.

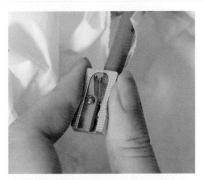

STEP 7 – Line the upper and lower lashes with a black kohl pencil to add definition to the eye area. Remember to sharpen the pencil before you use it.

STEP 8 – If necessary, curl the lashes before you apply black mascara to the upper lashes and to the centre of the lower lashes to open up the eyes.

STEP 9 – Groom the brows with an eyebrow brush or disposable mascara wand.

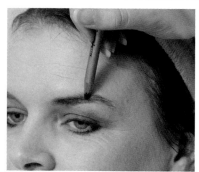

STEP 10 – Define the brows with an eyebrow pencil. Remember to sharpen the pencil before you use it and blunt it slightly on a tissue to stop you creating harsh lines.

STEP 11 – Apply blusher to the cheeks and blend towards the temples.

STEP 12 – Apply highlighter to the areas you want to enhance, such as the brow bone, the cheekbone, the centre of the nose and the cupid's bow.

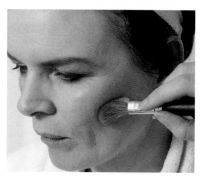

STEP 13 – Apply shader to the areas you want to hide, such as the hollow of the cheeks, either side of the nose, and correct the face shape if necessary.

STEP 14 – Add lip liner to define the lip shape and even out any imperfections.

STEP 15 – Apply two coats of lipstick with a brush.

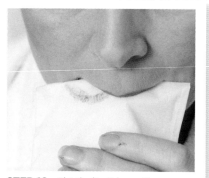

STEP 16 – Blot the lipstick on a tissue.

STEP 17 – Add a small amount of gloss to enhance the lips.

You don't have to stick to this step-by-step guide – it's just an example.

HANDY HINTS

If you carry out a make-up lesson by doing one step on one side of the face and letting your client repeat it on the other side, make sure the first step is complete before you move on to the next one.

WHY DON'T YOU...

Refer to Unit B8 for other step-by-step guides to different make-up applications on different complexions.

A client trying out application of make-up for herself

When you've finished, take off the headband or towel protecting your client's hair and let them see the finished result. Ask them for their feedback before you give them any promotional material and provide aftercare and home care advice. Explain that you've used a colour chart and tell them which products you've used so they don't forget what you've just taught them.

When you're sure your client is happy with the finished result, give them some samples of the products you've used to try at home. You could also offer them a discount on any products they buy on the same day.

HANDY HINTS

Remember to use a variety of open and closed questions to ensure your client knows what they're doing and understands each process and why products are applied in a certain way.

HANDY HINTS

It's important to get feedback from your client before the end of the treatment so that you can change anything they're unhappy with. If this happens, make any alterations on the make-up chart as well.

WHY DON'T YOU...
Work through SmartScreen worksheet 3 to test your knowledge on planning a make-up lesson.

SmartScreen B9 worksheet 3

WHY DON'T YOU...
Refer to Unit B8 to remind yourself of the necessary aftercare advice to give after a make-up service.

The final make-up look

HANDY HINTS

Where spaces are limited, it's a good idea to promote an event and offer it on a first-come, first-serve basis so you don't have more people turn up than you can manage. Remember, if it's a success, you can always repeat the event for those who missed out the first time.

SKIN CARE SEMINAR

You've been asked to give a skin care seminar to an audience to boost sales and increase business. There are two ways to do this:

- perform a demonstration on one model while the audience watches
- provide a talk to a small group of people and let them practise and test the products as you go round and help each person.

Below is a guide to the latter option. As you demonstrate each product, discuss its benefits and the product's key ingredients. Encourage the audience to ask questions to make sure they're clear on the instructions and advice you're giving.

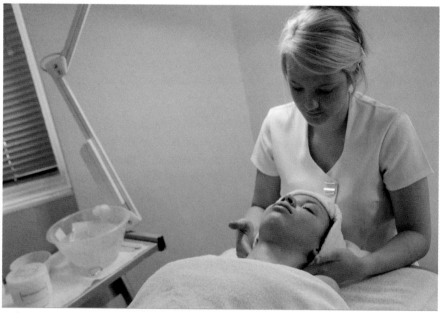

A therapist performing a skin analysis

1 Place some tables in the middle of the room and some chairs around the edge. This means everyone has their own 'station' and they're all facing one another other as well as facing you.

2 Place a large sheet over the tables and put a selection of products in the centre so that everyone can reach them without overstretching.

3 At each station, place any promotional material, such as a face chart, product leaflets and price lists for the business, as well as a mirror.

4 Place one pair of heated mitts for each member of the audience into a hot towel cabbie.

5 Begin by introducing yourself and explain the purpose of the event. Ask the audience to tell you why they're there and what they expect from the seminar.

6 Start by discussing the skin and why a good skin care routine is important. Explain why people should avoid using soap and why it's a good idea to exfoliate on a regular basis.

7 When you've finished talking, move on to the practical demonstration. Start with eye and lip make-up removal. Demonstrate the correct procedure on one person while the rest of the audience copies your techniques. Remember to assist anyone who might need it.

8 Introduce the cleansers that are available and invite the audience to choose the type of cleanser they would normally go for. Observe the techniques they use and provide support to those who need it.

9 Instruct the audience to have a good look at their skin in the mirror and write down what they see on the face chart. Suggest they ask their neighbour to look at their skin as well. Explain this is a skin analysis and will allow them to choose the right products for their complexion.

10 As you walk around, help each person decide what type of skin they have. Use a magnifying lamp if necessary.

11 When each person has identified their skin type and condition, make sure they write it down so they don't forget.

12 Move on to a deep cleanse (see Unit B4 for guidance) and ask each person to choose an appropriate cleanser to suit their skin. Demonstrate on another model how to cleanse the skin and remove all make-up traces.

13 Ask your audience to remove the cleanser gently with the heated mitts and choose an appropriate toner. You could use cotton wool or facial pads for this step.

14 Move on to the exfoliation and ask each person to choose one product suitable for their skin. Check that everyone knows how to apply and use it effectively. Ask them to remove the exfoliator with heated mitts and explain that they can use a warm face cloth or warm water at home.

15 Show the audience how to apply their chosen mask to the entire face with their fingers. This reduces the risk of cross-infection as you don't want your audience sharing mask brushes.

16 While the mask is on, invite the audience to write on their chart the products they've used so far and how they've been used. This way, if they choose to buy any of the products, they'll never forget how to use them.

17 When it's time to take the masks off, ask your audience to use their heated mitts and explain that they can use warm water or a warm face cloth at home.

18 Finish with a spray tonic to rebalance the skin.

19 Apply any speciality products, such as eye and neck creams or gels, and explain how and why they should use them.

20 Invite the audience to choose an appropriate moisturiser and ask them to apply it to the entire face, and neck if necessary.

When you've finished, ask each person to complete a feedback form before they leave. When you're happy everyone has enjoyed themselves and understands how the products work, invite them to try other products from the tester stand. Give everyone a goodie bag to take home with them that includes some samples of the products they've used, as well as samples of other products they might be interested in. You could also give them a gift voucher for a taster facial, or a discount off a future treatment to encourage them to return. As an incentive, you could offer an additional discount or a free mini back massage for any bookings made on the day. If the audience has paid to attend the seminar, you could tell them that this discount can be redeemed against any products they buy on the day.

During a seminar, clients should use their fingers to apply face masks

HANDY HINTS

In a seminar, a spray tonic is more suitable as it reduces waste.

HANDY HINTS

Make sure your responses to any questions are clear and check that you've fully answered the person's question before moving on to the next part of the demonstration.

HANDY HINTS

Make sure you're available until the last person has left so you're there to answer any questions. Not everyone is comfortable asking questions in front of a group.

B9 SKIN CARE AND MAKE-UP

A client purchasing skin care products

WHY DON'T YOU...
Refer to Unit B4 to remind yourself of the necessary aftercare advice to give following a facial skin care treatment.

EVALUATE THE SUCCESS OF SKIN CARE AND MAKE-UP INSTRUCTION

When the event is over, it's important to get feedback from your client or audience to evaluate its success. This can be done in a number of ways:

- question-and-answer session
- questionnaire
- guestbook
- feedback form.

QUESTION-AND-ANSWER SESSION

This is an informative way of finding out whether or not your audience found the information you gave valuable and interesting. It's also a way of testing their knowledge and seeing how much they remember. If you make notes during the session, you'll be able to refer to them and improve on anything your client or audience felt was missing or lacking.

QUESTIONNAIRE

This is a good way of obtaining feedback from clients because it means you can develop your own questions based around the event. The feedback you receive should be more relevant and specific rather than generalised. If you really want the audience to be honest, make the questionnaires anonymous and make a point of not watching over them as they complete them. Instead, make yourself busy by tidying up and putting all the equipment and products away. You could even let the audience put their completed questionnaires in a box as they leave.

GUESTBOOK

This is another informal way of gaining feedback after an event, but you might not get as much detailed information as you'd hoped for because the audience isn't answering specific questions. Instead, they simply write in their overall comments on how the event went.

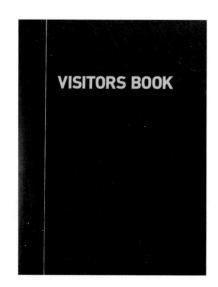

FEEDBACK FORM

This is similar to a questionnaire but has statements that the audience can agree or disagree with to varying degrees. This is very specific feedback so it's important that you make sure the statements are relevant to the event rather than being general. You also need to check there's no medium or safe answer, such as 'Don't know'.

When you've got everyone's feedback, check that they don't need any more help with anything they've learnt. Finally, tell your client or audience where they can buy the products you've recommended if they can't get them through you or the business.

ACTIVITY

Because it's important to evaluate the success of the event, why don't you ask yourself the following questions to see if you could make any improvements in the future:

- Were there enough products for everyone?
- Did the event drag on because there weren't enough products and equipment for everyone?
- Did you have the right products available?
- Were you organised enough?
- Did you feel confident in your own knowledge, skills and ability?
- If not, is there anything you or your employer could do, such as additional training?
- Did your client or audience enjoy themselves?
- Did the audience interact with each other?
- Did your client interact well with you?
- Was your event engaging and informative?
- Did you speak for too long and lose your audience's interest?

It's important to ask yourself these questions and answer them as honestly and as frankly as you can. It will let you make the necessary improvements so that future events are even more successful.

WHY DON'T YOU...
Read through SmartScreen handout 16 to give you an idea of how to obtain feedback from clients after instructional events.

SmartScreen B9 handout 16

END OF UNIT SUMMARY

Now you've reached the end of the unit, you should feel confident in the theory and practical aspects of all areas of instructional activities and events. Use the checklist below to see if there are any areas you feel you need to recap before beginning the end of unit assessment:

- maintain safe and effective methods of working when providing skin care and make-up instruction
- consult, plan and prepare for skin care and make-up instruction
- deliver skin care and make-up instruction
- evaluate the success of skin care and make-up instruction.

Using the questions below, test your knowledge of Unit B9 to see just how much information you've retained. These questions will help you revise what you've learnt in this chapter.

Turn to pages 415–417 for the answers.

1 What are the main Acts that are relevant to this type of service?

2 What are your responsibilities under the Disability Discrimination Act?

3 Why is it important to complete consultations for both one-to-one and group instruction?

4 Explain what environment is best suited to these types of event?

5 What are the restrictions highlighted by Habia regarding the application of products, treatments and equipment for clients under 16 years?

6 Explain how glasses might affect eye make-up during make-up application.

7 Give reasons why it's a good idea to make up only half the face during a make-up lesson.

8 Why is it important to talk about what you're doing and why you're doing it during an instructional event?

9 During a make-up lesson, why should you record the products you've used on a face chart?

10 During a seminar, why is it important to check everyone has access to the products they need?

11 Why is it a good idea to have a colour wheel handy during a make-up lesson?

12 Explain why mirrors should be available for instructional events?

13 Discuss why it's a good idea to offer promotions and discounts on the day of the event.

14 What promotional material should you hand out to encourage repeat custom?

15 How can you encourage clients to buy products and book more treatments before they leave?

16 What methods of feedback can you use after an instructional event?

17 What are the advantages and disadvantages of each?

18 Why is it important to evaluate the success of the event?

19 Why should you reflect on the event as well?

20 How can this feedback help you make improvements?

WHY DON'T YOU...
Test your knowledge further by logging into SmartScreen and completing the revision activities before attempting the sample GOLA revision questions.

G4
FULFIL SALON RECEPTION DUTIES

The reception area, or front of house, is the place where you'll first meet your clients and customers. Reception areas in hair and beauty salons can feel a little intimidating, so it's vital you make anyone who enters feel welcome and create a lasting first impression.

In this chapter you'll learn how to:

- maintain the reception area
- attend to clients and enquiries
- make appointments for salon services
- handle payments from clients.

This unit will be used in conjunction with all other units to make sure your clients and customers are made to feel welcome and want to return.

Clients relaxing in a relaxation room

Customer

Someone who makes a purchase but has not yet received a treatment.

Client

Someone who receives a treatment at the salon.

MAINTAIN THE RECEPTION AREA

A reception is the first area a **customer** or **client** will see when entering any business and will provide that all-important first impression. For a salon reception area to offer a welcoming atmosphere, the owner needs to consider the amount of space available and decide on a decor that will suit the salon's image. A spa reception area should feel relaxing and calming with neutral colours, natural textures and dimmed lighting. A city salon might prefer a fresh approach with bright lights and eye-catching colour schemes.

A calm reception area

Maintain the cleanliness of the reception area by disinfecting all surfaces at least once a week to remove dust, dirt and the build-up of bacteria. Vacuum the floors and, if necessary, mop them at the start and end of every day to make sure the reception is clean and inviting.

RECEPTION AND PRODUCT DISPLAYS

The reception desk is the single most important piece of furniture and will be the main focal point for clients and customers entering the salon. Clients need to be able to recognise where to go for enquiries, appointment booking and telling the receptionist they've arrived for their treatment.

A client making an appointment

Another important aspect of all reception areas is the product displays and how well they're maintained and promoted. For example, if the product displays are dusty, this looks as if they haven't been updated for quite some time and sends out the message that the products on offer aren't important. It's vital the displays are well maintained and updated at least every season to keep up with current and emerging industry trends. Make sure you maintain stock levels by having a few of each product available on display so that clients who want to buy something aren't kept waiting while you check the stock cupboards.

ACTIVITY

Product displays need to be eye-catching and well maintained. Which of these is more appealing to your customers?

If you're given the responsibility of maintaining the reception area and product displays, familiarise yourself with the products and how much they cost. You'll also need to check for any defects in products while the customer is paying so they're satisfied with every purchase. Make sure you're aware of any special offers and discounts on products to avoid confusion during payment. Each of these factors are discussed in more depth later in the unit.

HANDY HINTS

In general, product displays should form the main areas of the reception, including the windows, to entice passers-by to come in, have a look and maybe book an appointment. There should also be a tester display stand with testers of all products available for clients and customers to try before they buy.

Make sure the salon window is attractive to customers.

Some of the types of stationery you will need to have to hand.

STATIONERY

To make sure the reception area is well stocked with stationery, use the following checklist:

- a selection of pens in different colours: for making notes, writing out gift cards, loyalty cards, taking messages and writing on appointment cards
- pencils: to write down appointments in the appointment book
- erasers: to remove cancellations and mistakes in the appointment book
- a pencil sharpener
- paper clips: to keep things together
- a stapler and staples: to staple receipts together
- a hole punch: so you can place appointment pages in the folder
- a calculator: to calculate payments
- a notepad
- a memo pad: for taking messages
- an address book: for local business details
- appointment cards: to give to clients when they make appointments
- price lists: so that clients know how much each treatment costs
- promotional literature: to promote new treatments and products
- client record cards: to be completed by each new client prior to their first treatment
- aftercare advice leaflets: to be given after each treatment
- a telephone: so that clients can contact the salon to make appointments
- an appointment system, such as appointment book or computer: to keep a record of appointments
- a waste paper bin.

The receptionist needs to make sure all these items are available to do their job effectively.

G4 SALON RECEPTION

HANDY HINTS

Always write appointments in pencil when you're using an appointment book so that you can correct any mistakes and change cancellations or re-scheduled appointments without making a mess of the book.

THE CITY & GUILDS TEXTBOOK

Therapists attending to a customer

WHY DON'T YOU...
Read through SmartScreen handout 1 to identify the role of the receptionist.

SmartScreen G4 handout 1

WHILE THEY WAIT ...

There are other things that a salon can offer to make clients and customers comfortable while they're waiting. Many salons and spas do this to enhance the experience and to encourage customers to come back. A spa might offer herbal teas, fresh fruit juices, water, light and healthy snacks, and spa books or journals. A salon might provide tea, coffee, water, biscuits and fashion magazines or industry journals. Again, it all depends on the image you're trying to create.

A client receiving refreshments from the receptionist

A client making an enquiry at a salon reception

RESPONSIBLE PERSON

It's also important you know who the responsible person is for the reception area so you know who to ask if there are any problems. For example, some salons employ a receptionist who is in charge of the reception area, making appointments, dealing with clients, and taking payments. Other salons choose not to employ a receptionist and train each of their therapists to take turns working in the reception area.

WHY DON'T YOU...
Have a go at SmartScreen worksheet 1 to see what you think makes a good first impression.

SmartScreen G4 worksheet 1

ATTEND TO CLIENTS AND ENQUIRIES

To create a good first impression, it's really important you acknowledge and deal with all customers and clients as soon as they arrive. Even if it's only eye contact, this shows you're polite, and makes the client feel important. Make sure you smile and welcome the client or customer to the salon before asking how you can help them. If a customer enters the salon while you're dealing with another client, acknowledge their presence by smiling at them and telling them you'll be with them shortly. Failure to provide this welcome when you're busy could be the difference between losing and gaining another loyal client.

A receptionist greeting a new customer

WHY DON'T YOU...
Read through SmartScreen handout 5 for further details on effective communication.

 SmartScreen G4 handout 5

EFFECTIVE COMMUNICATION

When you're communicating with clients, make sure you speak and adjust your language to suit the situation. For example, when you take a client through to a treatment area, lower your voice so that you don't disturb other clients receiving treatments; this will encourage your client to follow your lead and reduce their tone of voice as well. If you're dealing with an enquiry, make sure you listen carefully. When you're on the phone, speak clearly and confidently and avoid the use of slang and obscenities as you'll instantly lose their respect and they will almost certainly take their custom elsewhere.

Your body language is also important. For example, standing with your arms folded across your chest creates an immediate barrier between you and your client and could make them feel uncomfortable. This is called negative body language as it creates the impression you're unapproachable; positive body language gives the impression you're relaxed, calm and friendly.

Look at the pictures below and discuss how the receptionist's actions would make you feel if you were a client entering a salon for the first time and what you would think of that salon's image.

TYPES OF ENQUIRY

It's important you're able to deal with all your customers' needs to avoid any confusion and upset. The types of enquiry you might have to deal with include:

- taking messages
- complaints
- telephone enquiries
- face-to-face enquiries
- email/Internet enquiries
- confirming appointments.

TAKING MESSAGES

When you take a message for a colleague, make sure you write down the message and ask the person's name and contact number so your colleague can return the call. Below is an example of how you can record a telephone message:

To: Sita	Tel. no: 01234 567890	Date: 24/04/2011
From: Julie	Taken by: Roxy	Time: 3:15pm
Message:		
Call Julie as soon as possible regarding her appointment with you on Friday please.		

It's important that you record a message correctly so the recipient can deal with it accordingly. If you pass on the wrong information, for example if you write down the wrong contact number, the call might not be returned. Or, if the message itself is wrong, it might not be dealt with in the right way.

COMPLAINTS

If a client wants to make a complaint, they're not likely to be in a good mood. They could be angry, upset or confused, so first of all try to calm them down. Listen carefully to why they're upset or angry. Suggest they sit down next to you in the seating area; this will make them feel like you want to listen and that you value their opinion. Tell them you'll help them in the best way you can, but don't make any promises because you could make things worse for yourself and the salon. Listen to all the facts and make sure you understand the complaint before reporting it to the responsible person. Offer the client some refreshments while you fetch the responsible person to deal with the complaint and take any necessary action.

TELEPHONE ENQUIRIES

Make sure you speak clearly and politely on the phone and remember to introduce yourself. Try to answer each call in the same way, by introducing yourself and the salon. For example, 'Good morning, The Retreat beauty salon, Lisa speaking. How can I help you?'. Answer with a smile so that you sound happy to be at work. The caller then knows they've called the right salon, the person they're speaking to, and that they're talking to someone who sounds like they enjoy their job.

A receptionist happy to be at work

WHY DON'T YOU...
Have a go at SmartScreen worksheet 7 to see if you can successfully take a telephone message.

SmartScreen G4 worksheet 7

An upset client being comforted by an empathetic receptionist

WHY DON'T YOU...
Think of the consequences of answering the phone simply by saying 'hello'.

G4 SALON RECEPTION

FACE-TO-FACE ENQUIRIES

When you're dealing with clients face to face, make sure you're friendly and welcome them with a smile. Introduce yourself with a handshake before asking how you can help them.

EMAIL/INTERNET ENQUIRIES

More and more businesses are communicating with their clients through the Internet and email. Many salons use networking sites to tell their clients about their latest offers and treatments and promote their services to a much wider audience. However, these resources should be updated on a regular basis. Some salons train one staff member to update the networking sites and deal with all enquiries received via email.

When you deal with enquiries, you must maintain confidentiality at all times to make sure your salon follows the guidelines set by the Data Protection Act (DPA).

CONFIRMING APPOINTMENTS

When a client arrives for a treatment, ask them for their full name and which treatment they've booked. If you're still not sure you've got the right person, ask them for the contact number they gave when they made the appointment. Repeat this information back to them and tell them who their therapist is. Offer to take their coat and invite them to take a seat while they wait.

A receptionist checking the appointment schedule

WHY DON'T YOU...
Think about the consequences of not responding to clients at all or waiting for them to speak first.

You could attract lots of new clients through the Internet.

WHY DON'T YOU...
Refer to Unit G20 to remind yourself of the Data Protection Act and its guidelines, before reading through SmartScreen handout 2.

 SmartScreen G4 handout 2

HANDY HINTS

More and more salons are going online with their records and they might use photographs as a form of evidence for returning clients to save time with future appointments. If your salon does this, take each new client's photo before completing the consultation card. When the therapist returns the consultation card, you can update the system with the client's details.

THE CONSULTATION PROCESS

When you give a new client a consultation card, ask them to fill it in honestly as it will include a great deal of personal information, such as contact details, their general health and lifestyle habits and their GP's contact details. This way if there are any contra-indications, the therapist can use open questioning techniques to find out more information before the treatment starts. Make sure your client signs and dates the consultation card to say the information is true to the best of their knowledge and they're consenting to the treatment. To the right is an example of a consultation card.

Although many salons leave their clients alone for a few minutes to complete the consultation card, some prefer their therapists to fill out the card to avoid any discrepancies later on. If this is your salon's procedure, make sure you use the correct consultation techniques to gather all the information you'll need. These include:

- questioning techniques
- visual techniques
- manual techniques
- reference to client records.

A receptionist asking a client to fill in a consultation card

Confidentiality
Not making information available to others as it contains personal details.

Open questions
These ask for a detailed response, and begin with 'what', 'who', 'when', 'why', 'how' and 'where'.

Closed questions
Ask for a yes or no response, and begin with 'do', 'can' and 'have'.

QUESTIONING TECHNIQUES

During the consultation, make sure you use a variety of **open** and **closed questions** in a polite manner so that your client feels comfortable around you. Remember to adapt your manner and tone of voice to suit the consultation and the person you're speaking to. When you ask if they have any contra-indications, use closed questions so that you get a simple yes or no answer. If your client does answer yes, use open questions to get more details. This means you can work out if your client needs medical referral, if the treatment will need adapting or if the treatment simply cannot go ahead. Check you've written down all your client's answers on the consultation card to prove the questions have been answered properly.

A therapist performing a consultation with various questioning techniques

HANDY HINTS

In beauty therapy, you'll meet a **diverse** range of clients and customers so you must treat them all equally and make them feel valued. This might seem difficult to the inexperienced therapist but if you watch those around you, you'll quickly realise how easy it is.

Diverse

Wide-ranging; different; refers to the differences between people, eg personality, beliefs, religion, race, upbringing and **social background**.

Social background

For example, the jobs a person's parents do, whether they're educated and how much money they have.

VISUAL TECHNIQUES

Use visual techniques during the consultation and the treatment so you can look for any contra-indications that might prevent or restrict the treatment. For example, if a client has booked a facial, you would, subtly, look at their skin during the consultation to see if there's anything that would contra-indicate the treatment. When you've finished the superficial cleanse, you can have a closer look at the skin type and condition.

MANUAL TECHNIQUES

Manual techniques allow you to feel your client's skin and get a more rounded picture. For example, during a skin analysis you'll not only look at your client's skin through the magnifying lamp but touch the skin to see how even the texture is.

REFERENCE TO CLIENT RECORDS

If your client has been to the salon before, they won't need to fill out a new consultation card. Take the existing card and ask them if their personal details have changed, if they have a new GP, or if their health has changed since their last appointment. If there are any changes, delete the old details and ask your client to check the new information and re-sign the card to agree that the new details are correct.

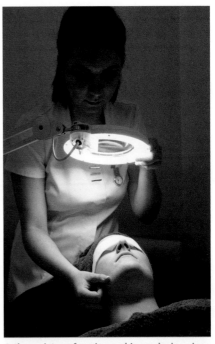

A therapist performing a skin analysis using visual and manual techniques

A therapist referring to client records for an existing client

A secure filing system

A secure online system

As many salons are choosing to put their records online, the receptionist might need the consultation card to update the system with the client's details before storing the hard copy somewhere safe.

When the treatment is finished, make a note on the card of the treatment you've performed, any skin reactions, the products you've used, and any further treatments you've recommended. If a different therapist carries out the next treatment, they can use this as a guide.

Once you have finished with a consultation card, place it in a lockable filing cabinet where it will be safe and secure.

CUSTOMERS' RIGHTS

Make sure you're aware of the customer's rights in terms of legislation that affects the salon, for example:

- Sale of Goods Act
- Services Act
- Data Protection Act.

SALE OF GOODS ACT

This Act requires that all goods must 'conform to contract', which basically means they must 'do exactly what they say on the box'. If a product doesn't do this, the customer can ask for their money back (provided it's within a reasonable time) or ask for the item to be repaired or replaced. The **purchaser** has to prove the product is faulty or doesn't 'conform to contract', and the **supplier** needs to make sure the purchaser is happy with the end result.

SERVICES ACT

By agreeing to provide a service, a salon enters into a contract of agreement with a client to ensure this service is provided to a high standard, by a trained person, in a reasonable time and at a reasonable cost. If this doesn't happen, the 'contract' is broken and the client could be entitled to compensation. This compensation can either be a refund or the client can choose to have the same treatment again free of charge.

HANDY HINTS

Many of these Acts will also come in handy for Unit G18.

Purchaser

Someone who buys a product.

Supplier

Someone who supplies resources, equipment and materials.

Customers checking out product displays

DATA PROTECTION ACT

This Act requires that all personal and confidential information is stored securely and that access is only given to authorised people. Clients have the right to view this information whether it's on a consultation card or a computer and ask for information to be changed if it's incorrect. Even friends and family shouldn't be allowed to see the information as this would be a breach of confidentiality.

WHY DON'T YOU...
Read through SmartScreen handout 3 for further details on these Acts and other legislation affecting retail and services.

 SmartScreen G4 handout 3

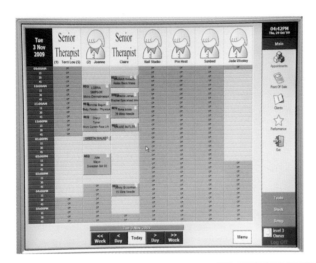

Some salons use an online booking system ...

MAKE APPOINTMENTS FOR SALON SERVICES

When you're making appointments, you should deal with each individual promptly and politely. You're most likely to make appointments either in person or on the telephone. Make sure there are no gaps between appointments by offering the client a slightly earlier or later time if you need to. Most clients understand how appointments work so don't mind coming in a little earlier or later if you ask them to. Every salon will have its own procedures for making appointments, most likely in an appointment book or through an online booking system.

... some prefer to use appointment books.

Either way, make sure you know how long each treatment takes so you can book the right amount of time. Below is a guideline of times for standard beauty treatments, the abbreviations you could use and average prices:

Treatment	Possible abbreviation	Time taken	Average cost of treatment
Indian head massage	IHM	45 minutes	£15–£40
Full body massage	FBM	60 minutes	£30–£60
Full body massage including head and face	FBMH&F	75 minutes	£50–£90
Back, neck and shoulder massage	BNS	30 minutes	£15–£30
Specialised facial	sp/fac	75–90 minutes	£50–£70
Facial	fac	60 minutes	£25–£50
Basic facial	–	30–45 minutes	£15–£30
Manicure	m/c	60 minutes	£20–£35
Pedicure	p/c	60–75 minutes	£25–£40
Mini or basic manicure	mini m/c	45 minutes	£15–£25
Mini or basic pedicure	mini p/c	50 minutes	£20–£35
File and polish	F&P	15 minutes	£10–£15
Full leg wax	FLW	45 minutes	£20–£25
Half leg	½ LW	30 minutes	£15–£20
Bikini line	BW	15 minutes	£10–£15
Underarm	UAW	15 minutes	£10–£15
Eyebrow wax	EBW	15 minutes	£8–£15
Upper lip wax	ULW	10 minutes	£8–£15
Chin wax	CW	10 minutes	£8–£15
Eyelash tint	ELT	20 minutes	£10–£20
Eyebrow tint	EBT	10 minutes	£8–£15
Eyebrow shape	EBS	15 minutes	£8–£15
Make-up	m/up	30–45 minutes	£20–£30
Trial make-up	trial m/up	60 minutes	£15–£25
Make-up lesson	m/up less	75 minutes	£15–£25
Artificial lashes (flare)	flare a/l	15–30 minutes	£15–£30
Artificial lashes (strip)	strip a/l	15 minutes	£15
Ear piercing	EP	15 minutes	£15–£30

 SmartScreen G4 worksheet 4

MAKING APPOINTMENTS IN PERSON

When you're making appointments, you'll need to use a variety of open and closed questions to get the information you need from the client. This information will include:

- the client's name
- their contact details
- service(s) required
- the preferred date and time.

Closed questions need a one-word answer and normally begin with 'do', 'does' and 'will'. Open questions need more in-depth responses and normally begin with 'when', 'who', 'why', 'what', 'where' and 'how'. When you've obtained this information and confirmed the appointment, tell the client how long the treatment will take, the estimated price and which member(s) of staff they're booked in with. Below is an example of someone making an appointment in person, and the conversation between the receptionist (Sarah) and the client (Holly) who wants to book a beauty therapy treatment.

WHY DON'T YOU...
Read through SmartScreen handout 4 for further details on making appointments.

 SmartScreen G4 handout 4

A client and receptionist agree on an appointment booking.

Sarah 'Good morning, welcome to The Retreat. My name's Sarah, how can I help you today?' *Open question*

Holly 'Good morning Sarah, I'd like to make an appointment for a couple of treatments if that's possible?' *Closed question*

Sarah 'Of course, what were you thinking of having?' *Open question*

Holly 'I'd like to book a facial, an eyelash tint and an eyebrow wax, and a half leg wax. It's my sister's birthday party at the weekend so I thought I'd treat myself.'

Sarah 'Oh lovely, well you've come to the right place! I would advise you have the facial a couple of days before to let your skin settle in time for the event, and have your waxing treatments at least 24 hours beforehand for the same reason. How does that sound?' *Open question*

Holly 'That sounds perfect. Is it possible to have the eyelash tint today, the facial tomorrow in the afternoon, and the waxing on Friday morning please?' *Closed question*

Sarah 'Unfortunately we can't do your eyelash tint today as we need to do a skin sensitivity test at least 24 hours before the treatment to check you're not allergic to anything. We're also fully booked tomorrow I'm afraid but I can book you in on Wednesday at 3:30pm?' *Closed question*

Holly 'OK, do I need a test if I've had a tint done elsewhere?' *Closed question*

Sarah 'Yes, because the other salon might not use the same products as we do so the ingredients could be different. It's a safety precaution to reduce the risk of a reaction during the treatment.'

Holly 'No problem. OK, so I'll go for that appointment for my facial and eyelash tint then please.'

Sarah 'Great, can I take your full name and a contact number please?' *Closed question*

Holly 'Yes, my name is Holly Jones and my phone number is 07894 561230.'

Sarah 'Thanks Holly, so that's your facial and eyelash tint booked in; now let's organise your waxing. I have a space free at 10am on Friday morning if that suits you? We will also need to do a sensitivity test for the waxing for the same reason.'

Holly 'That's fine. Can I have these tests done today?' *Closed question*

Sarah 'Yes, when I've confirmed your booking I'll ask one of our therapists to do the tests.'

Holly 'OK then.'

Sarah 'Great. I'll write these appointments down for you on a card and I'll make a note you've had the sensitivity tests so there's no problems when you arrive. Just to confirm then, your facial and eyelash tint are booked for Wednesday at 3:30pm with Jenny and these will take about 90 minutes. Then your half leg and eyebrow wax are booked for Friday morning at 10am with Lisa and this will take about 45 minutes. Does that sound OK?' *Closed question*

Holly 'Perfect, thank you for your help.'

Sarah 'No problem Holly, here's your appointment card with our details if you need to cancel or re-arrange your appointments. If you'd like to take a seat, I'll go and get one of our therapists to do your skin tests.'

MAKING APPOINTMENTS OVER THE TELEPHONE

When you're making appointments over the telephone, make sure you answer with a smile. When you've asked why the client is calling and made the appointment, repeat all the details back to them and check they've written it down so they don't forget.

WHY DON'T YOU...
Have a go at SmartScreen worksheet 5 to see if you can successfully book appointments.

SmartScreen G4 worksheet 5

HANDLE PAYMENTS FROM CLIENTS

When the client has finished their treatment, you need to make sure they pay before leaving. Ask them if they enjoyed their treatment and whether they want to buy any of the products their therapist recommended. If they do, put the products in a bag and add the cost to the total charge. Use a calculator or the till to work out the final price. Tell the client the total price without shouting it out for everyone to hear.

If you're dealing with product purchases, double check the condition and quality before placing them in the bag. This shows the client you want them to be happy with their purchases and that you've checked there's no damage, such as loose packaging or cracked/leaking containers.

Check your salon accepts the client's method of payment and make sure the payment is processed correctly. Methods of payment include:

- cash
- cash equivalents
- cheques
- credit or debit cards.

A therapist checking products for faults

A therapist handing over an appointment card to a client, as well as her purchases

WHY DON'T YOU...
Have a go at SmartScreen worksheet 12 to identify the limits of your authority when dealing with clients, maintaining the reception area and handling payments.

SmartScreen G4 worksheet 12

CASH

Most people don't tend to carry large amounts of money with them any more but businesses still accept cash provided it's a valid currency. In the UK, this includes English and Scottish currency, and some businesses also accept Euros. When you're handling cash, always count the money in front of the client and check all notes for the watermark and silver strip before you process the payment. If you have to give change, count it out as you hand it back to the client as this will avoid any disputes later on. If the client believes you've short changed them, remain polite and don't assume the customer has made a mistake. Ask them how much they think they're missing and explain that the money is checked at the end of each day. Inform the responsible person and, if necessary, put the money to one side for the client to collect the following day, and remember to take their contact details.

> **HANDY HINTS**
>
> Check the watermark of English notes by holding them up to the light so you can see the Queen's face. Check the silver strip as well, which should run from top to bottom on the back of the note on the right-hand side. You can also use a counterfeit detection pen to check the authenticity of a bank note; make a streak along the note and if it turns yellow or remains clear, the note is authentic, if it turns brown or black, the iodine in the pen has reacted with the material used to make the counterfeit.

Make sure the till is never short of change. There is usually a float that's counted at the start and end of each day and this usually provides the till with enough change. Remember to keep an eye on this and tell the responsible person if the money runs short.

THE DIFFERENCES BETWEEN ENGLISH, SCOTTISH AND EURO BANK NOTES

English notes are made of cotton and linen. They always have a picture of the Queen's head on the front and the exact same picture in the watermark. Each note has a silver security strip that appears as a dashed line which becomes a solid dark line when the note is held up to the light.

Scottish notes are made of 100 per cent cotton paper and should feel crisp and firm. They also have a security thread along their height and a watermark, which matches the portrait on the front. There is also a hologram that changes colour as you tilt the note.

Euro notes are made of 100 per cent cotton material and feel hard and stiff. When you hold them up to the light, Euro bank notes show their value in each corner of both sides, and the hologram changes from the value number to a window or door symbol. When you hold them under UV light, the star symbols appear orange, flag symbols appear green and you can see the signature of the president of the European Central bank.

CASH EQUIVALENTS

This includes traveller's cheques, gift vouchers and loyalty schemes, and can be used as an alternative to cash payments.

TRAVELLER'S CHEQUES

Traveller's cheques can be accepted as long as they're the correct currency, ie **Sterling** in the UK. When you accept traveller's cheques, make sure you check the signature by asking for the person's passport as well as ensuring the client signs it in your presence.

> **HANDY HINTS**
>
> If a client tries to pay for their purchases with an invalid currency, politely explain to them that you don't accept that currency and ask if they have another method of payment they could use instead.

Sterling

This is currency used in the UK and is also referred to as the 'Great British Pound' (GBP).

GIFT VOUCHERS

Gift vouchers are pre-paid and can either have a monetary value or be used for a specific treatment. If a person wants to buy a gift voucher, tell them the expiry date; in most cases this is six months, but it can be anywhere between three and 12 months. If the voucher is for monetary value rather than a specific treatment, explain that if the client wants a treatment worth more than the value of the gift voucher, they'll need to pay the difference.

LOYALTY SCHEMES

Loyalty schemes are a good way of ensuring repeat custom and are popular amongst clients. After a client's first treatment, give them a loyalty card with a stamp on it to show they've received a treatment. Then, each time they have a treatment, stamp the loyalty card until it's full and then the client can receive a free treatment, usually a back massage or a mini facial. This is a fantastic way of encouraging your client to return and is also a nice way to thank them for their loyalty and custom.

CHEQUES

Although cheques aren't used that much any more, they're still an acceptable method of payment. The client must also provide a cheque guarantee card, which will have a maximum amount that they can spend in one go. When you're processing cheques, ask the client to fill in the payee's name and the amount before signing and dating it. It's your responsibility to make a note of the card number on the back of the cheque and check that the card hasn't expired. You also need to check that the sort code and account numbers on the cheque match those on the card, that the total amount doesn't exceed the limit, and that the signature on the card matches the one on the cheque. If a cheque has been completed incorrectly, tell the client politely and explain that you cannot accept it. Ask them to write a new cheque and hand the old one back.

HANDY HINTS
Some salons accept cheques for higher amounts than the guarantee card states. However, you'll need additional identification, such as a driver's licence. Check this with you manager first.

CREDIT OR DEBIT CARDS

These are probably the most common methods of payment as they're normally the most secure. A credit card gives a person additional credit that they must pay back in an agreed time, usually 30 days, and is available from most banks or credit providers. A debit card gives a person access to their own money and is provided by the bank when the account is opened. Processing payments for both of these cards is exactly the same. Place the card in the electronic card reader or terminal and enter the total amount. Pass the terminal to the client, ask them to check the amount before pressing enter, and ask them to enter their Personal Identification Number (PIN). The terminal will process the payment by requesting authorisation from the client's account or credit provider. When this is authorised, place the first receipt in the till and give the second copy to the client. Remember not all terminals work this way so make sure you read the manufacturer's instructions beforehand.

HANDY HINTS
Cheque guarantee cards are being phased out by July 2011.

SmartScreen G4 worksheet 11

WHY DON'T YOU...

Have a go at SmartScreen worksheet 11 to identify the best course of action when dealing with different payment discrepancies.

HANDY HINTS

Not all salons follow this procedure for dealing with declined cards. Check with your salon manager how you should handle this.

DECLINED CARDS

In some cases, cards can be declined. This could be due to a lack of funds in the person's account or, if someone is spending more than usual, the bank might be concerned that they're not who they say they are. If this happens, explain to the client that their card has been declined and try the same card again, just in case the problem is with the card reader. If the problem continues, tell the client clearly, but discreetly, that you'll need another method of payment. If there are further problems, invite the client to take a seat while you find the responsible person to deal with the situation.

A client making a payment with a credit/debit card

WHY DON'T YOU...

Have a go at SmartScreen worksheet 9 to identify your salon's security methods.

SmartScreen G4 worksheet 9

When you're dealing with all methods of payment, make sure they're kept safe and secure. It's a common mistake for salons to place their reception desk right next to the front door, making them an easy target for criminals. Tills should be kept secure and out of direct sight of any windows. When the money is counted at the end of the day, store it in a locked cupboard until it's taken to the bank. Keep floats separately for added security.

A receptionist handing the receipt to a client as proof of purchase

HANDY HINTS

Regardless of what payment method the client has used, always offer them a copy of the receipt for their own personal records.

Fraud

Deceiving people by using counterfeit money or bank cards. This is a crime.

HANDY HINTS

If you suspect a person of **fraud** while you're processing a payment, for example forged bank notes or fraudulent cards, keep hold of the payment method and tell the responsible person discreetly so they can deal with the situation. This will save any embarrassment for the client and makes sure you're following salon protocol.

SPECIAL OFFERS

It's normal practice for salons to promote special offers on a regular basis. These might be **seasonal offers** or ongoing promotions, or might be a deal to promote a new treatment the salon wants to introduce. Promotions are also a great way of drumming up business if there's been a drop in sales. You can give leaflets to each client when they make an appointment or to local businesses who are happy to promote your services. You can place adverts in local newspapers or magazines, or you could even contact the local radio station and offer a free treatment for some free airtime in return. The most popular types of promotions are the ones that include something for free. These are usually 'buy one get one free' or '3 for 2' offers where the client pays for one or two treatments and receives the cheapest one free. It's a good idea to think about which treatments you want to include in this offer; if you include them all, you could end up losing more money than you thought. For example, if your facials are already popular, there's no need to promote them as part of a special offer. Instead, why not promote a new treatment that hasn't quite taken off yet and that you want to make more people aware of.

DISCOUNTS

This means you're offering a product or service at a reduced price. Again, this is popular when there's a dip in sales and bookings or to say thank you to loyal customers. Perhaps you have a client who wants to book a treatment you've recommended but they just can't afford it; you could offer them a discount the first time in the hope they enjoy the treatment and pay full price next time. If a client introduces a friend to the salon, you could reward them by offering them a discount on their next treatment. Make sure you check your salon's procedure when you're offering discounts – often it's the role of the salon manager.

Seasonal offer

Something that relates to the season, eg waxing is ideal for spring and summer to prepare for holidays and the warmer weather, whereas fake tans are good for the festive season, when people have parties to dress up for.

Advertising your salon in a magazine will make potential new clients aware of the business

ACTIVITY

Think of some special offers and discounts for your salon and suggest them to your tutor.

END OF UNIT SUMMARY

Now you've reached the end of the unit, and before you test your knowledge with the end of unit assessment, check the following list to see if you feel confident in all areas covered. If there are still any areas you're unsure of, go back over them in the book and ask your tutor for additional support:

- maintain the reception area
- attend to clients and enquiries
- make appointments for salon services
- handle payments from clients.

Now that you have an understanding of how to maintain a reception area and how to conduct yourself when you're working on reception, let's see how much you can remember. These questions will help you revise what you've learnt in this chapter.

Turn to pages 417–418 for the answers.

1   How can you make sure the reception area is clean and tidy at all times?

2   What stationery does a receptionist need?

3   How can you ensure there's adequate stock on display at all times?

4   When you're maintaining stock levels, what should you be looking for?

5   Describe how a beauty salon can create the right first impression.

6   Why is it important to offer refreshments to all clients and customers?

7   What is the difference between negative and positive body language?

8   Why is it important to attend to clients and customers promptly and politely?

9   What are the different types of enquiry you're likely to deal with on reception?

10 Explain the correct procedure for confirming an appointment.

11 What information do you need when you're taking a message for a colleague?

12 Why is important to communicate to clients and customers clearly?

13 Which **two** Acts must you be aware of when you're offering products and services?

14 How can you balance the attention you give to one client without ignoring another?

15 What information do you need when you're taking a booking?

16 How can you make sure salon time is used productively when you're making appointments?

17 What payment methods are accepted in most salons?

18 Why must you make sure the customer takes a copy of the receipt?

19 What other identification do you need if you've been given a cheque that exceeds the limit on the cheque guarantee card?

20 How would you deal with a card that has been declined?

WHY DON'T YOU...
Test your knowledge further by logging into SmartScreen and completing the revision activities before attempting the sample GOLA revision questions.

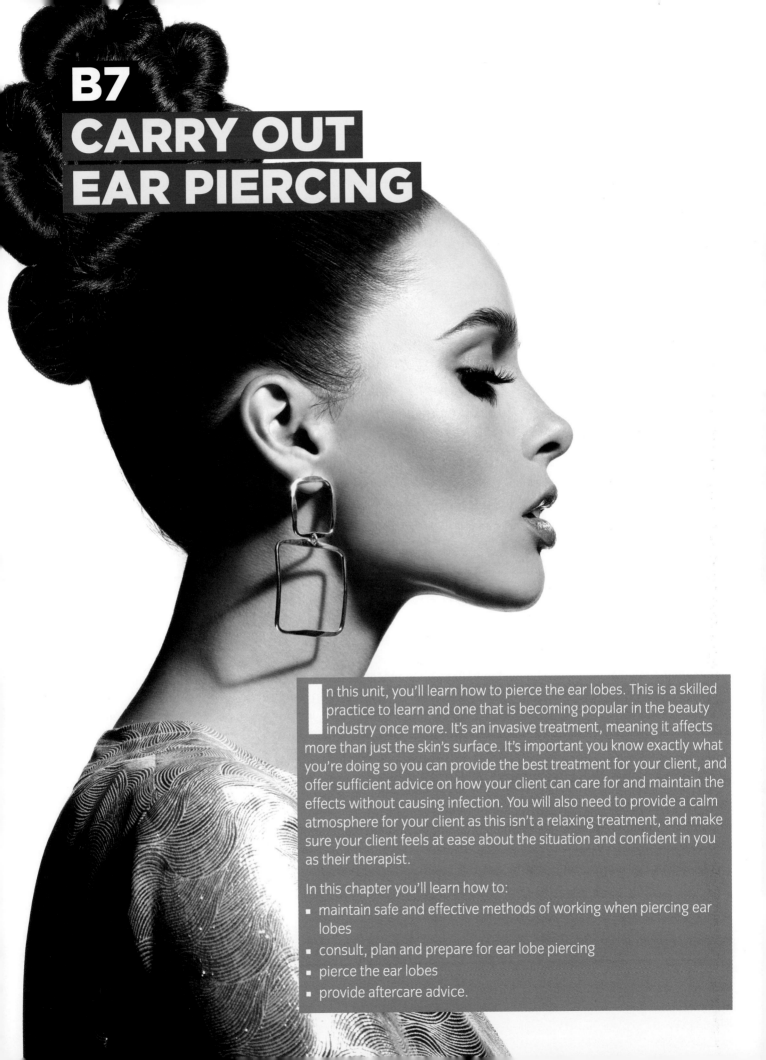

B7
CARRY OUT EAR PIERCING

In this unit, you'll learn how to pierce the ear lobes. This is a skilled practice to learn and one that is becoming popular in the beauty industry once more. It's an invasive treatment, meaning it affects more than just the skin's surface. It's important you know exactly what you're doing so you can provide the best treatment for your client, and offer sufficient advice on how your client can care for and maintain the effects without causing infection. You will also need to provide a calm atmosphere for your client as this isn't a relaxing treatment, and make sure your client feels at ease about the situation and confident in you as their therapist.

In this chapter you'll learn how to:

- maintain safe and effective methods of working when piercing ear lobes
- consult, plan and prepare for ear lobe piercing
- pierce the ear lobes
- provide aftercare advice.

HANDY HINTS

When you're providing an ear piercing service, it's important to use the skills you've learnt from the following units:

Unit G20   Ensure responsibility for actions to reduce risks to health and safety

Unit G18   Promote additional services or products to clients

Unit G4   Fulfil salon reception duties.

By-laws

Local laws passed from a higher authority and can vary from place to place. Contact your local HSE for more information about your area's by-laws.

WHY DON'T YOU...

Look back at Unit G20 to refresh your memory on each of these Acts, and all the others, before continuing with this unit. Or read through SmartScreen handouts 5 and 8 on data protection and health and safety legislation.

SmartScreen B7 handouts 5 and 8

HANDY HINTS

The Local Government Act 2003 recommends that anyone offering ear piercing treatments is immunised against hepatitis B as a precautionary method against the risk of cross-infection.

WHY DON'T YOU...

Have a go at SmartScreen worksheet 3 to test your knowledge on disinfection and sterilisation.

SmartScreen B7 worksheet 3

MAINTAIN SAFE AND EFFECTIVE METHODS OF WORKING WHEN PIERCING EAR LOBES

When you're providing ear piercing treatments, it's vital that you're aware of, and understand, the health and safety legislation affecting your practice. It's also important that you familiarise yourself with any local **by-laws** as these can differ from one area to another. The following legislation is of particular interest in relation to this unit:

- Data Protection Act (DPA)
- Disability Discrimination Act (DDA)
- Control of Substances Hazardous to Health (COSHH)
- Reporting of Injuries, Diseases and Dangerous Occurrences Regulations (RIDDOR)
- Provision and Use of Work Equipment Regulations (PUWER).

Each of these Acts is described fully in Unit G20 along with all other health and safety legislation.

As well as the above legislation, there's also the Local Government Act 2003 (a recent update from the Local Government Miscellaneous Provisions Act 1982), which outlines the by-laws that you should follow when you're offering ear piercing treatments. As an overview, this Act requires any salon (and its employees) offering this treatment to be registered with the local Health and Safety Executive (HSE). The HSE sends an inspector to ensure the salon is following all by-laws and all relevant health and safety legislation before providing the business with a certificate of registration. Only then can the salon offer these treatments to clients.

SALON ENVIRONMENT

Now you're aware of the local by-laws and health and safety legislation affecting this treatment, you need to focus on creating the right environment. Disinfect your gun with an appropriate solution and place it in a UV cabinet for ten minutes on each side prior to use (refer to Unit G20 for further guidance on sterilisation and disinfection procedures). Other equipment, including pre-packed sterilised items and disposable items, don't need further sterilisation or disinfection. On the top shelf of the trolley, you'll need the following items:

- an ear piercing gun such as
  - a disposable gun (these are intended for single use only and are pre-loaded with studs)
  - a re-usable gun (this doesn't come into contact with the ear at all)

Re-usable ear piercing guns

- hand disinfectant
- a selection of hypo-allergenic studs (pre-sterilised and pre-packed by the manufacturer)
- pre-packed alcohol-based sterile wipes
- disinfecting solution
- a small bowl of cotton wool pads
- disposable gloves (ideally powder-free, nitrile/vinyl gloves to prevent sensitisation)
- aftercare solution
- a sterile skin marker pen.

On the second shelf you'll need:
- a headband
- a mirror
- a small towel
- a medium towel.

On the bottom shelf you'll need:
- client record card
- aftercare advice leaflet.

Hypo-allergenic studs

Alcohol-based sterile wipes

HANDY HINTS

It's important to use an approved piercing gun as it's designed to avoid all contact with the ear lobe and eliminate the risk of cross-infection.

An ideal trolley set up for an ear piercing service

WHY DON'T YOU...
Read through SmartScreen handout 4 for further information on the equipment and materials required for this service.

 SmartScreen B7 handout 4

When you've prepared the trolley, make sure you have a lined pedal bin for all your waste and that your client will be comfortable; sitting is the best position and normally there should be a high chair provided, similar to those used by make-up artists. However, this might not be available – a treatment couch is fine as long as it's height adjustable to prevent poor posture and overstretching. Protect the couch with a sheet, cover this lengthways with two large towels, and place couch roll over the top. Bring the head of the couch into an upright position to allow suitable access to the ear lobes and minimise the risk of injury to your client and yourself.

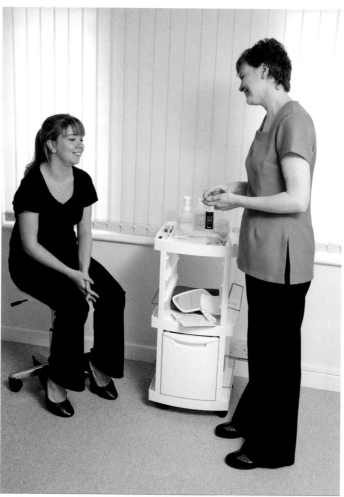

It's best to seat your client in an appropriate chair

WHY DON'T YOU...
Work through SmartScreen worksheets 1 and 2 to see how well you prepare your environment and yourself.

SmartScreen B7 worksheets 1 and 2

To create the right environment, refer to Unit G20 and focus your attention on temperature, lighting and general comfort. You'll need adequate lighting so you can see what you're doing and where to pierce. Maintain comfort for your client by encouraging them to relax throughout the treatment so they can enjoy it as much as possible, for example, by playing calming music and ensuring the room is warm enough. The local by-laws for this treatment will require that the environment and set-up adhere to the relevant health and safety legislation and guidelines.

Check your own comfort by wearing supporting shoes and maintaining your posture as you'll be standing for the duration of this treatment. Make sure your own personal hygiene is of a high standard and reflects the guidelines set by the local by-laws. Remember to wash your hands prior to the treatment and use the hand disinfectant as and when is necessary. You must wear disposable gloves at all times as this is an invasive treatment and some clients' ear lobes might bleed a little, so you must reduce the risk of cross-infection to maintain a safe and hygienic working environment.

You should also adhere to the industry accepted times to provide a commercially viable treatment. Ear piercing is usually a quick treatment with 15 minutes for the consultation and aftercare advice and 15 minutes for the actual service. Ear piercing is an inexpensive treatment with prices beginning from as little as £8 to as much as £15.

CONSULT, PLAN AND PREPARE FOR EAR LOBE PIERCING

As with any other beauty treatment, you should carry out a consultation to determine your client's suitability. Focus your attention on finding out if they have any contra-indications, if they are 16 or over and identify where on the ear lobe they would like to be pierced. Below is a list of the contra-indications to ear piercing that require medical referral. You need to establish whether there are any contra-indications to prevent the risk of injury or cross-infection:

- systemic medical conditions: risk of aggravating the condition and causing discomfort or distress to your client
- serious localised skin infections: risk of cross-infection and exacerbating the condition
- ear lobe infections: as above
- **haemophilia**: due to a lack of blood clotting, the skin is unlikely to heal as well, or as quickly as it should
- nervous client: your client might panic or jump, which could result in incorrect placement of the studs.

If you identify any of the above contra-indications, remember to refer your client to their GP in a tactful manner to avoid causing distress and alarm. Under no circumstances should you name the condition no matter how certain you are; you're not qualified to do so and you might be wrong. Instead, inform your client you're aware of a contra-indication and you don't want to worsen this by performing the treatment. Advise

Haemophilia
A disorder of the blood where there aren't enough platelets to clot the blood where the skin is damaged.

SmartScreen B7 handout 10 and worksheet 5

them to see their GP for a full and proper diagnosis. The following is a list of contra-indications that restrict treatment:

- scar tissue less than six months old
- previous ear piercings.

For both of these conditions, make sure the new piercing is at least 1 cm away from the scar tissue or existing piercing(s) to avoid the risk of infection and additional swelling.

You must also find out how old your client is because if they're a minor, you must have written parental/guardian consent before you go ahead with the treatment. Usually, anyone who is aged 16 years or under is considered a minor; however, this age does vary from region to region. Many parents/guardians want to get their children's ears pierced when they're young but they must provide written consent and be present for the duration of the treatment.

HANDY HINTS

When you're treating young children, you might want to ask a colleague to assist you with the treatment so both ears can be pierced at the same time, providing there are two guns available. This reduces the chance of the child crying or panicking. Although it's generally quite a painless treatment, the sound of the ear being pierced could upset small children.

WHY DON'T YOU...
Read through SmartScreen handout 6 for further information on the consultation.

 SmartScreen B7 handout 6

Remember that your insurance policy might not cover you for performing ear piercing services on minors, so it's important you confirm this before offering the treatment.

WHY DON'T YOU...
Read through SmartScreen handout 9 for further information on client preparation.

When you've completed the consultation and your client has signed and dated the consultation card, you need to prepare your client and plan the treatment. Ask your client to remove their shoes and sit on the treatment couch or chair, cover their feet with the small towel and cross the medium towel over their shoulders to protect their clothing.

 SmartScreen B7 handout 9

Below is a step-by-step guide to preparing the treatment area.

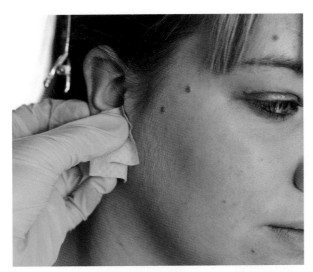

STEP 1 – Cleanse the ears thoroughly using pre-packed alcohol-based sterile wipes. These often come as part of a starter kit and are recommended or produced by the gun manufacturer. This will minimise waste and reduce the risk of cross-infection.

STEP 2 – Take the mirror and discuss where your client would like the piercing. While your client holds the mirror, use the surgical marker pen to mark where the piercings will be. Recommend a central location as it will appear balanced and symmetrical.

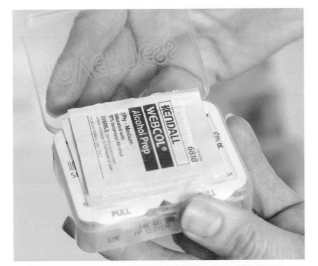

STEP 3 – Check that the packaging of the studs isn't damaged, damp, wet or out of date as the studs will no longer be sterile and must be thrown away in the appropriate hazardous waste bin. If there's no identification on the pre-sterilised package, you'll need to contact the manufacturer before using the studs as they might need to be sent back and replaced.

HANDY HINTS

On each packet of studs, there should be a red spot identifying that they've been sterilised. If this red spot isn't present, don't use the studs as they'll need to be sent back to the manufacturer.

ACTIVITY

Ask a friend if you can practise making crosses on their ears, so that you can get used to making the same piercing location on each ear. Make them as symmetrical as possible!

PIERCE THE EAR LOBES

When you've prepared the treatment area, proceed with the treatment as smoothly as possible. Below is a step-by-step guide on how to pierce the ear lobes accurately and safely. However, make sure you read the manufacturer's instructions first as there might be some differences.

STEP 1 – Remove the backing paper of the stud pack. Pull back the plunger knob on the back of the gun until you here it click.

STEP 2 – Hold the plastic cartridge by its plastic mount and remove from its packaging, ensuring you don't touch the backing clasp (butterfly) or stud to avoid cross-infection. Separate the two parts of the cartridge; do this by positioning the part with the backing clasp into the slot of the gun, pushing it down until it doesn't go any further. Position the part holding the stud against the stud barrel of the gun, placing a protective ring around the stud.

STEP 3 – Hold the ear in your non-working hand and keep the gun in a horizontal position. Bring the stem of the stud in line with the mark on the ear lobe. Squeeze the trigger gently until it stops and check the stem of the stud is still in line with the mark on the ear lobe. Squeeze the trigger again so the ear is pierced with the backing clasp placed on the back of the stud.

STEP 4 – Hold the ear gently and move the gun down and away from the ear lobe.

STEP 5 – Discard the plastic ring into the waste bin by holding the gun upside down.

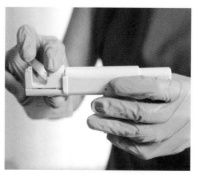

STEP 6 – Pull back the plunger knob as described in step 1.

STEP 7 – Remove the backing clasp holder from its slot, invert and replace. Repeat steps 3–5 on the second ear.

STEP 8 – Show your client their pierced ears using a hand mirror.

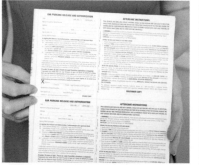

STEP 9 – Provide aftercare and home care advice and product recommendations.

When the treatment is complete and you've given your client the appropriate aftercare and home care advice, wipe the gun with an appropriate disinfecting solution and place it in the UV cabinet.

In the event of a gun malfunction, what often happens is that the backing clasp doesn't attach to the stud even though the actual piercing of the ear has been successful. If this happens, you can attach it manually but do this firmly and with confidence so you don't cause any undue distress. If the stud needs any adjustment after the piercing is complete, remove your gloves, disinfect your hands and apply a new set of gloves to prevent the risk of infection.

WHY DON'T YOU...
Read through SmartScreen handout 3 to find out about the anatomy of the ears and refer to the anatomy and physiology chapter for diagrams and further information.

 SmartScreen B7 handout 3

PROVIDE AFTERCARE ADVICE

It's vital that you give both aftercare and home care advice to each client after every treatment and ear piercing is no different. When you provide this advice, it's not enough simply to tell your client what they should and shouldn't do. You also need to explain why they must follow this advice and highlight the risks involved if they don't.

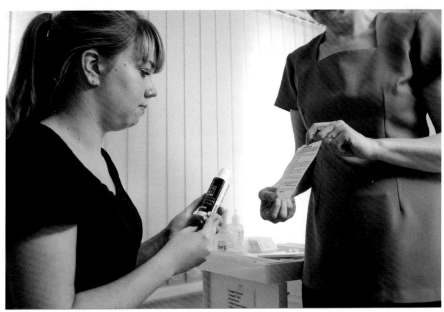

A client with aftercare solution and being given an advice leaflet

HANDY HINTS

It's a good idea to give your client an aftercare advice leaflet with all of this information clearly outlined so they don't forget what you've recommended.

AFTERCARE ADVICE

Give this advice to all clients after an ear piercing treatment and tell them to follow it for 6–8 weeks to ensure effective skin and cartilage healing:

- Don't remove the studs.
- Cleanse the area twice a day using a suitable disinfectant aftercare solution applied with a clean cotton ball.
- Prior to cleansing the ears, wash your hands with soap and warm water for at least 30 seconds.
- Don't touch the ears unless it's to cleanse or rotate the earrings.
- Take care when shampooing and applying perfume and hair spray to avoid sensitisation and the risk of infection.
- Rotate the studs with your index finger and thumb once a day to prevent them from sticking as the skin heals (remember to wash your hands thoroughly beforehand).
- Avoid using any other cleansing solutions than those recommended by the salon and the manufacturer. This includes essential oils, such as tea tree, because sensitisation can occur.
- Don't have any other ear lobe piercings as the skin is healing and scar tissue will be present. This means the lobes will be swollen and the process will not only be painful but also there's a risk of cross-infection.

WHY DON'T YOU...

Read through SmartScreen handout 12 for further information on the aftercare advice to give your client after ear piercing.

 SmartScreen B7 handout 12

After 6–8 weeks, tell your client they can remove their studs and replace them with others. If they want to do so, recommend they disinfect their hands first and try not to tug at the ear while they separate the back clasp and stud.

HOME CARE ADVICE

As always, this is more client specific and should reflect the individual needs of your client. The only piece of advice to give is to avoid costume earrings after the initial 6–8-week period. If your client is allergic to nickel, recommend they wear only gold earrings as costume jewellery is cheaply made and almost always contains nickel, which can cause skin sensitisation.

A retail stand for earrings

CONTRA-ACTIONS

If any of the following contra-actions occur, it's likely your client hasn't followed your aftercare and home care advice. In which case, you need to know how to deal with such occurrences:

- Removing studs before the skin has healed and not replacing them with other earrings will cause the holes to close up. If this occurs and your client doesn't want the holes to close up, they will need to book in for another ear piercing treatment.

- If the skin isn't cleansed at least twice a day, infection is likely to occur as dirt, shampoo and other products build up around the area. If infection does occur, the skin will appear erythemic, swollen and inflamed with pus or a serum-like fluid weeping from the hole. In this instance, tell your client to contact you so you can remind them of the aftercare advice and cleansing techniques to use. In severe cases, advise your client to contact their GP.

- Keloid scarring might also occur after the ear lobe has been pierced due to the amount of collagen produced as the skin heals. Advise your client not to have any other ear lobe piercings as it's likely further keloid scarring might occur. For clients who are prone to keloid scarring but are determined to have their ears pierced, make it clear that there's an increased risk of this and that only one piercing is recommended.

HANDY HINTS

Facial and body piercings go through phases in popularity and so it's always important to remain alert to the possible risks associated with cartilage piercings and those piercings in and around the mucous membranes, such as in the nose and mouth. Here there's an even higher risk of developing more serious infections. However, you're not qualified to pierce these areas.

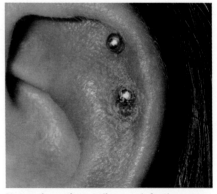

Never pierce the cartilage as infection can occur.

WHY DON'T YOU...
Read through SmartScreen handout 11 for further information on the possible contra-actions to ear piercing.

 SmartScreen B7 handout 11

B7 EAR PIERCING

Chlorhexidine acetate

A medical antiseptic with bactericidal properties.

Isopropyl alcohol

Has sterilising qualities.

PRODUCT RECOMMENDATIONS

The manufacturer should supply small bottles of aftercare solution that you can give to your client and this is included in the price of the treatment. These products generally contain ingredients called **chlorhexidine acetate** and **isopropyl alcohol**.

WHY DON'T YOU...
Work through SmartScreen worksheet 5 to see if you can remember why certain conditions are contra-indicated.

 SmartScreen B7 worksheet 5

END OF UNIT SUMMARY

Now you've reached the end of the unit, you should feel confident in the theory and practical aspects of ear piercing. Use the checklist below to see if there are any areas you feel you need to recap before beginning the end of unit assessment:

- maintain safe and effective methods of working when piercing ear lobes
- consult, plan and prepare for ear lobe piercing
- pierce the ear lobes
- provide aftercare advice.

TEST YOUR KNOWLEDGE B7

Using the questions below, test your knowledge of Unit B7 to see how much information you've retained. These questions will help you revise what you've learnt in this chapter.

Turn to pages 418–421 for the answers.

1 Why is it important to be aware of the different health and safety legislation before you offer ear piercing?

2 Explain the requirements of the Local Government Act 2003.

3 What is a by-law?

4 Why should a person offering piercings of any kind be immunised against the hepatitis B virus?

5 Explain why it's important to obtain written parental consent when you're treating minors.

6 How long should an ear piercing treatment last without the consultation and aftercare advice?

7 What PPE should be made available, and worn, when you're providing an ear piercing treatment?

8 Explain how to ensure the piercing gun is disinfected.

9 Why is it important to maintain hygiene standards in relation to the risk of cross-infection?

10 Why is it important to ensure your client is positioned correctly and comfortably before you pierce the ear lobes?

11 Why are the ear lobes marked prior to piercing?

12 Which contra-indications to ear piercing require medical referral?

13 List all the equipment needed for an ear piercing treatment.

14 Why are pre-packed studs recommended?

15 Why is it important to use the recommended piercing gun for this treatment?

16 Explain the correct procedure for ear piercing.

17 What aftercare advice should you give to each client and why is it important they adhere to this for 6–8 weeks?

18 Why is it important for your client to use the recommended aftercare solution?

19 What are the possible contra-actions to ear piercing?

20 How would you deal with these contra-actions?

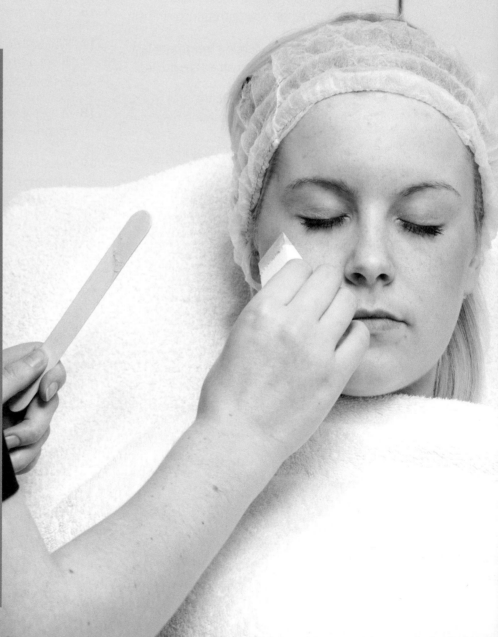

B10
ENHANCE APPEARANCE USING SKIN CAMOUFLAGE

Skin camouflage was first developed during World War II by cosmetic surgeons to conceal major burns on soldiers and pilots. Today, camouflage is probably the most rewarding and highly skilled service you can offer as a beauty therapist. It provides an instant difference to your client's skin complexion by diminishing any imperfections and enhancing the overall appearance of their skin. Clients who request this service might feel self-conscious and have low self-esteem. It's up to you to make them feel welcome and at ease in your company as soon as you meet them so they feel comfortable and confident in your care throughout the service.

In this chapter you'll learn how to:

- maintain safe and effective methods of working when providing skin camouflage
- consult, plan and prepare for skin camouflage
- carry out skin camouflage
- provide aftercare advice.

MAINTAIN SAFE AND EFFECTIVE METHODS OF WORKING WHEN PROVIDING SKIN CAMOUFLAGE

As with all beauty treatments, it's important you understand and adhere to the relevant health and safety legislation throughout to ensure you perform a safe and enjoyable treatment for your client. The main legislation affecting skin camouflage is:

- Data Protection Act (DPA)
- Disability Discriminations Act (DDA)
- Control of Substances Hazardous to Health (COSHH)
- Provision and Use of Work Equipment Regulations (PUWER).

Each of these Acts is described fully in Unit G20 along with all other health and safety legislation.

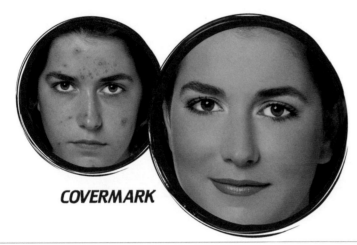

COVERMARK

Skin camouflage can really improve the confidence of some clients.

SALON ENVIRONMENT

Before beginning a treatment, it's important that you've set up your work area properly. To reduce the risk of cross-infection, disinfect all non-metal implements and work surfaces; check Unit G20 for further assistance with this. Start with the trolley and disinfect the surfaces with an appropriate product. Protect the trolley with couch roll and place the following items on the top shelf:

- a selection of cleansers
- a selection of toners
- a selection of moisturisers
- camouflage creams
- camouflage powders
- setting products
- a selection of make-up brushes
- foundation sponges
- velour puffs
- tissues
- a small bowl for damp and dry cotton pads and cotton swabs.

HANDY HINTS

When you're providing skin camouflage, it's important to use the skills you've learnt in the following units:

Unit G20 Ensure responsibility for actions to reduce risks to health and safety

Unit G18 Promote additional services or products to clients

Unit B8 Provide make-up services

Unit G8 Develop and maintain your effectiveness at work

Unit B4 Provide facial skin care treatments.

HANDY HINTS

It's common for make-up artists to use **isopropyl alcohol** to clean their brushes as it's particularly effective at removing products with a high oil content.

Isopropyl alcohol

Widely used as a cleaning fluid, especially for dissolving oil.

There are many camouflage make-up products available for this service. However, the British Association of Skin Camouflage recommends the following, which are available to professionals and non-professionals both online and through the NHS:

- Covermark
- Dermacolor
- Keromask
- Veil.

You will also need your make-up kit if you're working on the face. Refer to Unit B8 to remind yourself of the make-up products you'll need.

On the second shelf you'll need the following:

- a small towel
- one square of couch roll
- a headband
- a mirror.

On the bottom shelf you should have the client record card and a pen, and a colour chart for your client to take home detailing the colours and products you've used. You should also have ready any aftercare advice leaflets you want to give your client at the end of the treatment.

WHY DON'T YOU...
Check out **www.skin-camouflage.net** for additional information on skin camouflage and how skin conditions affecting the natural skin colour can impact on a person's quality of life and wellbeing.

HANDY HINTS

Remember to wash your make-up brushes in warm soapy water after each make-up and skin camouflage service and leave them to dry on a flat surface. This ensures they're clean and hygienic the next time you use them.

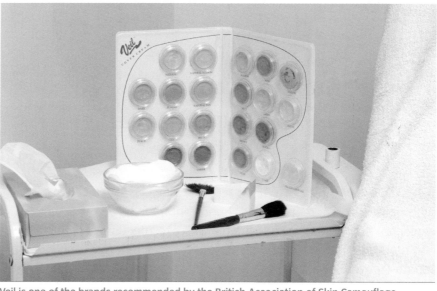

Veil is one of the brands recommended by the British Association of Skin Camouflage.

PREPARING THE TREATMENT AREA

Make sure the treatment couch is covered with a protective sheet. Place a pillow at the head with one large towel covering the pillow and upper half of couch, and cover the full length of the couch with couch roll. Remember to have some pillows, blankets and towels for additional comfort and support. You'll also need a lined metal pedal bin for all your waste. As you'll be standing for the duration of this service, ensure you maintain a good posture: keep your legs shoulder width apart and bend slightly at the knee. Check that the couch is height adjustable and the trolley is nearby to avoid any unnecessary stretching that could result in fatigue or injury.

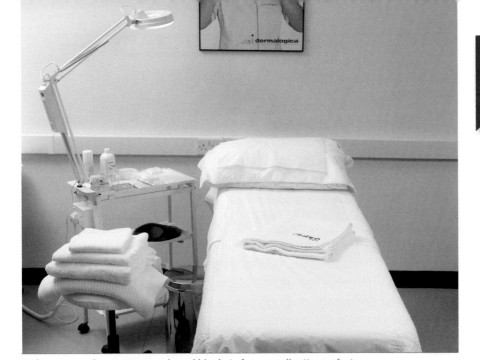

WHY DON'T YOU...
Refer to Unit B8 to remind yourself of how different lighting affects the appearance of make-up.

Make sure you have extra towels and blankets for your client's comfort.

To provide the right environment for this service, you need to make sure your client feels relaxed when they enter the treatment area and that the area is suitable for you to work safely and comfortably. You need to think about your client's general comfort and the lighting so you can see what you're doing. Remember that natural daylight or white light is ideal when you want to produce a natural look.

While there are no set times for the application of skin camouflage, treat it as a make-up lesson unless your client has booked in for a special occasion. Let your client try out the techniques you've demonstrated before they leave to ensure they're happy with the finished result.

WHY DON'T YOU...
Refer to Unit G4 to remind yourself of the techniques required for an effective consultation.

CONSULT, PLAN AND PREPARE FOR SKIN CAMOUFLAGE

It's always important to perform a consultation and obtain your client's signature before beginning any treatment to safeguard yourself and the salon. However, as part of a skin camouflage service, you also need to identify what your client's main areas of concern are. The only way this can be achieved is by using a variety of open and closed questions.

HANDY HINTS
Remember that if you're working on a minor aged under 16 years, you'll need informed and signed parental or guardian consent and the parent or guardian must stay for the duration of the service.

Remember that when you greet your client at the reception area, you need to be polite and friendly in the same way you would be with any other client. It's vital that you don't treat this client any differently. Make sure that you're respectful and reassuring at all times to encourage them to relax and open up about their skin concerns. First, it might be a good idea to explain the purpose of skin camouflage and how different results are achieved. This will ensure your client understands the process behind skin camouflage and will encourage them to ask any questions they're unsure of.

A therapist performing a consultation for skin camouflage

WHY DON'T YOU...
Refer to Unit G4 to remind yourself how to interpret positive and negative body language.

When you've covered these areas, ask your client to identify their main area, or areas, of concern: ask what they want you to focus on and what they would like you to conceal or diminish. This way your client must tell you rather than you simply guessing and making a mistake; this could be embarrassing for you and could be humiliating for your client. It's important to avoid insensitive questions, for example asking your client why their skin has such imperfections and what caused it. If your client chooses to open up then that's fine and you should take it as a compliment as it shows they feel comfortable in your presence. But it's highly unprofessional for you to ask anything your client might not want to discuss. The last thing you want to do is make your client feel uncomfortable before the service has even started.

When you've identified the area(s) of concern, make sure your client's expectations are realistic and achievable. If they're not, it's your responsibility to make this clear to them and explain you'll try your hardest to achieve the best results you can.

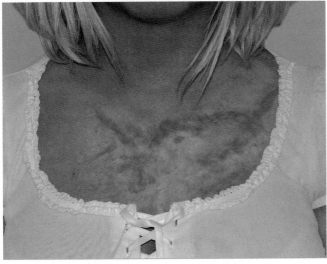
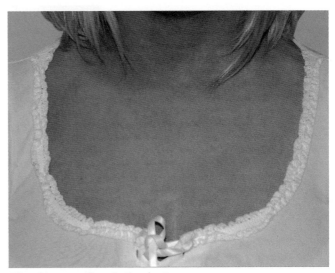

Before skin camouflage to the chest

After skin camouflage to the chest

Now you need to identify whether or not your client has any contra-indications that could prevent or restrict skin camouflage. Below is a list of contra-indications that require medical referral:

- Structural changes to the area to be camouflaged: because of the risk of pain and discomfort or an underlying medical condition you're unaware of. For example, if your client has metal plates or pins, there's likely to be scar tissue present around the area.
- Suspicious moles: a mole could be malignant so it's important you don't work over it until your client's GP has given a proper diagnosis. Moles tend to appear brown in colour and can range in shapes and sizes. However, a suspicious mole can be inflamed, swollen and tender with an irregular edge.
- Skin infections: risk of cross-infection.

If you identify one of the above contra-indications, explain to your client that the treatment cannot go ahead but you mustn't name the condition in case you're wrong. Instead, tell your client that you've identified a contra-indication and that applying skin camouflage products could make it worse; then advise them to see their GP for a proper diagnosis.

The following contra-indications restrict skin camouflage but don't require medical referral:

- Conditions adjacent to the area to be camouflaged which are sore and tender: watch your pressure when you're applying camouflage make-up and check with your client throughout to make sure they're comfortable.

When the consultation is complete and you've identified the area(s) of concern, you're ready to begin the service.

CARRY OUT SKIN CAMOUFLAGE

Before you can start, you need to make sure your client is prepared for the service. If you're working on the face, ask your client to remove their top if it has a high neck, wrap a large towel around their torso under the arms and ask them to lie supine on the couch. If your client is wearing a round-necked top that exposes enough of the neck and the area of concern isn't on or around the décolleté, then simply protect it with a square of couch roll and tuck it in at the neckline. Place a blanket over your client, wrap their hair in a small towel or headband and tuck in two small tissues at the hairline to protect it.

If your client requires skin camouflage to the face, neck or décolleté and plans to recreate this effect at home, you might want to give them a mirror so they can watch the techniques you use.

If you're applying skin camouflage to the face, you'll need to perform a superficial cleanse and tone and analyse the skin to determine your client's skin type and condition. This will help you decide which camouflage techniques you'll need to use.

If you're applying skin camouflage to any other part of the body, make sure the area is adequately exposed and you maintain your client's modesty with towels. Protect any clothes with couch roll if necessary.

As part of the analysis, you need to identify the following skin conditions, which you're likely to come across during skin camouflage:

- hypo-pigmentation, such as vitiligo
- hyper-pigmentation, such as chloasma and melasma
- erythema, such as acne rosacea and thread veins
- stretch marks.

WHY DON'T YOU...
Refer to Unit B4 to remind yourself of the eye and lip cleanse, superficial cleanse and skin analysis.

HYPO-PIGMENTATION

Vitiligo is a condition where the skin becomes much lighter in patches due to the melanocytes dying or not functioning. Melanocytes produce melanin, the skin's own pigment, the quantity of which determines our skin tone. This condition is common amongst Afro-Caribbean skins and can be extremely distressing for your client; its cause is unknown. People who suffer with this condition can suffer with depression as a result. Vitiligo can occur anywhere on the face and body.

HYPER-PIGMENTATION

Conditions, such as chloasma and melasma occur as a result of increased production of the female hormones oestrogen and progesterone, which stimulate the melanocytes to produce more melanin. This causes dark, irregular patches of skin to form on the face and the back of the hands. The skin in these areas can also feel quite rough in texture compared with the rest of the skin. Although both melasma and chloasma are more common in pregnant women and those taking hormone replacement therapy (HRT), they can also affect men and women at any age and can be caused by other factors, such as perfumes and **photo-toxic** oils applied to the skin. Ephilides (freckles) are also a type of hyper-pigmentation.

ERYTHEMA

Acne rosacea is an erythemic condition of the face that primarily affects the T-zone and cheeks. The cause is unknown; however, recent studies suggest intestinal bacteria can play a part in the condition as well as elevated levels of enzymes in the stratum corneum. The skin appears red and will feel quite rough in texture. Erythema can also accompany pustules and papules – see Unit B4 to remind yourself of what these look like.

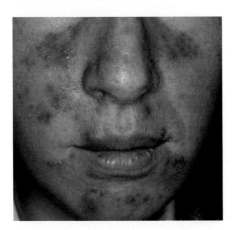

Thread veins are superficial veins that have become dilated and have risen to the skin's surface. They're normally found on the cheeks of the face or on the legs and are also called spider veins. The cause of this condition could be an underlying vascular problem, which would require medical referral for a proper diagnosis. However, they're often **hereditary**.

Hereditary
Passed on in the genes.

STRETCH MARKS

Stretch marks are commonly found around the abdomen, the thighs and the backs of the upper arms as a result of the skin stretching quickly, during a growth spurt, rapid weight gain or during pregnancy. This causes the dermis to tear as there's insufficient elastin production to keep it supple. Fresh stretch marks appear red initially as there's still blood supply to the area, but over time this blood supply decreases, which causes the stretch marks to diminish and become quite silvery in appearance. While stretch marks will fade, they will rarely disappear once they occur. If your client has red stretch marks, camouflage make-up is ideal for disguising the erythema surrounding the area.

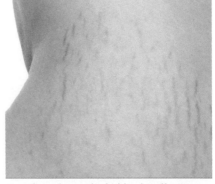

Stretch marks can be hidden by effective make-up.

THE FITZPATRICK CLASSIFICATION TABLE

When you've identified the possible conditions requiring skin camouflage, you need to be aware of your client's natural skin colour as this will indicate the **photosensitivity** of the skin. According to the Fitzpatrick Classification Scale, a person's skin is classified by their tolerance to UV light and how likely they are to get skin cancer. This scale was developed in 1975 by Thomas Fitzpatrick at the Harvard Medical School. Below is the Fitzpatrick scale identifying skin photosensitivity amongst the different skin groups.

Photosensitivity
A chemical or electrical reaction to light.

Skin type	Features	Characteristics
1	White and very fair. Red or blonde hair. Blue eyes and freckles.	Burns – never tans
2	White and fair. Red or blonde hair. Blue, hazel or green eyes.	Usually burns, sometimes tans (but with difficulty)
3	Creamy white skin and fair. Any eye or hair colour.	Sometimes mild burn, tends to tan gradually
4	Brown skin (usually Mediterranean)	Rarely burns, tans easily
5	Dark brown skin (mid-eastern skin types)	Very rarely burns, tans very easily
6	Black	Never burns, tans very easily

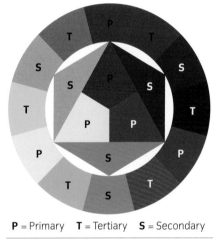

P = Primary   **T** = Tertiary   **S** = Secondary

The colour wheel

Now you need to look at your client's skin colour to make sure you choose colours that will not only conceal the area(s) of concern but complement their natural skin tone. This is where a colour wheel comes in handy. You can instantly see which colours contrast and which complement each another. This shows you the primary, secondary and tertiary colours.

The primary colours are red, yellow and blue from which all other colours are made. Secondary colours are produced when two of the primary colours are mixed, for example yellow and blue produce green, red and yellow produce orange, and red and blue produce purple. Tertiary colours are produced when a primary and secondary colour are mixed together.

Looking at the colour wheel, you'll see that the colours sitting opposite each other are complementary and will work well together. For example, green and red are opposite; green neutralises red so they complement one another very well. You'll also find that any three colours next to each other are harmonious, meaning they can be applied together to produce flattering results. For example, green, blue/green and blue eyeshadow can be applied around the eye area to enhance the natural eye colour.

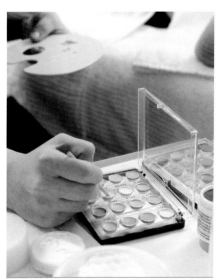

The colour wheel will be very useful for choosing make-up to suit your client's skin tone.

HANDY HINTS

Remember the following colour corrections as outlined in Unit B8:

- Green neutralises red so is perfect for dilated capillaries and high colour.
- Yellow or peach diminishes areas of blue, such as blue veins.
- Lilac diminishes yellow undertones and sallow complexions as well as dark circles.
- Concealers vary in colour and are designed to hide skin imperfections that don't require colour correction.

When you've determined your client's skin type, condition and skin colour, you need to finish preparing the skin by performing a deep cleanse, tone and moisturise (refer to Unit B4).

CAMOUFLAGE PRODUCTS

You can use the following products to camouflage the skin to provide different effects and benefits:

- camouflage cream
- camouflage powder
- setting products.

CAMOUFLAGE CREAM

Camouflage creams are mixed and applied after you've made any necessary colour corrections to rebalance the skin colour. They tend to contain no or very little oil to make them durable and waterproof. Apply camouflage creams with clean fingers in a patting motion to give an even coverage.

CAMOUFLAGE POWDER

Camouflage powder is applied to set the camouflage cream and provide a waterproof finish. Apply with a velour puff and leave to set for roughly ten minutes. Brush off any excess powder with a large powder brush or a damp cotton pad.

SETTING PRODUCTS

Apply setting sprays after powder to provide sun protection and make the finished result last even longer.

INGREDIENTS

It's important that you know what the main and active ingredients are in camouflage products and how these ingredients can affect the appearance of make-up, especially where flash photography is concerned. The following are ingredients that produce very little reaction in the skin and provide good coverage without clogging the pores:

- titanium dioxide
- iron oxide
- mica.

TITANIUM DIOXIDE

Titaniun dioxide is an organic mineral of white pigment that is becoming a popular ingredient in make-up products. It was originally used in camouflage make-up for its highly refractive qualities; it absorbs UV light effectively and provides a suitable form of SPF. However, because it's a naturally occurring white pigment and has a high **refractive index**, this ingredient can make a person appear extremely white and almost luminous under flash photography.

Refractive index
The speed at which light passes through a substance.

IRON OXIDE

Iron oxide is another naturally occurring pigment also widely used in cosmetics but for different reasons; iron oxide produces many colours from ochre reds and yellows to charcoal and carbon black. It's also used as a natural SPF but can also cause a person's skin to appear luminous under flash photography.

MICA

Mica is used in pearlescent pigments or mineral make-up containing organic oxides. It's coated with titanium dioxide to produce a reflective, metallic-looking pigment where the intensity depends on the application. As mica is extremely reflective, you need to apply a large amount to produce intense results under flash photography and fluorescent light. However, in natural or white light, you need very little as reflection causes the colours to appear intense even when you apply a small amount.

THE SKIN CAMOUFLAGE SERVICE

When you've prepared the skin, bring your client into an upright position and check they're comfortable. You're now ready to begin the skin camouflage service. Below is a step-by-step guide to applying skin camouflage. These steps can be used for any area of the face, neck, chest, shoulders, limbs or back to conceal pigmentation, erythema and tattoos.

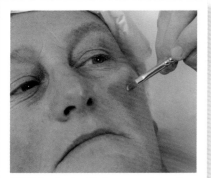

STEP 1 – Begin with the appropriate colour corrections for areas that require it, such as broken capillaries.

STEP 2 – Choose the camouflage colour(s) that will suit your client's natural skin tone. You might need to mix two or more colours together to get an exact match.

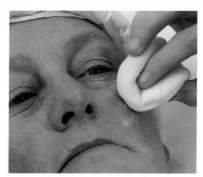

STEP 3 – Test this mixture on a small area of skin near to the area(s) of concern so you're sure it's a natural match.

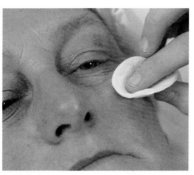

STEP 4 – When you're happy with the colour mix, build up several thin layers with your fingers using a patting motion, or use a dry foundation sponge if you prefer.

STEP 5 – Blend this out past the area(s) of concern so there's a natural progression to the natural skin colour. You might want to use a synthetic brush on smaller areas or a damp sponge for additional blending.

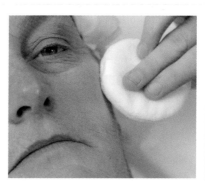

STEP 6 – When you're satisfied with the colour, set the mixture by applying the fixing powder with a velour puff and leave to set for ten minutes.

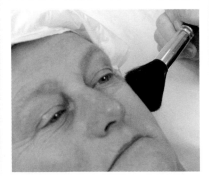

STEP 7 – Remove any excess powder with a large sable powder brush or damp cotton pad.

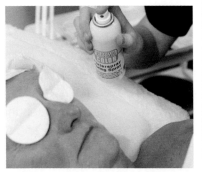

STEP 8 – For further protection and durability, use a fixing spray. Make sure you cover your client's eyes before spraying.

STEP 9 – Allow your client to see the finished result and check they're satisfied with the effects.

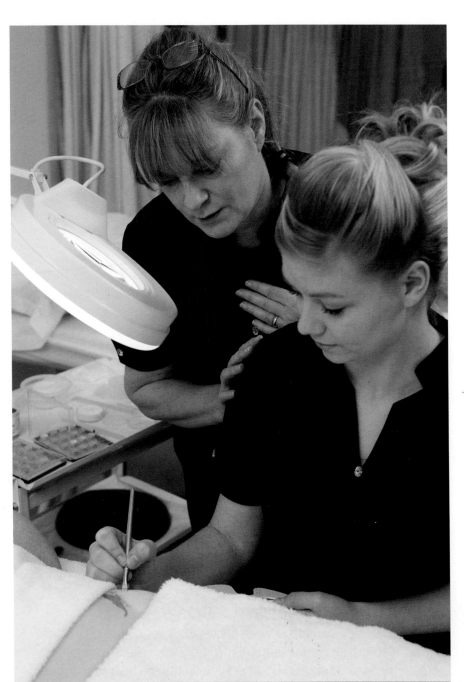

A student practising camouflage make-up to cover a tattoo.

HANDY HINTS

Remember these are just guidelines and you must check the manufacturer's instructions to make sure you're achieving the correct density, colour and effect.

HANDY HINTS

If your client wants to apply skin camouflage themselves, you might want to let them have a go before they leave. When you apply the camouflage initially, apply it only to half of the area and let your client have a go after each step you demonstrate. This way you can give instructions and additional support so that your client is confident in their own application when they leave.

HANDY HINTS

If your client requires skin camouflage to an area they cannot reach, they might want to bring a partner or friend along with them who can apply the skin camouflage for them at home. In which case, make your instructions clear so that your client and the person you're instructing leave feeling confident in the application.

When the treatment is over, it's important you give the appropriate aftercare advice to ensure your client maintains the results. Give the same aftercare advice to every client after skin camouflage; home care advice is more specific to their individual needs. This should include product recommendations and advice on skin care routines.

AFTERCARE ADVICE

Aftercare advice is important so that your clients know how to maintain the look for as long as possible. Below is a list of aftercare advice you should give to every client. Tell them to follow the advice for 24 hours after skin camouflage:

- Avoid heat treatments, such as saunas, steam rooms and hot tubs as the temperatures could cause the make-up to run.
- Avoid overexposure to UV light as this could aggravate any pigmentation disorders.
- Avoid using oily make-up and skin care products on top of the skin camouflage as it might cause smudging or remove the camouflage altogether.
- Swimming is fine as the make-up is waterproof and durable. However, don't rub the skin dry with a towel; use a patting motion to prevent smudging or removing the make-up.
- Remove skin camouflage 24 hours after application to avoid clogging the pores.

HOME CARE ADVICE

Home care advice is more client specific. It will depend on their needs and requirements as well as their skin condition and the area to which you applied the skin camouflage. For example, if your client suffers from vitiligo, advise them to avoid exposure to UV light and protect their skin with a suitable SPF when they're outdoors. This home care advice should also include skin care recommendations so that your clients follow the correct skin care routine with the products best suited to their skin type and condition. If your client doesn't follow the recommended skin care routine, it's important you advise them that this could affect the condition they're concerned about and possibly make it worse.

SKIN CAMOUFLAGE REMOVAL

Advise your client that to remove skin camouflage, they should use an oil-based make-up remover to break down and dissolve the make-up. Very often skin camouflage manufacturers will recommend their own line of skin care and make-up removal products which work in harmony with the make-up to remove it effectively.

PRODUCT RECOMMENDATIONS

At the end of the skin camouflage service, it's a good idea to provide product recommendations as it's highly likely your client will want to recreate this look on their own. Give your clients the best product

WHY DON'T YOU...
Refer to Unit B4 to remind yourself of which skin care products suit which skin types and conditions.

B10 SKIN CAMOUFLAGE

recommendations to suit their individual needs and recap any techniques you used. A product display at the main reception area will raise the profile of skin camouflage so that clients don't feel embarrassed about asking for more details on such services.

CONTRA-ACTIONS

In the unlikely event of a contra-action occurring during or after skin camouflage application, you need to know how to deal with it so there's as little reaction as possible and you avoid aggravating the skin. The main contra-action to watch out for during this service is an allergic reaction.

ALLERGIC REACTIONS

This is caused by a reaction to the product itself or an ingredient in the product(s) and can be identified as redness and warmth in the skin. If an allergic reaction occurs, stop the treatment immediately, remove the make-up and apply a cold compress to the area to reduce the heat and bring down any erythema. Apply a calamine mask made with a rose water toner to cool and soothe the skin. Advise your client to continue to apply cool compresses over the next 24 hours, by which time the reaction should have gone. Recommend they seek GP assistance if it hasn't.

END OF UNIT SUMMARY

Now you've reached the end of the unit, you should feel confident in the theory and practical aspects of all areas of skin camouflage. Use the checklist below to see if there are any areas you feel you need to recap before beginning the end of unit assessment:

- maintain safe and effective methods of working when providing skin camouflage
- consult, plan and prepare for skin camouflage
- carry out skin camouflage
- provide aftercare advice.

The beginnings of camouflage make-up to a tattoo

Using the questions below, test your knowledge of Unit B10 to see just how much information you've retained. These questions will help you revise what you've learnt in this chapter.

Turn to pages 421–422 for the answers.

1 Give the reasons why a client might book a skin camouflage treatment.

2 Explain what is meant by the term hypo-pigmentation.

3 What is vitiligo?

4 Why is lighting important in relation to skin camouflage?

5 As a guide, how long should skin camouflage services take?

6 Why is it important to ask your client to identify their area(s) of concern?

7 Explain why it's important to remain empathetic and reassuring when you're dealing with a client during skin camouflage services.

8 Why is it important to ensure your client's expectations are realistic and achievable?

9 Which contra-indications to skin camouflage require medical referral and why?

10 What skin camouflage products are available and how are they used?

11 Why is it important to use these products in a logical order?

12 What is it that makes the finished result waterproof?

13 How long should skin camouflage be left on the skin and why?

14 Why is it important to understand how different lighting can affect the appearance of skin camouflage?

15 Explain what titanium dioxide is and why it's used in skin camouflage.

16 Why is it important to ensure your client can recreate the same effects themselves before they leave the salon?

17 What aftercare advice should you give to all clients after skin camouflage services?

18 Why should you give your client product and skin care recommendations as well?

19 What contra-action might occur as a result of skin camouflage?

20 How should this contra-action be dealt with?

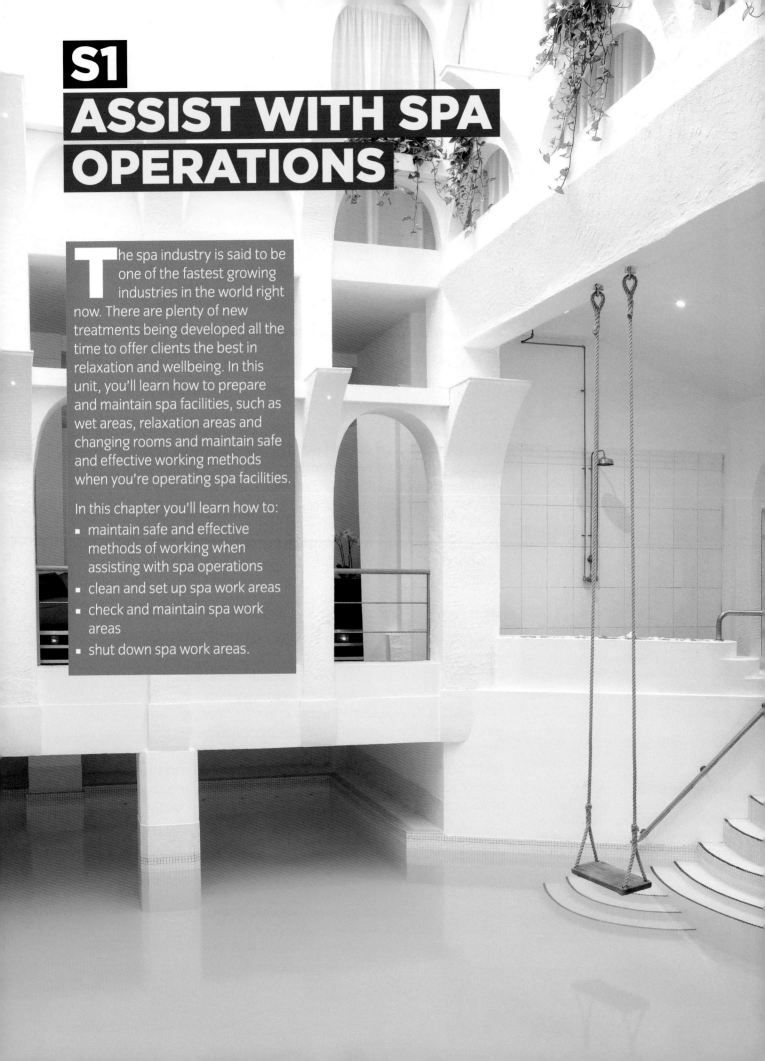

S1
ASSIST WITH SPA OPERATIONS

The spa industry is said to be one of the fastest growing industries in the world right now. There are plenty of new treatments being developed all the time to offer clients the best in relaxation and wellbeing. In this unit, you'll learn how to prepare and maintain spa facilities, such as wet areas, relaxation areas and changing rooms and maintain safe and effective working methods when you're operating spa facilities.

In this chapter you'll learn how to:

- maintain safe and effective methods of working when assisting with spa operations
- clean and set up spa work areas
- check and maintain spa work areas
- shut down spa work areas.

WHY DON'T YOU...

Refer to Unit G20 to refresh your memory of these Acts before continuing with this unit.

By-law

Local laws passed from a higher authority, which can vary from place to place.

HANDY HINTS

To find out more on your area's by-laws, contact your local HSE for more information.

WHY DON'T YOU...

Have a go at SmartScreen worksheet 2 to test your knowledge of the relevant health and safety legislation.

 SmartScreen S1 worksheet 2

Contact dermatitis

A skin condition caused by overexposure to an allergen over a prolonged period of time. This can result in irritation and inflammation and, in severe cases, cracking and weeping of the skin.

WHY DON'T YOU...

Refer to Unit B6 for more detailed information on contact dermatitis.

MAINTAIN SAFE AND EFFECTIVE METHODS OF WORKING WHEN ASSISTING WITH SPA OPERATIONS

As with all beauty treatments, it's important you understand and adhere to the relevant health and safety legislation throughout to ensure you perform a safe and enjoyable treatment for your client. The main legislation affecting spa operations is:

- Control of Substances Hazardous to Health (COSHH)
- Electricity at Work Regulations (EAWR)
- Reporting of Injuries, Diseases and Dangerous Occurrences Regulations (RIDDOR)
- Personal Protective Equipment (PPE)
- Provision and Use of Work Equipment Regulations (PUWER).

Each of these Acts is described fully in Unit G20 along with the other health and safety legislation.

As well as this legislation, there's also the Local Government Act 2003 (a recent update from the Local Government Miscellaneous Provisions Act 1982), which outlines the **by-laws** that you need to follow when you're operating spa work areas. As an overview, this Act requires any salon (and its employees) offering dry and wet heat treatments to be registered with the local Health and Safety Executive (HSE). The HSE sends an inspector to ensure the salon is following all by-laws and all relevant health and safety legislation before providing the business with a certificate of registration. Only then can the salon offer these treatments to clients.

BEFORE YOU BEGIN

Before you can invite clients to use your salon's spa facilities, it's important to check they're in safe working order and hygienic to reduce the risks of injury and cross-infection. Clean work surfaces with an appropriate disinfectant and use more heavy-duty industrial preparations if necessary. When you're using cleaning materials, make sure you wear the personal protective equipment (PPE) provided by your employer to protect your skin. This should include rubber gloves and an apron to prevent skin conditions, such as **contact dermatitis** and protect your uniform from damage and stains. You can also use a protective face mask so you don't breathe in any chemicals.

HANDY HINTS

When you're assisting with spa operations, it's important to use the skills you've learnt in the following units:

Unit G20 Ensure responsibility for actions to reduce risks to health and safety

Unit G18 Promote additional services or products to clients

Unit G8 Develop and maintain your effectiveness at work.

CLEANING SPA FACILITIES

Clean spa facilities at the start and end of every day to make sure they're hygienic. This prevents the build-up of bacteria, which can lead to mould, especially in wet areas.

You must also maintain this cleanliness throughout the working day. Your manager might set up a rota so that everyone helps out. This is a more effective use of everyone's time.

HANDY HINTS
Remember to maintain your posture at all times as cleaning can be strenuous work. Refer to Unit G20 to remind yourself of the correct posture so that you don't cause unnecessary injury to yourself.

WHY DON'T YOU...
Have a go at SmartScreen worksheet 1 to test your knowledge on maintaining the spa environment.

 SmartScreen S1 worksheet 1

Spa facilities must be cleaned twice a day.

When you're cleaning spa facilities, make sure that you dispose of all waste correctly. If you come across any hazardous waste, such as a cotton pad coated in blood, place it in the hazardous waste bin that the local authority will take away and **incinerate**.

Remember that if you come across any safety issues or difficulties when you're checking hygiene levels, you must report them to the relevant person immediately. Trying to deal with them yourself could make matters worse, or you could injure yourself and others.

Incinerate
Burn to ashes.

WHY DON'T YOU...
Refer to Unit G20 to remind yourself of the COSHH regulations regarding waste disposal and storage of chemicals used to maintain and clean spa facilities.

CONTRA-INDICATIONS TO HEAT TREATMENTS

The following is a list of contra-indications to heat treatments:

- High or low blood pressure: risk of fainting.
- History of thrombosis: risk of blood clotting.
- Respiratory disorders, such as asthma or bronchitis: risk of making the condition worse.
- Systemic disorders, such as epilepsy or diabetes: risk of seizures. A lack of **tactile sensation** could allow the hot water to scald the skin.
- Immediately after a heavy meal: risk of feeling nauseous.
- After alcohol consumption: risk of fainting or nausea.
- Severe skin conditions, such as psoriasis or eczema: risk of making the condition worse.
- Skin diseases: risk of cross-infection.
- Pregnancy: could cause premature labour (worse case scenario).

Tactile sensation
The sensation produced by pressure receptors in the skin.

HANDY HINTS
More information on skin diseases and conditions can be found in the anatomy and physiology chapter.

WHY DON'T YOU...
Refer to SmartScreen handout 2 for more details on the effects of spa therapy.

 SmartScreen S1 handout 2

Sebaceous gland
This gland is attached to the hair follicle in the skin and produces sebum, which is the skin's own natural moisture.

Sudoriferous gland
Sweat gland.

GENERAL EFFECTS OF HEAT TREATMENTS

The following is a list of general effects on the body of both dry and wet heat treatments:

- stimulates blood circulation
- stimulates lymphatic flow
- produces erythema
- disperses lactic acid
- eases tension in the muscles
- promotes a feeling of wellbeing
- decreases blood pressure
- stimulates **sebaceous** and **sudoriferous glands**.

There are also potential contra-actions to heat treatments and these are described later in the unit. To reduce the risk of clients feeling faint, nauseous or dizzy, make sure they drink plenty of water at regular intervals during heat treatments so their bodies remain hydrated. They should also take cool showers at regular intervals.

CLEAN AND SET UP SPA WORK AREAS

WHY DON'T YOU...
Work through SmartScreen worksheet 4 to develop more knowledge of waterborne diseases.

 SmartScreen S1 worksheet 4

It's important to check that the spa work areas and facilities are cleaned and set up according to salon policies and the manufacturer's instructions. Your job might be to maintain:

- wet areas
- treatment areas
- changing rooms
- relaxation areas
- service areas.

WET AREAS

Wet areas include saunas, steam rooms/baths and spa pools. These areas need specific maintenance to prevent the build-up of mould which can lead to cross-infection and other conditions, such as **Legionnaires' disease**. It's also important you're aware of the manufacturer's instructions regarding the recommended number of clients for each facility.

Legionnaires' disease
A type of pneumonia caused by the inhalation of water droplets contaminated with the Legionella pneumophila bacterium. This is a potentially fatal disease but is easy to prevent by maintaining high standards of hygiene in wet areas. Legionnaires' disease can be found in wet areas with stagnant water. Air conditioners and humidifiers also carry the risk of this disease. For more information, read the HSE information handbook.

SAUNAS

Clients must sit on towels while in the sauna.

Saunas are usually made of timber. The dry heat can reach temperatures between 70 and 110°C and the humidity levels stop the skin from burning. To reach the right temperature, switch the sauna on about 30 minutes before use to make sure the heat penetrates all the surfaces evenly. When you've set the temperature, check all air vents are open and free from obstruction. The heater and rocks get very hot, so make sure you tell your clients not to touch them or sit too close. Usually, guards are fitted around the heating elements to offer some protection. Clients can pour water over the rocks to create a blast of steam to help with perspiration.

It's important you make sure your clients are aware of the safety requirements so they enjoy the treatment to its fullest:

- Clients should wear appropriate swimwear.
- Place a clean towel on the bench to maintain hygiene. However, some clients sit on their own towel, which they take in and out with them.
- Clients should start by sitting on the lower benches to acclimatise before moving up to the higher benches.
- Clients shouldn't stay in the sauna for more than ten minutes at a time before taking a warm shower.
- If clients want to stay in the sauna for longer, they should have a warm shower every 5–10 minutes and shouldn't stay in the sauna for more than 30 minutes in total as this could lead to dizziness, fainting and nausea.
- Many clients like to stay in the sauna for longer than is necessary. This is why you must tell your clients about the safety measures and display them on the wall as a reminder. You could check on your client at regular intervals to see if they have any reaction to the heat.

WHY DON'T YOU...
Read through SmartScreen handout 16 for more information on sauna treatments.

SmartScreen S1 handout 16

Effects of dry heat

Dry heat produces the following effects on the skin and body:

- cleanses the skin
- prepares the body for further treatment
- relaxes the body
- relaxes the pores
- eases aches and pains
- slightly lowers blood pressure.

Cleaning a sauna

Start by vacuuming the floor to pick up dust and hair, then use a detergent to mop up stains and water spillages. Wash the benches with a mild detergent and wipe away any soapy residue. Avoid using harsh chemicals as they can damage the timber. Wash the rocks when they're cool with a non-abrasive cloth.

STEAM ROOM/BATH

WHY DON'T YOU...
Read through SmartScreen handout 14 for more information on maintaining spa hygiene.

SmartScreen S1 handout 14

Your clients can enjoy the steam room without using towels.

A steam room is usually made of ceramic tiles, whereas a steam bath is made of fibreglass; both use moist heat to warm the skin and body. There's no difference between a steam room and bath except that a steam room can hold a number of clients, whereas a steam bath is for one person only. As both use moist heat, the temperature is much lower than a sauna, usually between 45–55°C, and the humidity much higher to encourage perspiration. A client shouldn't stay in the steam room/bath for longer than 15–20 minutes to reduce the risks of fainting, dizziness and nausea.

Steam bath

When you're preparing a steam bath, fill the tank with enough water to cover the heating element and switch it on at the mains. Set the temperature and turn the timer to 30 minutes to make sure the bath is properly heated before use.

It's important that you make sure your clients are aware of the safety requirements so that they enjoy the treatment to its fullest:

- Clients should wear appropriate swimwear, or wrap themselves in a towel. Recommend they protect their back with a towel as this is where the steam rises and it can scald the lower back quite easily.
- Place a clean towel on the bench, not only to maintain hygiene but also to stop the skin from scalding.
- To maintain hygiene, suggest your clients wear flip flops into the steam bath.
- When your client is comfortable, close the steam bath door and place two small towels around the opening at the top to stop any heat from escaping.

Steam room

The safety requirements for a steam room are fairly similar to those for a steam bath except you don't need to put any towels on the floor. As the steam room can be used by several people at a time, you don't have to put any towels around the openings. Just remind your clients to close the door on entering and leaving to stop any heat from escaping.

Effects of moist heat

Moist heat produces the following effects on the skin and body:

- softens the skin
- **desquamation**
- stimulates sebaceous and sudoriferous glands
- decreases blood pressure
- increases heart rate due to stimulation of blood circulation
- increases lymphatic flow.

Cleaning the steam bath/room

Clean the steam bath/room with an appropriate mild detergent to maintain hygiene levels. Make sure the steam bath has cooled down and wipe away any soapy residue. Leave the door open to let all surfaces dry properly. Leave the water tank to cool before you empty it and wash it out. If it's not cleaned after each use, mould will form, which could lead to cross-infection and disease.

WHY DON'T YOU...
Read through SmartScreen handout 16 for more information on steam treatments.

SmartScreen S1 handout 16

Desquamation
The skin's own natural exfoliation process.

Hydrotherapy

External use of water to treat disease or illness.

Water erosion

Gradual wearing away of material caused by the action of water.

Scaling

The build-up of limescale and bacteria on a surface caused by water.

pH

The level of acidity and alkalinity measured on the pH scale, which goes from 0–14 with 7 being neutral: 0–6.9 is a low pH and is acid; 7.1–14 is a high pH and is alkaline. The ideal water pH is anywhere between 7.2 and 7.8.

Water hardness

The level of calcium present in the water, which, if high, can cause corrosion, staining and scaling.

WHY DON'T YOU...

Refer to SmartScreen handout 15 for more information on water testing.

 SmartScreen S1 handout 15

HANDY HINTS

Failure to produce accurate or up-to-date maintenance records could result in a fine or the salon could lose its licence.

SPA POOL

Clients can use spa pools before or after a sauna or steam to stimulate blood and lymphatic circulation and produce a **hydrotherapy** effect on the body. The temperature of a spa pool is usually between 36–40°C. Use chemical disinfectants, such as sodium and calcium hypochlorite, to clean the water and minimise **water erosion**, **scaling** and staining. Water in the pool is tested for the following:

- **pH** (alkalinity/acidity)
- **water hardness** (calcium content)
- temperature.

Collectively, these measurements are known as the Langlier Index or the Palintest Balanced Water Index. Water samples are taken and tested to see if they're at acceptable operating levels. The amount of disinfectant you should use depends on how often the spa pool is used and the results of the water tests. The pH and chlorine levels must also be controlled and recorded. Your local authority could ask to see these records and check they're accurate and up to date. If you use the wrong amount of chemicals, you could affect a client's breathing, cause an allergic skin reaction and affect the eyes. You should also check water levels on a regular basis to prevent any flooding.

If your client wants to use the spa pool, make them aware of the following safety requirements:

- Clients should wear appropriate swimwear.
- Clients should not stay in the spa pool for longer than 15–20 minutes because of the risk of fainting or nausea.
- Shower prior to entering the spa pool.
- Shower after leaving the spa pool.

Make sure your clients know how long they can stay in the spa pool.

Effects of the spa pool

The following effects are produced when clients use the spa pool:

- increases blood flow
- relieves pain
- eases muscle tension
- increases metabolism
- prepares the body for further treatment.

ACTIVITY

Research the benefits of newer spa developments, such as the Rasul, Turkish Hammam, dry flotation tank and cryotherapy to see how they compare with traditional facilities.

HANDY HINTS

With more and more developments in the spa industry, there are other dry and wet heat treatments available that will enhance any spa experience.

WHY DON'T YOU...
Read through SmartScreen handout 17 for more information on hydrotherapy treatments.

 SmartScreen S1 handout 17

Ask the senior therapist how to clean and maintain the cryotherapy chamber.

Aroma-stone
A small electrical heated appliance used to warm essential oils so they're dispersed into the air.

TREATMENT AREAS

Make sure you prepare all treatment areas at the start of each day so that the therapists don't fall behind on their treatments. You can make this much easier by preparing each treatment room at the end of the day for the very first treatment the next morning. Clean each area with a vacuum cleaner to remove any dirt and dust. Wash the floors with a detergent suitable for each type of flooring, for example, laminate and wooden floors need a much milder detergent than tiles or lino.

Sterilise or disinfect all implements and tools and place any hazardous waste in the appropriate bins ready for collection. Put any laundry in laundry bags ready for washing the following morning or collecting.

Clean all areas between treatments to make sure they stay hygienic and presentable. Change the towels for each new client to avoid the risk of cross-infection, and re-sterilise or disinfect implements and work surfaces using the appropriate methods.

When you've finished preparing the treatment areas, check the salon's working temperature and adjust the heat or air conditioning so that your clients don't get too hot or too cold. Make sure you have additional pillows and blankets for extra warmth and comfort and dim the lighting. Play calming music in the background, light some scented candles or place a few drops of essential oil in an oil burner or **aroma-stone**. All of these factors will help you to create a relaxing and soothing atmosphere for your client when they enter the treatment area.

Check products are all stocked up and replenish or re-order anything you're short of.

A clean and tidy treatment room

CHANGING ROOMS

Most spas offer changing rooms and lockers for clients to store their personal belongings. This stops the treatment areas getting cluttered and puts responsibility for their belongings onto the client. Clean the changing rooms in the same way as other areas and wash down with an appropriate detergent to maintain hygiene standards and avoid the risk of cross-infection. Clients use changing rooms to change into a more comfortable robe and slippers before their treatment. This prevents the risk of staining or damaging your client's own clothing and encourages them to relax before the treatment has even begun. Some changing rooms have a seated area with mirrors and hair dryers, some even offer body lotions, hand lotions, bags for wet wear, and a shower area with shampoos and shower gels.

It's important to clean the changing rooms too.

ROBES AND SLIPPERS

If your spa or salon has changing rooms and provides clients with robes and slippers, it could be your responsibility to keep these items stocked up. For example, your job might be to check each locker has a clean robe and pair of slippers at the start and end of each day and replace these items when a client has left.

Most spas provide disposable slippers that are put in the bin when each client leaves. This shows your clients you're conscious about hygiene. Place a laundry basket in the changing rooms for clients to put their dirty robes into.

RELAXATION AREAS

Many spas also offer relaxation areas for clients to use after they've had a treatment. Relaxation areas have soft lighting and calming music to help clients relax and improve their whole experience. Clients can relax on reclining couches with overhead lights and read any promotional literature or magazines left in the room. Encourage clients to drink plenty of water or herbal teas to treat the body from within as well as the skin. Therapists take clients to the relaxation area between treatments so they're away from the hustle and bustle of the main areas. This also allows the therapist to prepare themselves and the treatment area for the next client/treatment.

Show your clients to the relaxation area.

SERVICE AREAS

This usually refers to the reception and waiting areas where clients can find retail stands and product displays. These areas should be maintained on a daily basis and treated in the same way as any treatment area. Vacuum the floors to stop the build-up of dirt, debris and dust, which can lead to and aggravate allergies. Clean product displays and update them weekly to maintain interest in the products. If products are running low, tell the relevant person so they can re-order them.

A well-maintained reception area could encourage a potential client to pay your salon a visit.

CHECK AND MAINTAIN SPA WORK AREAS

While it's important to provide clear instructions to clients on how to use dry and wet heat treatment areas, it's also important to provide clear reminders so they don't forget. Your salon should display posters throughout the spa areas to make sure clients know exactly how to use each area. This will allow them to get the best out of their treatments and reduce the risk of cross-infection, injury or illness.

Remember to check water and air temperatures regularly according to the manufacturer's instructions and report any discrepancies to the responsible person. Refer to the beginning of the unit to remind yourself how to do this.

POSSIBLE CONTRA-ACTIONS TO HEAT TREATMENTS

The following contra-actions can occur during or after a heat treatment if a client doesn't follow the safety precautions. You need to be aware of the symptoms and how to deal with them.

THE TREATMENT DURATION IS TOO LONG

This can cause a decrease in blood pressure and dehydration. When you are dehydrated, cells can absorb fluid from other organs in the body, which might cause your client to feel faint. If this occurs, encourage them to rest and drink plenty of water to restore hydration levels before you let them leave the salon.

DRY HEAT APPLICATION – RELATIVE HUMIDITY TOO LOW

If the humidity is too low in the sauna, a client could become severely dehydrated or experience breathing difficulties due to the lack of moisture in the air. As the air temperature is higher than normal, this might make the breathing problems worse. If this happens, advise your client to drink plenty of water to restore hydration levels and tell them to lie down with their legs raised to avoid fainting. If necessary, refer them to their GP.

FAINTING

This occurs when blood flow to the brain is significantly reduced and the brain isn't getting enough oxygen. A person might experience dizziness, sweating and feeling 'odd' before they faint. If a client complains of these symptoms when they're having a dry or wet heat treatment, stop immediately, offer them a drink of water and stay with them until they feel better.

NAUSEA

This term is used to describe a feeling of sickness and can be accompanied by light-headedness and an increase in body or skin temperature. If a client complains of these symptoms during a dry or wet heat treatment, stop immediately and take them to a quiet area, offer them some water and stay with them until the symptoms pass.

HEADACHES

There are a number of causes for headaches, such as inflammation of the sinuses, straining of the eyes, dehydration and hunger. If a client experiences a headache during a dry or wet heat treatment, stop immediately and offer them some water. Don't offer them pain relief, such as paracetamol or ibuprofen as they could be allergic to it. If the headache doesn't go away, advise them to go home and get plenty of rest and water over the next 24 hours and seek GP advice if symptoms get worse.

CRAMP

Cramp is caused by excessive perspiration and can be relieved by stretching the muscle and gently massaging the affected area(s). Encourage your client to drink plenty of water over the next 24 hours to rehydrate the body.

WHY DON'T YOU...
Read through SmartScreen handout 21 for appropriate aftercare advice following spa therapy.

SmartScreen S1 handout 21

WHY DON'T YOU...
Have a go at SmartScreen worksheet 3 to test your knowledge on recommended spa therapy times.

SmartScreen S1 worksheet 3

WHY DON'T YOU...
Have a go at SmartScreen worksheet 5 to test your knowledge on safe working temperatures for spa facilities.

 SmartScreen S1 worksheet 5

SCALDING/BURNING OF THE SKIN

A client can burn their skin if the air is hot or they touch a hot component, such as the heater or rocks in a sauna or the water tank in a steam bath/room. If this happens, take your client out of the sauna or steam bath/room immediately and apply a cold compress to the burn for several minutes and repeat if necessary. When the skin is cool, apply a dry dressing to prevent any infection and tell your client to remove the dressing after three days to allow the skin to heal. If they get any blisters, tell your client to leave them alone as this is the skin's way of healing itself. If the burn hasn't improved in three days, advise them to seek medical assistance.

NOSEBLEED

This is quite rare and is caused by irritation of the mucous membranes in the nose or the effects of high temperature on the circulatory system. Take your client out of the treatment area and place a towel on their knee. Tell them to tilt their head forwards and gently pinch the bridge of their nose for ten minutes, by which time the bleeding should have slowed or stopped. NEVER tell a client to tilt their head back as this can result in choking. If the bleeding hasn't stopped after 30 minutes, seek medical assistance.

ALLERGIC REACTIONS TO CHEMICALS IN SPA POOLS

This is usually caused by high temperatures mixed with the effects of the chemicals. Tell your client to leave the spa pool and take a cool shower to reduce skin temperature. Recommend they avoid shower gels and body creams which can make the reaction worse. If the reaction hasn't gone down after 24 hours, advise them to see their GP.

SHUT DOWN SPA WORK AREAS

WHY DON'T YOU...
Read through SmartScreen handout 19 for more information on assisting with the shutdown of spa treatment areas and facilities.

 SmartScreen S1 handout 19

At the end of the working day, turn off spa facilities correctly otherwise they could get damaged. Make sure you follow the salon's and the manufacturer's instructions for health and safety reasons:

- Check all electrical equipment and facilities are switched off before cleaning to avoid electric shocks.
- Test that the water is clean, check the chemical concentrations and record the results appropriately.
- Make sure the floors are clean and free from water, dirt, debris and dust.
- Wash all tools and implements in warm soapy water before you disinfect or sterilise them.

PREPARING FOR THE FOLLOWING DAY

It's important to make sure that all work areas are prepared for the following day:

- Clean all surfaces in the sauna and steam baths/rooms with an appropriate detergent after you've switched them off at the mains.
- Wash sauna rocks when they're cool completely and empty the water bucket before washing that as well.
- Prepare the treatment rooms for the first treatment of the following day.
- Check all lockers in the changing rooms have a clean bath robe and a new pair of slippers.
- Check relaxation areas for used cups and wipe down all chairs and loungers with an appropriate disinfectant.
- Make sure all candles, oil burners and incense sticks are put out to reduce the risk of fire.
- Clean all tables in the service areas with an appropriate disinfectant to prevent staining.
- Replenish all towels on the treatment couches.

Clients are more likely to relax if all spa areas are cleaned properly.

- Check all resources are stocked up for the treatments booked for the following day.

When you've cleaned, re-stocked and prepared all the areas for the following day, check that all the facilities have been turned off and tell whoever is responsible for locking up as they might want to double check everything before they close the salon or spa.

END OF UNIT SUMMARY

Now you've reached the end of the unit, you should feel confident in the theory and practical aspects of assisting with spa operations. Use the checklist below to see if there are any areas you feel you need to recap before beginning the end of unit assessment:

- maintain safe and effective methods of working when assisting with spa operations
- clean and set up spa work areas
- check and maintain spa work areas
- shut down spa work areas.

Using the questions below, test your knowledge of Unit S1 to see just how much information you've retained. These questions will help you revise what you've learnt in this chapter.

Turn to pages 422–423 for the answers.

1 Why is it important to maintain personal hygiene, protection and appearance when you're assisting with spa operations?

2 List the personal protective equipment that you should wear when you're cleaning spa facilities.

3 How can you make sure your working methods reduce the risk of cross-infection and minimise the risk of harm or injury?

4 Explain why it's important to maintain the correct posture when you're assisting with spa operations.

5 Why should you report any problems or difficulties to the responsible person?

6 Why is it important to check you're using the correct cleaning materials for specific spa facilities?

7 Explain why tools and equipment must be sterilised or disinfected before they're used.

8 Why should you clean spa facilities and work areas at regular intervals?

9 How can you create and maintain the correct environmental conditions for your client?

10 Why is it important to explain all safety requirements and put them on display?

11 What are the general effects of dry and wet heat treatments?

12 What are the possible contra-actions to dry and wet heat treatments?

13 What test is used to check the water's pH, hardness and temperature in a spa pool?

14 Why is it important to make sure these tests are recorded and kept up to date?

15 How would you deal with any chemical concentration problems or temperature fluctuations?

16 Explain why clients shouldn't be left unattended for too long during dry and wet heat treatments?

17 Why is it important to check all electrical equipment and facilities are switched off at the mains before you clean at the end of the day?

18 Why should you make sure the responsible person is happy with how you've shut down the equipment and facilities?

19 Give **three** examples of dry or wet heat treatments.

20 What is Legionnaires' disease and how can you catch it?

WHY DON'T YOU...
Test your knowledge further by logging into SmartScreen and completing the sample GOLA revision questions.

TEST YOUR KNOWLEDGE ANSWERS

Anatomy and physiology

1 How many layers make up the epidermis and what are their names?

Five: stratum corneum (horny layer)

stratum lucidum (clear layer)

stratum granulosum (granular layer)

stratum spinosum (prickle cell layer)

stratum germinativum (basal layer).

2 What does mitosis mean?

Mitosis is the division of cells, which occurs in the stratum germinativum.

3 Explain the term keratinisation.

The hardening of a cell caused by the production of a protein called keratin and the degeneration of its nucleus.

4 How many layers make up the nail plate?

There are hundreds of layers packed together in three layers that make up the nail plate.

5 What is the function of the matrix?

To produce new cells by cell mitosis.

6 Describe the hair growth cycle.

Anagen: early anagen and anagen are known as the active stages because the follicle is forming or is fully formed and the cells stay attached to the base of the follicle. Cell mitosis occurs in this stage, continuously producing new cells and allowing the hair to grow up towards the skin's surface. The follicle grows down towards the dermis and forms the dermal papilla, which provides nourishment for the hair to grow.

Catagen: also known as the transitional stage because the hair begins to detach from the life-giving dermal papilla and causes the follicle to disintegrate. The hair rises towards the skin's surface while it's still attached to the follicle wall.

Telogen: the final stage of the hair growth cycle, known as the resting stage as the hair is dead. The dermal papilla has withdrawn completely from the disintegrated follicle and will only be stimulated again at the start of a new hair growth cycle. It's at this point the hair is shed from the follicle and the cycle can begin again.

7 What is the bulk of the ear called?

The pinna.

8 What fibres are found in muscles?

Actin and myosin.

9 What is skeletal muscle made up of?

Skeletal muscle is made up of 75 per cent water, 5 per cent inorganic substances and 20 per cent muscle forming cells called myoblasts.

10 What are the action and location of the frontalis muscle?

This is located on the forehead and its action is to raise the brows.

11 What are the action and location of the sternocleidomastoid muscle?

The sternocleidomastoid is located at the side of the neck extending from below the ear to the sternum. Its action is to pull the head down towards the chest and extend it back, as well as moving it from side to side.

12 What are the action and location of the thenar eminence muscle?

This is located at the base of the thumb and controls the thumb's movement.

13 What are the action and location of the soleus muscle?

The soleus is located beneath the gastrocnemius muscle at the back of the lower leg, and its action is to plantar flex the foot.

14 What is the difference between cancellous and compact bone tissue?

Cancellous bone tissue is soft and spongy, whereas compact bone tissue is hard and solid.

15 Where are the carpals and what are their individual names?

The carpal bones form the wrist and their individual names are:

- scaphoid
- capitate
- lunate
- pisiform
- trapezium
- trapezoid
- triquetral
- hamate.

16 How many discs make up the cervical vertebrae?
Seven.

17 Is blood a two-way or one-way network?
Blood is a two-way network.

18 What are erythrocytes?
Erythrocytes are red blood cells.

19 Where would you find the parotid lymph nodes?
The parotid lymph nodes are located just in front of the ear.

20 What is the function of the lymphatic system?
The function of the lymphatic system is to eliminate waste and toxins from the body by filtering the blood.

G20 Ensure responsibility for actions to reduce risks to Health and safety

1 Identify what is meant by the terms hazard, risk and control.
Hazard: something with the potential to cause harm.
Risk: the likelihood of that hazard's potential being realised.
Control: the steps taken to reduce or eliminate the risk.

2 Give **one** example of a low-risk hazard.
One of the following: trailing wires; liquid next to electrical equipment; failed light bulb.

3 Give **one** example of a high-risk hazard.
One of the following: frayed wires; flammable liquids and chemicals; heavy boxes.

4 State your obligations under HASAWA 1974.
To maintain a safe working environment.

5 What is the purpose of a risk assessment?
To identify and evaluate the possible risks in the salon before taking steps to reduce or eliminate them.

6 What are your obligations under COSHH 2002?
To ensure all chemicals and hazardous substances are stored, handled, used and disposed of safely.

7 What does SHUD stand for?
Storage; Handling; Usage; Disposal.

8 List the hazard symbols and state what they mean.
Irritant: this symbol means a substance is hazardous and could be dangerous if not used correctly. Ensure you wear PPE when you're using such substances as they're often irritants. They aren't necessarily corrosive but could cause an immune response in the body that can result in itching, burning, redness and swelling.
Flammable: this symbol means a substance can catch fire quite easily when exposed to high temperatures. Keep it stored in a cool, dry cupboard away from direct sunlight.
Explosive: this symbol means a substance has the potential to be explosive when exposed to shock, pressure or high temperature. It should be stored in a dry cupboard at normal room temperature and away from direct sunlight.
Oxidising: this symbol means that the substance itself might not be combustible but can cause other materials to combust by providing them with oxygen. Store these types of chemical separately from other chemicals to make sure there's no reaction between them.
Toxic: these types of substance could be potentially lethal if they enter the body as they're poisonous. The ways in which a substance can enter the body are through inhalation, absorption and ingestion. Ensure you wear gloves, an apron and a mask at all times when you're dealing with these chemicals.
Corrosive: this substance is extremely dangerous and will attack living tissue, including the skin and eyes. Ensure you wear appropriate gloves, an apron and a mask when you're dealing with these chemicals.

9 List the types of PPE your employer should provide and when you should wear them.
Wear gloves when you're performing manual extractions to prevent cross-infection; wear an apron when you're waxing to protect your uniform; wear closed-toe, flat shoes to protect your feet; and wear a suitable uniform to make sure you're following the correct dress code.

10 How often should a PAT test be performed and who should do it?
Every 12 months by a qualified electrician to ensure the equipment is in working order.

11 List **five** key factors to follow under the DPA. Five of the following:

- Data should only be used for the specific purposes for which it was collected.
- Data must not be disclosed to other parties without the consent of the individual, unless there's legislation or other overriding legitimate reasons to share the information (for example, the prevention or detection of crime). It's an offence for other parties to obtain this personal data without authorisation.
- Individuals have a right of access to the information held about them, subject to certain exceptions (for example, information held for the prevention or detection of crime).
- Personal information shouldn't be kept for longer than is necessary and must be kept up to date.
- Personal information shouldn't be sent outside the European Economic Area unless the individual has consented or adequate protection is in place.
- Businesses holding personal information are required to have adequate security measures in place. These include technical measures (such as firewalls) and organisational measures (such as staff training).
- Individuals have the right to have factually incorrect information corrected (note: this doesn't extend to matters of opinion).

12 What type of fire extinguisher would you use on a computer fire?

One with a blue label as it contains powder.

13 When would you use a fire blanket?

If a person or their clothing caught fire, or on chip pan fires.

14 What are the **four** key factors to consider when you're creating the ideal salon environment?

Lighting, ventilation, heating and general comfort.

15 What is the correct working temperature for a salon?

16–18°C.

16 What is considered to be good personal presentation?

Wear your hair off your face, a clean, pressed uniform and closed-toe flat shoes. Apply subtle day make-up to enhance your natural features, and make sure you've got short, manicured and clean nails. Make sure you (and your breath) smell clean.

17 What is the difference between pathogenic and non-pathogenic bacteria?

Pathogenic bacteria cause disease; non-pathogenic bacteria are harmless.

18 Explain how an autoclave sterilises metal implements.

With moist heat, the autoclave reaches an optimum temperature of 120°C.

19 How long should you leave small metal implements in the glass bead steriliser?

30 seconds.

20 What is the difference between sterilisation and disinfection?

Sterilisation destroys all bacteria; disinfection only destroys some and inhibits the growth of others.

G18 Promote additional services or products to clients

1 Why is it important to make sure your knowledge of the services and products your salon offers is always up to date?

So that you're up to date with current and emerging industry trends, and so you know the recommendations you provide are accurate.

2 What can you do if you're unsure about a new service or product?

Ask a colleague who knows about it so they can help you to remember.

3 Explain the term 'planting the seed'.

Letting your client know what is going to benefit them when you're proposing a treatment plan so they'll be thinking about it throughout the treatment.

4 How can you identify opportunities to recommend additional services or products?

By always being alert and listening to your client's needs and expectations.

5 What is meant by the term 'link-selling'?

The recommendation of products and/or services to meet a client's needs and expectations.

6 Give **one** example of link-selling.

Recommending a back massage to a client who has had a facial, because you've identified tension in the neck and shoulders.

7 How should you adapt your communication methods when you're providing recommendations?

You should ensure that you don't draw attention to yourself as this will make your client feel uncomfortable. If you're speaking to a client during a relaxing treatment, lower the tone of your voice so you don't startle them.

8 Explain why it's important to provide accurate information when you're recommending services and products.

So your client knows they can trust your recommendations.

9 Why is it important to encourage your client to ask questions regarding the recommendations you've made?

Because they might not fully understand the reasons why you're recommending a service or product, and might want to find out more.

10 What is meant by the term 'up-selling'?

Recommending a product or service that isn't directly linked to a client's needs and expectations but you think will enhance their salon or home experience.

11 Explain the difference between a hard sell and a recommendation.

A hard sell occurs because a client feels pressured into buying a product or service they aren't really interested in. A recommendation informs your client of a product or service that will enhance their experience.

12 What action should you take when your client shows no interest in the recommendations you're making?

You should say to your client that if they change their mind, they know where to find you for further details and then close the discussion.

13 If your client is interested, how can you move the situation forward to close the sale?

By providing further information, such as key ingredients and the benefits they provide, then take your client to the reception area to make their purchases.

14 If it's not your responsibility to close sales, how can you make sure this happens?

Take your client to the reception area and invite them to take a seat while the receptionist gets their purchases ready. Remember to tell the receptionist everything your client needs to pay for.

15 Why is it important to refer your client to other therapists when your knowledge of a particular service or product is limited?

So they can obtain all the information they need before making a decision.

16 Explain how a client's use of additional services or products will benefit the salon.

If a client chooses to buy additional products or services, the salon's profit margins will increase, the therapist will make a commission and both parties will secure another client to add to the client base.

17 What **seven** factors influence a client's decision to buy into a service or product?

- cost
- time
- your experiences
- smell
- sight
- texture
- visualisation.

18 Why is it important to ensure the information you give is balanced and to the point?

Because if you waffle or talk too much, your client might stop listening to you and lose interest.

19 How can you overcome any nervousness when you're recommending additional services or products?

By practising and role playing with your colleagues.

20 Why is it important for you always to provide recommendations to your clients?

Because not providing recommendations could lose you a client and they might take their money elsewhere.

G8 Develop and maintain your effectiveness at work

1 Why is it important to understand your contract?

So you're aware of your role and responsibilities, the limits of your authority, who to approach with certain problems and questions, and when to ask for assistance.

2 Why is it important to understand the roles and responsibilities of your colleagues as well as your own?

So you know who to approach when you need assistance with something.

3 Explain why it's important to understand your own strengths and weaknesses.

So you can enhance your existing skills and build on your confidence and abilities if you have any weaknesses.

4 Why is it important to agree to the targets your manager has set?

So you both understand and agree on what you need to achieve.

5 Why is it important to ask for additional support if you feel your targets aren't achievable or you're worried about not reaching them?

To ensure you can get the additional support you need rather than getting into further problems.

6 What does CPD mean and why is it important?

Continuous professional development. It's important because it allows you to keep ahead of current and emerging industry trends.

7 What does NOS mean and where can you find out more about them?

National occupational standards. You can find out more about these by accessing **www.habia.org**.

8 Why is it important to understand NOS?

So you know the guidelines on how to perform each treatment effectively and to the right standard required by a beauty therapist.

9 What is Habia?

The Hair and Beauty Industry Authority.

10 What steps can you take to ensure you're up to date with current and emerging trends?

Read trade journals, attend training courses and exhibitions and look at what competitors are offering.

11 What is a target?

A long-term goal to work towards.

12 What is an objective and how is it identified?

A short-term goal that helps you achieve your long-term target. Objectives are identified as being SMART – Specific, Measurable, Achievable, Realistic and Time bound.

13 How long do probationary periods tend to last for beauty therapists and why?

Three months. This is usually the length of time it takes for you to build up a client base.

14 Why should incentives be put in place when you're agreeing targets?

To give you something to work towards and give you motivation to reach your targets.

15 What is an appraisal?

A meeting between you and your manager to determine how well you're performing in your job and identify any strengths and weaknesses.

16 What is a personal development plan?

This is something that allows you to identify your weaknesses and areas for development. It can be updated regularly to make sure you're always developing and building on your skills.

17 Why is it important to put personal differences to one side when you're at work?

To maintain a happy working atmosphere and avoid tension between the team.

18 Why is it important to resolve issues right away with the appropriate person?

So that problems are faced and they don't get blown out of proportion. Also to make sure feelings are dealt with and they don't fester.

19 Explain why you need to be aware of and understand your salon's appeal and grievance procedures.

So you know where you stand in certain situations. If you feel you're being bullied or discriminated against, you know the right way to deal with it.

20 How can you ensure you're an effective team player?

By understanding your role and responsibilities as well as your team's.

B4 Provide facial skin care treatment

1 Why is it important to create the right environment for a facial?

To ensure your client feels comfortable and can relax and enjoy the treatment.

2 What health and safety measures do you need to follow?

- COSHH – Control of Substances Hazardous to Health
- EAWR – Electricity at Work Regulations
- PUWER – Provision and Use of Work Equipment Regulations.

3 How do you sterilise your metal implements?

Wash in warm soapy water and place them in a glass bead steriliser for 30–60 seconds or in the autoclave for 30 minutes.

4 Explain why you need to disinfect all non-metal and disposable implements and work surfaces.

To ensure they're clean and ready for use and to reduce the risk of cross-infection.

5 Why is it important to establish your client's current skin care routine?

So you know what your client is doing at home and help you give the best home care recommendations to improve and build on their home regimes.

6 Describe **three** contra-indications to a facial that require medical referral and explain why. Three of the following:

- bacterial infections, such as impetigo, conjunctivitis and boils: risk of cross-infection and further skin damage
- viral infections, such as herpes simplex and warts: risk of cross-infection
- fungal infections, such as ringworm: risk of cross-infection
- parasitic infections, such as scabies and pediculosis: risk of cross-infection
- systemic medical conditions: risk of injury and skin damage

- severe skin conditions, such as inflamed psoriasis: risk of making the condition worse
- acne: risk of cross-infection and risk of a skin reaction
- eye infections: risk of cross-infection.

7 Explain how you would prepare your client for a facial treatment.

Ask them to remove their top and shoes and ask them to move their bra straps under their arms to expose their shoulders and décolleté. Explain how they should lie on the couch and check they're covered with towels and blankets. Wrap their hair in a towel to protect it.

8 What is the difference between a superficial and deep cleanse?

A superficial cleanse prepares the skin for analysis and removes any dirt from the skin. A deep cleanse prepares the skin for further treatment by removing all make-up, dirt and grime from the skin and leaving it clear.

9 Why is it important to perform a skin analysis and what might the consequences be if you don't do this?

So you know your client's skin type and condition and what products to use to improve and enhance this. If you don't perform a skin analysis, you might use the wrong products, which could lead to an allergic reaction. It might also exacerbate existing skin conditions such as dryness.

10 Why should you recommend your clients exfoliate?

To remove the build-up of dead skin cells and blockages. This will result in a brighter complexion with a smooth, even texture.

11 What are the benefits of skin warming?

Prepares the skin for further treatment; deep cleanses; aids desquamation; temporarily hydrates the superficial layers of the stratum corneum; and relax the pores and the muscles.

12 Name the benefits of using ozone on the skin.

Ozone is healing, drying and antibacterial.

13 Describe how to perform a manual comedone extraction.

After you've steamed the skin, put on some gloves and wrap clean tissue around each index finger. Stretch the skin surrounding the blockage and gently squeeze underneath to release the blockage and draw it out from the skin.

14 What **three** techniques are used in massage and what are their benefits on the skin?

Effleurage: prepares the skin for deeper movements, aids desquamation and stimulates lymphatic and blood circulation.

Petrissage: aids relaxation, releases tension and stimulates cell mitosis.

Tapotement: temporarily tones the skin.

15 What is the difference between a setting and non-setting mask?

A setting mask sets on the skin, so you should apply it only for approximately 15 minutes. Setting masks generally contain clays to draw out impurities and lift away dead skin cells. You can apply a non-setting mask for longer as it doesn't set on the skin and won't dry it out. Instead, it's likely to be more nourishing as it will contain more moisture.

16 Why is it important to tone the skin?

Toning rebalances the skin's pH and restores its natural balance so the skin can function effectively.

17 What **two** components make up the acid mantle?

Sebum and sweat.

18 How often should a client have a facial and why?

It depends on their skin type and condition, however, a client can have a facial as often as once a week.

19 Name and describe the **two** contra-actions that might occur during a facial and explain how you would deal with them.

Excessive erythema: this could be a result of your client being touch sensitive; you'll notice this quickly in the skin. Adjust your pressure throughout the treatment, especially during the facial massage to avoid stimulating this further. If excessive erythema occurs during the treatment, stop immediately and apply a cold compress to reduce the heat and bring down the erythema. You can also apply a calamine mask made with a rose water toner to cool and soothe the skin. Advise your client to continue applying cool compresses over the next 24 hours. If the reaction still hasn't disappeared, recommend

they seek GP assistance. Excessive erythema could also be part of an adverse skin reaction.

Irritation: this is usually caused by a stimulant in a product and is more common in sensitive skin, although it can happen to anyone. If this contra-action occurs during the treatment, stop immediately and remove the product with cool water to reduce the heat and the temptation for your client to scratch their skin. Follow this with a calamine mask made with a rose water toner to cool and soothe the skin, or you can apply a cool compress. Apply aloe vera gel to soothe the skin and advise your client to continue this process over the next 24 hours. Recommend they seek GP assistance if the reaction hasn't gone away after this time.

20 What aftercare advice should you give to every client after a facial and why?

Because the skin and the underlying structures have been stimulated, this has brought newer cells to the surface and encouraged cell renewal in the epidermis. Therefore, it's important to make sure the skin isn't stimulated any more as this could cause a contra-action. For 24–48 hours after the treatment, the advice is:

- Avoid make-up.
- Avoid heat treatments, such as steam, sauna or hot tubs.
- Avoid swimming.
- Avoid UV treatments or sun exposure.
- Drink plenty of water, ideally two litres a day.
- Avoid caffeine, alcohol and smoking.
- Eat a light healthy diet.

B5 Enhance the appearance of eyebrows and lashes

1 Why is it important to ensure adequate lighting for all eye treatments?

To make sure you can see what you're doing and don't get any product in your client's eyes.

2 Explain why you should perform a mirror consultation before an eyebrow shape.

So your client can see what you plan to do before agreeing to the proposed treatment plan.

3 List the contra-indications to eye treatments that require medical referral.

Stye, conjunctivitis and blepharitis.

4 List the contra-indications to eye treatments that require modifications, and explain how you would apply these modifications.

- Eczema: if the skin is open and weeping, you shouldn't proceed with the treatment. If it's not open and weeping, continuously check the skin's reaction and communicate with your client throughout, taking care not to damage the skin.
- Psoriasis: treat in the same way as eczema.
- Bruising: work around the area and avoid applying too much pressure.

5 Why is it important to ensure the eyebrow shape complements a person's face shape?

Because the eyebrows frame the face and have a balancing effect on a person's face shape.

6 Explain how and why we measure the eyebrows before shaping them.

To make sure you create the correct shape with the arch in the right place and to make sure the length is correct.

Measure the eyebrows using the following process:

1 Begin with the orange wood stick resting next to the right nostril so it's aligned with the right eyebrow. Any hairs to the left of the orange wood stick need to be removed to neaten the space between the brows.

2 Asking your client to look up, bring the orange wood stick to an angle so it's still resting against the right nostril but the other end will rest directly over the iris. Where it ends over the brow will indicate where the arch needs to be.

3 Bring the end of the orange wood stick to the outer corner of your client's eye. Any hairs to the right of the orange wood stick need to be removed to prevent 'bringing the eyes down'.

7 What type of eyebrow shape is most suited to a heart face shape?

Oblique.

8 Why do square face shapes suit a tapered arch of medium thickness?

Because it helps to soften angular features.

9 What corrections would you make to the eyebrows for a client with wide-set eyes?

Make sure you don't tweeze too much from between the brows and start the eyebrows a little further in rather than in line with the inner

corner of the eyes. Take away more from the outer ends to create the illusion of them being closer together.

10 Explain the term oxidisation.

This is a chemical reaction that takes place when hydrogen peroxide is mixed with tint colour when it's exposed to air. This produces the dye that is applied to the lashes or brows.

11 Why are red and grey hair the most resistant to tinting?

Grey hair is resistant to tinting because there's no natural pigment present. Red hair is resistant because it has the strongest pigment of all the hair colours.

12 Explain why it's important to make sure the finished tint result complements the natural hair colour.

So that the finished result is natural and doesn't look out of place on your client's face.

13 What type of look would individual lashes complement the most?

A natural look.

14 Explain how strip lashes are applied and removed.

Separate the lashes by brushing them with the brow/lash brush. Take the strip lashes out of the box and measure them against your client's natural eye shape (they'll have a small amount of adhesive on them to let you hold them in place while you measure for size). Check which lash is for the left and right eye; the shorter lashes fit the inside of the eye while the longer lashes fit the outer eye area. Cut the width to fit the natural eye with a pair of scissors. If the length needs reducing, use the feathering cutting technique to maintain a natural effect. Place a small amount of adhesive in a foil-lined container or on a disposable spatula. Apply a small amount of adhesive to the base of the lash using the rounded end of the orange wood stick and make sure you're following the manufacturer's instructions. The adhesive is white but dries clear and takes about five minutes to set. Ask your client to look down and, with one hand, lift the brow to support the eyelid. Hold the strip lash with sterile tweezers and position the strip lash as close as possible to the base of the natural lashes, about 2 mm from the edge of both the inner corner and outer edge of the eyelid. Gently press the strip lash and natural lashes together from corner to corner with the rounded end of an orange stick or your fingers to make sure they're secure. Repeat this process on the other eye. Brush the lashes gently from under the natural lashes to blend both false and natural lashes together. Ask your client to check the finished result in the mirror and provide aftercare and home care advice.

To remove strip lashes, support the eyelid at the corner of the eye and gently peel the strip away from the lid, working from the outer to the inner corner of the eye. Using tweezers, gently peel the adhesive off the strip lashes. If you've used synthetic lashes, wash them in warm soapy water and rinse in warm water before you put them away. If the strip lashes are made of natural hair, follow the manufacturer's instructions on how to clean them.

15 When would you recommend strip lashes?

For an evening look.

16 Explain how you should care for and store strip lashes.

To maintain the curl of the lashes, place them side by side on a tissue, wrap them around a pencil and secure with a rubber band. When the lashes have curled back, put them in the original container for storage.

17 How should you apply individual lashes?

Separate the natural lashes by brushing them with a brow/lash brush. Select shorter lashes for the inside of the eye and longer lashes for the outer eye area. Place a small amount of adhesive in a foil-lined container or on a disposable spatula. Ask your client to look down and, with one hand, lift the brow to support the eyelid. Use sterilised tweezers to remove the shorter lashes from the tray and hold each lash as close to the centre as possible. Pass the underside of the lash from the root and just beyond through the adhesive, making sure you follow the manufacturer's instructions. The adhesive is white initially but dries clear and takes about five minutes to set. Start applying the lashes about 2 mm from the inner corner of the eyes. Use a stroking movement to apply the false lashes on top of the natural lashes, making sure you cover the length of the natural lash with adhesive. Secure the false lash as close to the root of the natural lash as possible to

create a natural effect. Check the lash is positioned correctly before moving on and repeating this process along the width of the eye. If the lash is incorrectly positioned, remove it while the adhesive is wet and re-apply. Continue applying the lashes one at a time, working each eye alternately. Use the appropriate length of eyelash to follow the contour of the eyes. This will make sure the overall effect is even, smooth and gradual. Apply eye make-up to complete the effect and remember not to apply mascara as it will loosen the adhesive. Brush the lashes gently, show your client the finished result in the mirror, and provide aftercare and home care advice.

18 Explain the aftercare advice you would give to a client after each eye treatment.

For eyebrow shaping:

Erythema is a normal reaction after an eyebrow shape due to the stimulation of the hair follicles and usually goes down in the first couple of hours, depending on your client's skin sensitivity. Give the following aftercare advice after every eyebrow shape to make sure the reaction doesn't get worse. The advice should be followed for up to 24 hours:

- Avoid heat treatments including sauna, steam and hot tubs as the pores are open and they might get infected.
- Avoid UV exposure as hyper-pigmentation might occur.
- Avoid swimming as irritation might occur.
- Avoid applying make-up as infection could occur.
- Apply a soothing antiseptic cream, such as aloe vera, to calm and soothe erythema.
- Groom the eyebrows into shape daily using a brow/lash brush, although a clean toothbrush will also do the job!
- Return for the next treatment in 4–6 weeks depending on previous hair removal treatment results.

For eyebrow and eyelash tinting:

- Avoid using an oil-based eye make-up remover as this will affect the longevity of the tint.
- Avoid rubbing and touching the eyes as this could cause cross-infection.
- For eyebrow tinting, return for the next treatment in 2–4 weeks depending on your client's hair growth rate.

- For eyelash tinting, return for the next treatment in 4–6 weeks depending on your client's hair growth rate.

For artificial lashes:
- Don't touch the eyes for two hours following treatment to allow the adhesive to fully dry.
- Avoid rubbing the eyes in general as this will loosen artificial lashes.
- Avoid using an oil-based eye make-up remover as this will dissolve the adhesive.
- Avoid heat as it might affect the lashes, making them frizzy if they're synthetic.
- Don't attempt to remove lashes – this will result in a loss of natural lashes. Instead, return to the salon for a safe and effective removal of any artificial lashes.
- If you lose an eyelash, return to the salon for a replacement fitting.

19 Identify **one** contra-action to each treatment and state how you would deal with it.

For eyebrow shaping:

Excessive erythema: occurs because the hair has been removed from the root of the follicle and is a minor histamine response. Apply an antiseptic agent, such as aloe vera, to soothe the area and reduce erythema; or, if severe, apply a cold compress first. You can prevent excessive erythema by stretching the skin properly.

For eyelash and eyebrow tinting, one of the following:
- Watery eyes: this could be caused by tint entering the eyes.
- Smarting of the eyes following treatment: this can be a natural occurrence for some clients but, to be safe, check that no tint has entered the eyes.
- Allergic reaction to petroleum jelly.
- Allergic reaction to the tint.
- Tint entering the eyes if your client opens their eyes during the treatment.

A tingling sensation is normal during an eyelash tint; however, burning, irritation and stinging aren't and are usually the result of tint entering the eyes.

Deal with the contra-actions listed above in the same way; by using an eyebath of purified or distilled water, which will rinse any product that has entered the eye, by following these simple steps:

- Tilt your client's head to one side and support with a small rolled-up towel.
- Place a small bowl of cool water beside the temple.
- Rinse from the inner to the outer edge of the eye with a sponge or a cotton pad and repeat until you've soothed the area and removed all the product.
- Repeat on the other eye before applying damp cotton pads to each eye to soothe the area.

For artificial lashes, one of the following:
- Watery eyes: this might be due to adhesive entering the eyes and should be treated with an eyebath.
- Lashes sticking together: apply adhesive remover to the lashes with a cotton swab and run along the lashes until the adhesive has dissolved enough to separate the lashes. If this isn't possible, continue until all the adhesive has dissolved and restart the treatment.
- Adhesive or adhesive remover entering the eye: apply an eyebath and damp cotton pads as outlined previously for an eyelash tint.

20 Explain how you would identify contact dermatitis, how you would deal with such a reaction and how this affects the treatment.

Contact dermatitis is the skin's response to an allergen or irritant it has been exposed to for the first time (acute) or over a period of time (chronic). It's identified by a rash, blisters or weals and is accompanied by irritation or burning, depending on the severity. If this occurs during any eye treatment, stop the treatment immediately and act fast to reduce the reaction as best you can:

- Apply a cold compress to the affected area (after applying an eyebath if this occurs during an eyelash tint) until the reaction has begun to subside.
- Apply a soothing lotion to the area, such as aloe vera. This will help heal and cool the skin and reduce erythema.

Ensure you give your client the following advice to stop the condition getting worse:
- Apply a soothing lotion, such as calamine or aloe vera, to soothe the area.
- If blisters occur, continue applying cold water compresses for around 30 minutes, three times a day.

- Antihistamines can relieve swelling and irritation.

Contact dermatitis is triggered by exposure to an irritant or allergen, which is why it's so important to stop the treatment as soon as you recognise a reaction. Explain to your client clearly what's going on and stress the importance of them following the aftercare advice. If your client suffers from contact dermatitis and you discover this on consultation, try to identify what the cause is before going ahead with the treatment to ensure this reaction doesn't occur.

B6 Carry out waxing services

1 Why is it important to ensure hygiene measures are in place for all waxing treatments?

To prevent the risk of cross-infection.

2 List **two** types of PPE that you should use during waxing.

Apron and gloves.

3 What PPE should your client have available during waxing treatments?

Disposable panties, towels and tissues.

4 Why is it important to ensure your client is in the correct position before you start any waxing treatment?

So you can stretch the skin and for your client's comfort.

5 Explain how you can minimise waste during waxing treatments.

By re-using wax strips for the same area on each client.

6 When the spatula you're using has been in contact with bodily fluid, why is it important to use a new one?

To avoid cross-infection.

7 What is meant by the term 'hazardous waste'?

This is waste which cannot be disposed of in general waste bags because it's soiled with blood or bodily fluids.

8 How long should a full leg wax take?

45 minutes.

9 Why is it important to adhere to the industry accepted times?

So that you don't keep clients and colleagues waiting and so that profit margins don't fall.

10 What are the contra-indications to waxing, and which ones require medical referral?

Medically controlled diabetes: lack of tactile sensation and the skin is prone to burning, bruising and abrasions and, as a result, infection.

The following contra-indications prevent waxing treatments and require medical referral:

- Severe and infectious skin conditions: the treatment could make the condition worse, secondary infection could occur and there's a risk of cross-infection.
- Severe varicose veins: painful for your client and could cause the veins to burst and cause an ulcer.

The following contra-indications also prevent waxing treatments but do not necessarily require medical referral:

- Thin or fragile skin: chance of bruising or tearing the skin open.
- Scar tissue under six months old: risk of opening the scar and causing a secondary infection.
- Certain medication, such as steroids: these thin the skin and increase the likelihood of the skin tearing or reacting.
- Heat rash: skin will not tolerate more heat if it's already hot and irritated.
- Sunburn: skin will be hot and painful and there could be a risk of further burning.
- Known allergies: many clients are allergic to products and ingredients, such as rosin which is found in sticking plasters and wax. An allergic (histamine) reaction could cause the skin to swell, become hot and irritated.

The following conditions could restrict a waxing treatment:

- Diabetes: lack of tactile sensation could cause burning and the skin is thin and fragile which can cause tearing and bruising.
- Moles: have their own cellular structure and waxing could alter this.
- Infected ingrowing hairs: will be painful and sore with the risk of secondary infection.

- Skin tags: could be removed with waxing and will bleed with the risk of secondary infection.
- Medication: could irritate the skin and make it fragile.

11 Why should you do a test patch and skin sensitivity test before you begin the treatment?

To check your client isn't allergic to any of the ingredients and to ensure the wax is at the right temperature.

12 Why is it important to perform a visual examination of the treatment area prior to waxing the hair and how is this done?

So the therapist knows which direction to apply the wax and which type of wax to use for client comfort. Cleanse the treatment area with pre-wax lotion before looking at the hair and the direction of growth.

13 Which type of hair is best suited to hot wax, and which is best suited to warm wax?

Hot wax is best for terminal hair and warm wax is best for vellus hair.

14 What are the melting and working temperatures of hot and warm wax?

Hot wax melts at 50°C and works at 55°C; warm wax melts at 47°C and works at 43°C.

15 List the **two** main ingredients of hot wax.
Beeswax and resin.

16 Explain why sugar paste is ideal for use on a sensitive skin.

Because it's made of only three ingredients and doesn't stick to the skin like warm wax does, it only sticks to the hair, resulting in less chance of allergic reactions.

17 List and describe the expected skin reactions to waxing.

Erythema: the correct term for redness. As heat has been applied to the area, local blood circulation has been stimulated, encouraging the skin to become erythemic. This often diminishes in the first couple of hours and is a perfectly normal reaction to waxing. Calm erythema by applying after-wax lotion or a soothing agent such as aloe vera. If you identify excessive erythema during the treatment, stop immediately and apply a cold compress followed by a soothing agent, such as aloe vera gel, which

will calm the skin and reduce the reaction.

Red spots around the follicle: as the hair has been removed from the follicle, there has been trauma to the area and surrounding tissue, which is why the skin is sometimes referred to as 'looking like a plucked chicken'. It's a minor, and normal, histamine reaction that diminishes in the first couple of hours and treatment is the same as with erythema. However, if this reaction gets worse throughout the treatment, you might find your client is displaying signs of a histamine reaction.

18 Explain what contact dermatitis is and how you can avoid it.

Contact dermatitis describes the skin's response when exposed to an irritant for the first time (acute), or over a period of time (chronic). The symptoms include dryness and cracking, a rash, blisters or weals, and irritation or burning. If this occurs during the treatment, stop immediately and apply a cold water compress to the area to cool and soothe before giving your client the following advice:

- Apply a soothing lotion, such as calamine or aloe vera to soothe the area.
- If blisters occur, continue applying cold water compresses for around 30 minutes, three times a day.
- Antihistamines can relieve irritation.

As contact dermatitis is triggered by exposure to an allergen, it's important the treatment is stopped immediately and shouldn't be repeated at a later date as the condition could get worse. If the initial reaction doesn't diminish in three days, advise your client to seek GP assistance. If your client suffers with contact dermatitis and you discover this during the consultation, try to identify what the cause is before going ahead with the treatment; rosin (found in plasters and wax) is a common cause of this condition. If your client is allergic to this ingredient, you might need to look at other options or find a different wax. If you're still in any doubt, ask your client to obtain GP approval first. You can avoid contact dermatitis by performing a skin sensitivity test.

19 Explain a histamine reaction and how to deal with it.

- Sometimes the trauma caused to the hair follicle stimulates an immune response, causing the mast cells in the dermis to release histamine into the skin. This sets off a chain reaction.

- Irritation and/or pain is caused by stimulation of the sensory nerve endings.
- Histamine is released and vasodilation occurs, stimulating local blood supply.
- With this increased blood supply come fresh oxygen, nutrients and leucocytes (white blood cells) to repair the damaged tissue.
- As a result of all of these points, localised skin temperature increases, making the skin feel warm to the touch.
- There's also a temporary increase in keratinised cells in the area, which results in the skin flaking when the histamine reaction has gone.

If you notice a histamine reaction, stop the treatment and apply a cool compress to the area until the reaction diminishes. Advise your client to continue applying a cool compress for the next 12–24 hours and suggest antihistamines that can further reduce the reaction. If the response continues, advise your client to seek GP assistance.

20 What aftercare and home care advice should you give to each client after a waxing treatment?

Give aftercare advice to every client after every type of waxing treatment and tell them to follow it for at least 24 hours:

- Avoid make-up (facial waxing only).
- Avoid showers or baths.
- Avoid heat treatments, such as steam, sauna, hot tubs and infra-red.
- Avoid sun exposure and UV treatments.
- Avoid applying perfumed products.
- Avoid deodorant or antiperspirant (underarm waxing only).
- Avoid touching the area.
- Avoid tight clothing as this will rub and cause friction and heat (body waxing only).
- Avoid tanning products or talcum powder.
- Avoid swimming.
- Avoid other beauty treatments that involve working on the area treated.

Home care advice is more client specific and will vary from client to client but should follow the same theme:

- Exfoliate between one and three times a week depending on whether or not your client suffers with ingrown hairs.

- Moisturise at least once a day to keep the skin hydrated and prevent the hair from becoming brittle.
- Increase water intake so that skin is hydrated; two litres per day is the recommended amount.
- If your client must wash in the next 24 hours, recommend a tepid shower to avoid the application of heat on heat and only use unperfumed products to minimise the risk of infection.
- If your client's skin is red afterwards, advise them to use aloe vera over the next 24 hours to cool and soothe the area, or apply a cold compress.

B34 Provide threading services

1 Explain why it's important to check your insurance before offering threading services.

To make sure you're insured to offer this service and to check the current guidelines on threading services.

2 List the contra-indications that restrict threading treatments.

Moles and skin tags: work around the area, avoiding it completely.

3 Why is it important not to remove the hairs from a mole?

If you worked over a mole, you could make it bleed, which could change the cellular structure and lead to further complications.

4 List the advantages and disadvantages of threading.

Advantages:

- It's completely safe and hygienic as you'll throw away the only implement you'll use to remove the hair, ie the cotton thread.
- You won't apply any chemicals to the skin.
- Clients with medical and health issues can benefit from threading services as it doesn't affect the skin in the same way as other hair removal methods.
- The service is less time consuming as you get more and more experienced.
- Threading is a cost effective service because you need very little equipment, implements and consumables.

- Threading can be much less painful than other methods of hair removal.
- Threading allows for a more precise finish as hairs are removed in rows. This is especially beneficial on the eyebrow area.
- It's ideal for more sensitive skin as you only remove the hair; the skin isn't affected at all.

Disadvantages:
- If applied incorrectly, threading can cause the hair to break at the surface and, as a result, regrowth will be much quicker.
- It can sometimes be hard to find an experienced therapist outside bigger cities.
- If the treatment area is not stretched, the lasso can pinch the skin.

5 Explain why threading is more suitable for sensitive skin than other temporary methods of hair removal, such as waxing?

Because it doesn't affect the skin in any way, so there's no risk of an allergic reaction.

6 Describe **two** of the three techniques you can use during threading services.

The hand technique: you use only your hands to manipulate the thread.

The neck technique: you anchor the thread around your neck for ease of use.

The mouth technique: you hold the thread in your teeth.

7 Explain how your client can assist you with stretching the skin.

When you're working on the brows, instruct your client to stretch above and below the brows with their fingers. When you're working on the upper lip, tell your client to purse their lips as they would for an upper lip wax.

8 What are the implications of using the mouth technique if you have a crown or a brace?

If you have a crown or a brace and choose to use the mouth technique, the thread could get caught and this would make the treatment ineffective.

9 What length of cotton thread do you need for threading?

2 feet, or 24 inches (61 cm).

10 Why is it important not to use the same thread on different areas even on the same client?

To ensure there's no risk of cross-infection.

11 How do you prepare the cotton thread for the hand technique?
- Take 2 feet/24 inches (61 cm) of cotton thread and form a loop.
- Tie the two free ends together securing this loop in place.
- Hold the cotton thread in both hands with your thumb and first three fingers and twist 8–10 times.
- Move the wound section of cotton by widening both hands alternately so that it works like a mini lasso, plucking the hairs from the root against the direction of hair growth.

12 How do you prepare the cotton thread for the mouth technique?
- Take 2 feet/24 inches (61 cm) of cotton thread.
- Place the free ends between your teeth and form a loop with your thumb and first three fingers.
- With your thumb and fingers still in this position, twist the cotton several times.
- Take one free end from your teeth and hold with your free hand, ensuring the distance between the wound cotton and your teeth is enough so you're not too close to your client and you can maintain adequate tension in the cotton during the whole service.

13 Why is it important to remove the hair against the direction of hair growth?

To ensure the hair is trapped and removed from the root of the follicle.

14 Explain how threading produces a more defined effect on the brows than tweezing or waxing.

Because hairs are removed in a line and this produces a more precise finish.

15 What aftercare advice should you give after every threading treatment?
- Avoid make-up.
- Avoid showering/bathing.
- Avoid heat treatments, such as steam, sauna, hot tubs and infra-red.
- Avoid sun exposure and UV treatments.

- Avoid applying perfumed products to the area.
- Avoid touching the area.
- Avoid tanning or bronzing products.
- Avoid swimming.
- Avoid other beauty treatments that involve working on the treated area.
- Return in the next 2–4 weeks to maintain the results.

16 When you're providing home care advice, what should it include?

Advice on exfoliation and moisturising to prevent ingrown hairs and dry skin. It should also include advice on how to safely wash the skin in the first 24 hours after treatment.

17 What are the possible contra-actions to threading?

- blood spots
- abrasions
- allergic reaction
- excessive erythema.

18 Explain how to deal with these contra-actions.

Blood spots: these can occur if you've removed a deep rooted hair or if your client hasn't stretched the area properly. If this occurs, stop the treatment and apply a damp cotton pad to mop up the blood. Make sure you dispose of it in a hazardous waste bag and not in the general waste before you continue. Give the appropriate aftercare advice to prevent a secondary infection in the follicle.

Abrasions: these can occur if you use poor quality cotton or synthetic thread instead of 100 per cent cotton as it tends to be a little harsher when it's rolled along the skin and can cause small abrasions. This is why it's vital you use 100 per cent cotton at all times because it's much softer and smoother and will only remove the hair and won't affect the skin. If an abrasion occurs, stop the treatment and apply a soothing agent, such as aloe vera, to help the skin heal and to soothe the area. Give your client the appropriate aftercare advice to make sure there isn't a secondary infection.

Allergic reaction: this can be caused by using a poor quality thread or synthetic thread rather than 100 per cent cotton thread. The allergic reaction can happen when the thread is rolled

along the skin. Your client might identify an allergic reaction as a tingling or itching sensation, which might lead to a stinging or burning sensation if not dealt with quickly enough. If your client scratches the area, erythema occurs along with oedema and possibly urticaria. If an allergic reaction occurs, stop the treatment and apply a cold compress and a soothing agent, such as aloe vera. Advise your client to continue applying cold compresses at home and follow the appropriate aftercare advice to make sure the reaction doesn't get worse.

Excessive erythema: this can occur alongside each of the above contra-actions and is the result of an increase in skin temperature. Stop the treatment and apply a cold compress to cool and soothe the area.

19 Why is it important for your client to exfoliate between treatments?

To prevent ingrown hairs.

20 How often should your client book a threading treatment?

Every 2–4 weeks depending on hair growth rate.

N2/N3 Provide manicure and pedicure services

1 Who is responsible for the health and safety of everyone in the salon?

All those working there, including you.

2 Why is it important not to discriminate against clients?

Because you're representing your business and no salon wants to be associated with prejudice. Discrimination can take many forms, eg age, race, gender, sexual orientation, cultural background, religious background and ability or disability. Refer to the Disabilities Discrimination Act – it's illegal to discriminate against people with a disability, such as blindness.

3 What types of personal protective equipment (PPE) should you be provided with and why?

Gloves, glasses and aprons – to reduce the risk of injury.

4 What is contact dermatitis and how can you avoid it?

A condition that causes inflammation of your skin. It's caused when somebody comes into contact with a particular substance that inflames their skin. There are two types of contact dermatitis – allergic and irritant contact dermatitis. You can avoid it by making sure you're not overexposed to certain products.

5 What methods should you use to clean and disinfect tools and equipment?

For metal tools, clean in soapy water and disinfect in the correct solution. Wipe down hard surfaces with disinfectant solution after every client. Wash fabrics at 60°C and dispose of single-use items.

6 How do you keep tools and materials in a hygienic condition?

Store them in a clean environment after you've disinfected them.

7 Why is it important to disinfect your hands?

To avoid cross-infection.

8 Why is it important to maintain standards of hygiene?

To prevent the spread of illness and disease.

9 Why is it important to position tools and equipment safely?

To avoid accidents and injuries.

10 How can you avoid injury to yourself and clients by correct positioning?

Make sure you're sitting straight and your back is supported by choosing the correct furniture.

11 During a pedicure, when and why should you wear safety glasses?

When you're clipping toenails in case any nails fly up into your eye.

12 How should you leave the work area?

In a tidy and hygienic condition, so that your colleagues don't have to tidy up after you.

13 Why are accurate records important and how does the Data Protection Act affect them?

Make sure you keep an accurate account of the consultation and services and your client's personal information and put them in a secure place. There are rules under the Data Protection Act that allow you to record certain essential information. This must only be relevant to your work and mustn't be shared with a third party unless the individual has given permission.

14 Name **four** consultation techniques and how they help.

Questioning, visual, manual and referring to records. These help your client understand what to expect from the service, help you understand whether your client's expectations are realistic, and give you an idea of what to recommend for the service and what to suggest for a possible on-going service plan. These techniques help you check whether your client understands any constraints to their expectations, whether they agree to your recommendations, or whether any provisions or compromises could affect the service plan you've recommended.

15 Name **two** questioning techniques and how you can use them during a consultation.

Open and closed questions. An example of an open question might be to ask your client to describe the condition of their skin and nails. A closed question would be a straightforward question that requires a yes or no answer.

16 Can you provide a manicure or pedicure service to anyone under 16 years?

Yes, but only with written consent and in the presence of their parent or guardian.

17 Name **four** contra-indications to a manicure and describe them.

Any four of the following: fungal, bacterial, viral and parasitic infections, severe nail separation, severe eczema, psoriasis, dermatitis.

18 What does a condition that might restrict the service mean?

A condition that isn't contra-indicated but might need you to adapt the service.

19 Why should you encourage your client to ask questions?

To make sure they understand what the recommended service involves.

20 Can you diagnose specific contra-indications?

No. You need to recognise the possibility of a contra-indication but you're not medically trained. If you identify a possible contra-indication, always refer your client to their doctor.

21 Name **four** treatable conditions that affect the nail or the skin around the nail.

Four of the following: weak, dry, brittle and ridged nails, dry, split and overgrown cuticles.

22 What is a service plan?

The service you and your client agree on following the consultation. It should include the details of the service, home care advice and any further treatments.

23 Why should you keep toenails short?

Because shoes can damage longer nails.

24 What are the benefits of using cuticle products during a manicure treatment?

To soften the cuticle and allow for easy removal.

25 Name the **three** main massage movements for a manicure of pedicure service.

Effleurage, petrissage and tapotement.

26 Why do you need to clean the nail plate before you paint the nails?

Because any oil or grease on the nail plate will make the polish peel and chip.

27 Why do you need to use a base and top coat?

You need a base coat to prevent the colour from staining the nail. You need a top coat to give a glossy finish and make the colour last longer.

28 Why is it important to keep to service times?

To avoid your next client having to wait and to make sure the service is commercially viable.

29 Why is aftercare advice important?

To help your client continue with a routine that will help improve the condition of their nails and skin.

30 What is a contra-action? Give **two** examples.

A reaction that occurs following an activity or use of a product. Any of the following are examples: swelling, irritation or excessive erythema.

N4 Carry out nail art services

1 Why might your client want a nail art service?

Any of the following reasons: for fun, they want to match an outfit/sandals, they have a special occasion, they like to keep up with trends, or they want to draw attention to their nails.

2 Name **five** useful nail art products.

Five of the following: transfers, glitter dust, striping tape, foils, paints flatstones, rhinestones.

3 Name **four** essential nail art tools.

Four of the following: scissors, brushes, marbelling/dotting tool, tweezers, palette, orange sticks.

4 Why should you keep your nail art tools in a box?

To keep them clean and protect from dust.

5 What is the recommended time for a nail art service?

30 minutes.

6 Explain why you should use a nail art sealer.

To protect all nail art.

7 What is the difference between a nail art sealer and a top coat?

A sealer is formulated for nail art; a top coat could affect the nail art product.

8 What do you need to find out from your client during the consultation?

Their colour and design preferences, the occasion, contra-indications and restrictions.

9 Why is it important to have a display of your nail art designs?

So your client has examples to look at as a starting point because descriptions aren't always enough.

10 What should you remember when you're applying foil adhesive?

That the foil will only stick to the adhesive and it must be clear before you apply the foil.

11 What are the **three** primary colours?

Red, yellow and blue.

12 Why is it useful to include black and white in your collection of nail art paints?

White lightens and black darkens any colour.

13 What is the easiest method of applying flatstones/rhinestones?

Placing them on a wet top coat.

14 How are these methods of nail art removed?

With nail polish remover.

15 List **four** pieces of aftercare advice.

Four of the following: wear gloves, re-apply a top coat regularly, use cuticle oil, use hand cream, don't use your nails as tools, remove the art with nail polish remover.

16 List **four** possible contra-actions.

Four of the following: irritation, swelling, erythema, loss of stones, lifting of striping tape.

N5 Apply and maintain nail enhancements to create a natural finish

1 Why is it important to minimise the production of dust and remove it from the atmosphere?

Dust is a potential health hazard.

2 Where is the best place to extract dust from the air?

Where it's generated, ie at the desk.

3 List **four** working practices that will reduce vapours in the salon.

Four of the following: a lined metal bin with a lid, keep all bottles closed and cover dappen dishes, good ventilation, desk extraction, change paper towels and keep brushes in closed containers.

4 List **three** working practices that will reduce dust.

Three of the following: apply overlays accurately, desk extraction, change paper towels and keep used files and buffers in closed containers.

5 List **four** working practices that will reduce the risk of overexposure.

Four of the following: avoid any liquid monomer touching your skin, eg don't touch your L&P brush with your fingers. Avoid the brush touching the skin around your client's nails. Don't rest your arm in dust on the paper towel. Discard it and replace with a clean one when you've finished the stages that create dust. Only wipe your L&P on the lint pad, NOT on the paper towel. Take care when you're removing the sticky layer on UV gel.

6 What is the minimum grit size that you should use on a natural nail and why?

240 grit. Any lower could damage the nail plate.

7 List **five** conditions that restrict the service.

Five of the following: minor separation, minor eczema, psoriasis, dermatitis, severely bitten or damaged nails, unknown swelling or redness associated with the nails.

8 List **three** circumstances where you would recommend a natural nail overlay.

To repair or strengthen the nails, prevent biting, or as a base for polish.

9 List **two** benefits and **two** negatives of the liquid and powder system.

Two of the following: the benefits are strength, coloured powders for French manicures and nail art, and nail correction.

The negatives are the system needs a high skill level and the smell is unpleasant for some.

10 List **two** benefits and **two** negatives of the UV gel system.

Two of the following: the benefits are strength and flexibility, colours for French manicures and nail art, nail correction and no smell.

The negatives are the system needs a high skill level and the nails can be difficult to remove.

11 List **two** benefits and **two** negatives of the wrap system.

The benefits are the system is relatively easy to learn and is good for delicate nails and repairs.

The negatives are that it's the weakest system and it might need a spray activator.

12 List **three** reasons why it's important to prepare the nail properly.

To avoid infection, to create a good bond with the overlay, and to keep the nail healthy.

13 What are the **three** zones of the nail?

Z1 is the free edge; Z2 is the centre stress area; Z3 is the cuticle area.

For the L&P system:

14 How do you know if the overlay is sufficiently cured?

Tap it with the handle of the brush and it should click.

15 How do you clean and store your L&P brush?

Clean the brush in monomer, reshape it on a towel and store it in a closed container.

16 How do you remove L&P overlays?

Soak them in acetone.

For the UV gel system:

17 How do you know how long to cure the gel under the UV lamp?

You should follow the manufacturer's instructions.

18 What is the inhibition layer and how should you deal with it?

It's the unreacted monomer and you should remove it with an alcohol-based cleanser.

19 How do you remove UV gels?

Buff them off or soak them in acetone depending on the type of gel.

For the wrap system:

20 How do you use a spray activator?

Spray a small amount from at least 12 inches (30 cm).

21 What is a heat spike and how do you avoid it?

Uncontrolled and fast polymerisation. Avoid it by using less activator.

22 How do you remove wraps?

Soak them in acetone.

For all systems:

23 What is the 'C' curve?

The curve of the nail or plastic tip from side to side.

24 Give **three** reasons why it's useful to remove most of the contact area of a tip.

Three of the following: it's easier to apply, there's less likelihood of air bubbles, it's easier to blend, and leaves more nail plate exposed to bond with the overlay.

25 What is the difference between an infill and a rebalance?

An infill is for minimal nail growth and just fills the growth area. Rebalance thins the whole overlay and replaces it with the correct structure for the stress area.

26 List **four** possible causes of lifting.

Four of the following: incorrect nail preparation, the overlay is touching the skin, the wrong ratio (L&P), insufficient cure (UV gels), overactivation (wraps), or the overlay is too thick or too thin in Z3.

27 What is the main cause of nail enhancements breaking and leaving overlay on the nail?

The nail enhancement was too long for your client.

28 When applying a tip and overlay to a bitten nail, how long should it be?

The enhancement must be no longer than the finger.

29 What would you do if there was a yellow/green discolouration under the overlay where it's lifted?

Remove the enhancement, dehydrate and re-apply.

30 List **four** important pieces of aftercare advice.

Four of the following:

- Tell your clients they must look out for any discolouration on the nail and show you as soon as possible.
- Any itching of the skin around the nails, swelling or other irritation anywhere on the body could be a sign of an allergic reaction. If this is suspected, your client must have the enhancements removed as soon as possible.
- Explain to your client that they shouldn't use their nails as tools.
- Massage nail oil into the nails and surrounding skin every day to maintain the enhancements and keep the natural nail flexible and moisturised.
- Suggest that your client wears gloves when they're doing work that involves detergents and other cleaning products.
- If your client finds that the nails are too long for their lifestyle, they should return so you can make them shorter.

B8 Provide make-up services

1 Why is it important to clean all make-up brushes before use?

To prevent cross-infection.

2 What health and safety measures do you need to follow during make-up services?

Follow the manufacturer's instructions when you're using make-up products and the Health and Safety at Work Act 1974 to make sure the treatment area is safe.

3 Why is it important to maintain good posture during make-up services?

To prevent unnecessary stretching which could lead to fatigue and injury.

4 How long should a make-up lesson take?

75 minutes.

5 Why is it important to establish your client's skin type and condition before you apply make-up?

So you know what type of products to choose to diminish any flaws and imperfections. For example, a cream foundation is better suited to drier and mature complexions as it provides a smooth and even finish.

6 List the contra-indications to make-up services that require medical referral and why.

- bacterial infections, such as impetigo, conjunctivitis and boils: risk of cross-infection and further skin damage
- viral infections, such as herpes simplex and warts: risk of cross-infection
- fungal infections, such as ringworm: risk of cross-infection
- parasitic infections, such as scabies and pediculosis: risk of cross-infection
- systemic medical conditions: risk of injury and skin damage
- severe skin conditions: risk of making the condition worse
- eye infections: risk of cross-infection.

7 How does lighting affect make-up application?

Natural light or white light is better for a day or bridal look as this is when you're most likely to see or wear this type of make-up. Fluorescent light intensifies darker colours and softens blues and greys, while incandescent light enhances frosted tones.

8 Explain how to prepare your client for make-up services.

Check they're covered with towels to avoid staining their clothes and protect their hair with a small towel. Use couch roll and tissues to protect the towels as well.

9 Why is it important to analyse the face, nose, eye and lip shapes before you apply make-up?

So you can apply any corrections with highlighter and shader to rebalance the features and give the illusion of an oval face shape and almond eyes (the 'ideal' shapes).

10 What corrections should you apply to rebalance a heart face shape and why?

Apply shader to the widest point (the temples) to reduce the width, and apply highlighter along the jawline to increase the width and balance the face.

11 What corrections should you apply to prominent eyes and why?

To diminish the appearance of bulging eyes, use a medium/dark eyeshadow in the centre of the upper eyelid. Add a darker shade at the outer corner and blend it in an upwards direction. Finish with highlighter on the brow bone to enhance this area.

12 How should you apply make-up to create a new lip line?

Conceal the natural lip line with foundation and set with powder. Create a new lip line with an appropriate liner before filling the lips with a matching shade of lipstick. Blot with tissue and apply another layer before a coating of gloss if necessary.

13 Why might you use colour correctors?

Green is used to neutralise red and helps hide dilated capillaries and rosy cheeks. Lilac brightens a sallow complexion and can be used for dark circles under the eyes. Peach/yellow neutralises blue and is good for hiding blue veins.

14 How do you know what foundation colour to use?

Test it on the jawline; the one that disappears is the one to choose.

15 Why should you apply powder over foundation?

To set it.

16 Why should you apply lip liner?

To create a new lip line and prevent lipstick or gloss from bleeding.

17 How should you use eyeliner to create a smoky effect?

Apply along the upper and lower lashlines and use a sponge applicator to smudge it.

18 Why shouldn't you use shimmers and cream eyeshadows on dry, dehydrated and mature skins?
Because it will enhance and draw attention to fine lines and wrinkles.

19 What aftercare advice should you give to each client after make-up application?

- Avoid heat treatment, such as steam, sauna or hot tubs.
- Avoid swimming.
- Avoid UV treatments.
- Use an oil-based eye make-up remover for stubborn eye make-up and waterproof mascara.
- Remember to cleanse, tone and moisturise twice daily to maintain the skin condition.
- Exfoliate one to three times a week to brighten the complexion.
- Apply an appropriate mask after exfoliating to clear the skin and bring natural radiance.

20 What are the **four** possible contra-actions to make-up services and how should you deal with them?

- Excessive perspiration: if your client is likely to perspire during or even after make-up application, use a mattefying powder to set the foundation and advise them to buy one as well. They can use this at home to prevent a high shine.
- Adverse skin reactions: this is usually caused by an allergic reaction to a product or an ingredient. If this occurs, treat in the same way as you would excessive erythema and give the same advice to ensure the reaction calms and dissipates. If it doesn't go down after 24 hours, advise them to seek GP assistance.
- Watery eyes: if your client's eyes water during the make-up service or after you've finished, use a tissue gently to absorb the tears. Check your client is OK before you continue or re-apply any make-up. If this reaction carries on, stop the treatment and remove all traces of make-up. Keep your client in a semi-reclined position to make sure that they don't get any product in their eyes. Apply a cool compress to the eyes to soothe them and advise your client that the treatment cannot continue. Recommend they see their GP for further advice.

- Excessive erythema: this is identified as redness and warmth in the skin and could be a result of your client being touch sensitive. If you notice this, adjust your pressure when you're applying make-up to the face. If excessive erythema occurs during the treatment, stop immediately, remove the make-up and apply a cold compress to reduce the heat and bring down the erythema. You can also apply a calamine mask made with a rose water toner to cool and soothe the skin. Advise your client to continue applying cool compresses over the next 24 hours, by which time the reaction should have disappeared and recommend they seek GP assistance if it hasn't. Excessive erythema could also be part of an adverse skin reaction.

B9 Instruct clients in the use and application of skin care products and make-up

1 What are the main Acts that are relevant to this type of service?
- Data Protection Act (DPA)
- Disability Discrimination Act (DDA)
- Control of Substances Hazardous to Health (COSHH)
- Provision and Use of Work Equipment Regulations (PUWER)
- Consumer Legislation Act

2 What are your responsibilities under the Disability Discrimination Act?
As an employee you must make sure that you do not discriminate against a customer, client, contractor or colleague with a disability. You also have a responsibility to observe and promote equal opportunities for disabled people.

3 Why is it important to complete consultations for both one-to-one and group instruction?
To ensure that all clients are suitable for the service and there's no risk of cross-infection or reaction.

4 Explain what environment is best suited to these types of event?
An ideal environment is one with sufficient lighting so you can see what you're doing, and one with adequate set-up so you're not

stretching unnecessarily and you're maintaining your comfort throughout.

5 What are the restrictions highlighted by Habia regarding the application of products, treatments and equipment for clients under 16 years?

To obtain written consent from a parent/guardian prior to the service taking place, ensure that a parent/guardian is present for the duration of the treatment, and to avoid using lash curlers during make-up application for safety purposes.

6 Explain how glasses might affect eye make-up during make-up application.

If your client is long sighted, their lenses will make their eyes look bigger and will draw more attention to the eye make-up. If your client is short sighted, the opposite will occur and the eyes will be less noticeable.

7 Give reasons why it's a good idea to make up only half the face during a make-up lesson.

Because this allows your client to view your techniques before trying to copy them and produce the same result on the other side.

8 Why is it important to talk about what you're doing and why you're doing it during an instructional event?

So that everyone is clear on what's happening and why it's being done that way. It also means that clients understand the processes and techniques you're using and leave feeling much more knowledgeable.

9 During a make-up lesson, why should you record the products you've used on a face chart?

So when your client leaves and tries to recreate the look in their own time, they don't forget what you used and where.

10 During a seminar, why is it important to check everyone has access to the products they need?

To prevent unnecessary stretching and to ensure the event runs as smoothly as possible.

11 Why is it a good idea to have a colour wheel handy during a make-up lesson?

So that you know what colours complement each other, which ones contrast well with each other and which colours you should avoid completely.

12 Explain why mirrors should be available for instructional events?

So that, during a make-up lesson, your client can observe the techniques you use. During a skin care seminar, the audience can see what they're doing and that they're doing it correctly.

13 Discuss why it's a good idea to offer promotions and discounts on the day of the event.

To ensure repeat custom and increase profits made from sales on the day. It's also a good idea because you're actively encouraging your clients to sample more products and services.

14 What promotional material should you hand out to encourage repeat custom?

Price lists; product leaflets; product samples; face charts; and gift vouchers.

15 How can you encourage clients to buy products and book more treatments before they leave?

Offer discounts on products and treatments booked on the day; offer discount vouchers which must be used on products in a certain time frame; offer gift vouchers or discounted treatments if clients make a booking before they leave; and let them try out testers and samples.

16 What methods of feedback can you use after an instructional event?

Questionnaires, feedback forms, question-and-answer sessions and guestbooks.

17 What are the advantages and disadvantages of each?

Questionnaires are very specific so will give you the relevant feedback. However, you must give your client time to complete the questionnaire to get an honest response and a true reflection of the event's success. Feedback forms tend to be much more generalised than questionnaires so might not offer the relevant feedback or a true reflection of the event's success. Guestbooks are very informal, which is better for the person providing the feedback but, as there's no guidance as to the type of feedback you want, it might not be a true reflection of the event's success. Question-and-answer sessions are fun and informal and allow you to gain an instant view of whether your audience found you and your information interesting. However, as this is verbal feedback, you won't have a record of it to refer to later on.

18 Why is it important to evaluate the success of the event?

It's important because it allows you to work on any negative points for future improvements. It also allows you to implement these improvements and ensure future success.

19 Why should you reflect on the event as well?

So that you can see whether your views match those of your client or audience, and whether your opinion of how successful the event was is accurate.

20 How can this feedback help you make improvements?

It will allow you to make the necessary improvements to ensure future events are even more successful than the last.

G4 Fulfil salon reception duties

1 How can you make sure the reception area is clean and tidy at all times?

By cleaning the surfaces every day or at least once a week with an appropriate disinfectant, vacuuming and mopping the floors at the start and end of each day.

2 What stationery does a receptionist need?
- a selection of pens in different colours
- pencils: to write down appointments in the appointment book
- erasers: to remove cancellations and mistakes in the appointment book
- a pencil sharpener: to keep pencils sharp
- paper clips: to keep things together
- a stapler and staples: to staple receipts together
- a hole punch: so you can place appointment pages in the folder
- a calculator: to calculate payments
- a notepad: to make any notes
- a memo pad: for taking messages
- an address book: for local business details
- appointment cards: to give to clients when they make appointments
- price lists: so that clients know how much each treatment costs
- promotional literature: to promote new treatments and products

- client record cards: to be completed by each new client prior to their first treatment
- aftercare advice leaflets: to be given after each treatment
- a telephone: so that clients can contact the salon to make appointments
- an appointment system, such as appointment book or computer: to keep a record of appointments
- a waste paper bin: for waste.

3 How can you ensure there's adequate stock on display at all times?

By ensuring there are several of each product on display and checking stock levels daily.

4 When you're maintaining stock levels, what should you be looking for?

Damages including cracked or broken seals and loose packaging.

5 Describe how a beauty salon can create the right first impression.

By creating the right atmosphere in the reception area to reflect the image of the salon. For example, a spa might be decorated with neutral colours with candles and dimmed lighting to create a feeling of wellbeing, whereas a city salon might be decorated with funky furniture and fresh colours to make their clients feel energised.

6 Why is it important to offer refreshments to all clients and customers?

To help them to relax while they wait for their therapist.

7 What is the difference between negative and positive body language?

Negative body language makes a person appear aloof, unapproachable and agressive, whereas positive body language makes a person come across as open and friendly.

8 Why is it important to attend to clients and customers promptly and politely?

To ensure that no one is left feeling as though they're not important.

9 What are the different types of enquiry you're likely to deal with on reception?
- appointment bookings
- clients arriving for appointments

- clients wanting to buy products or vouchers
- complaints
- clients wanting to find out more about the services your salon offers.

10 Explain the correct procedure for confirming an appointment.

When a client arrives in the salon, ask for their full name and the contact number they gave when they made the appointment. Mark them as arrived in the book or on the booking system and invite them to take a seat while they wait for their therapist. Ask if they would like any refreshments.

11 What information do you need when you're taking a message for a colleague?

The name and contact number of the person giving the message, who the message is for, the date and time the message was taken, and who it was taken by, and the message itself.

12 Why is important to communicate to clients and customers clearly?

To check they fully understand the information you're giving and to avoid confusion, embarrassment or any disputes.

13 Which **two** Acts must you be aware of when you're offering products and services?

The Sale of Goods Act

The Services Act.

14 How can you balance the attention you give to one client without ignoring another?

When you're dealing with one client and another enters the reception area, smile at them and say you'll be with them shortly before returning your attention to your client you were dealing with first. This shows you've acknowledged the other person and lets them know that although you're busy, you're aware of their presence and you haven't ignored them.

15 What information do you need when you're taking a booking?

- client name
- client contact details
- service required
- date
- time.

16 How can you make sure salon time is used productively when you're making appointments?

By offering times a little earlier or later than requested by your client where necessary. For example, if a client wants a facial at 3:15pm but the only therapist available is free at 3:00pm, offer your client this time so there aren't any gaps in the appointment book.

17 What payment methods are accepted in most salons?

- cash
- cash alternative, such as traveller's cheques, gift vouchers, loyalty schemes
- cheques
- credit and debit cards.

18 Why must you make sure the customer takes a copy of the receipt?

As proof of payment and for their own records.

19 What other identification do you need if you've been given a cheque that exceeds the limit on the cheque guarantee card?

A driver's licence.

20 How would you deal with a card that has been declined?

Try the card again to make sure it's not the card terminal that is at fault. If the card is declined again, ask if your client has another payment method they could use. If not, find the responsible person to deal with the situation.

B7 Carry out ear piercing

1 Why is it important to be aware of the different health and safety legislation before you offer ear piercing?

To ensure you can provide the best, most effective and safest ear piercing service available.

2 Explain the requirements of the Local Government Act 2003.

As an overview, this Act requires any salons (and its employees) offering this treatment to be registered with the local HSE who sends an inspector to ensure all by-laws and all relevant health and safety legislation are being followed before providing the business with a certificate of registration. Only then can the salon offer these treatments to clients.

3 What is a by-law?

A by-law is a local law passed from a higher authority and can vary from place to place.

4 Why should a person offering piercings of any kind be immunised against the hepatitis B virus?

To avoid the risk of cross-infection.

5 Explain why it's important to obtain written parental consent when you're treating minors.

Because they're too young to consent to the treatment themselves so they must have a parent or guardian with them who is over 18 years old.

6 How long should an ear piercing treatment last without the consultation and aftercare advice?

Around 15 minutes.

7 What PPE should be made available, and worn, when you're providing an ear piercing treatment?

Disposable gloves.

8 Explain how to ensure the piercing gun is disinfected.

By using an appropriate disinfectant solution and placing it in the UV cabinet for ten minutes on each side.

9 Why is it important to maintain hygiene standards in relation to the risk of cross-infection?

To avoid complaints, legal action and an unprofessional image.

10 Why is it important to ensure your client is positioned correctly and comfortably before you pierce the ear lobes?

So the piercings are balanced and symmetrical.

11 Why are the ear lobes marked prior to piercing?

To ensure the finished result is even and balanced, and to ensure the client is happy.

12 Which contra-indications to ear piercing require medical referral?

- Systemic medical conditions: risk of aggravating the condition and causing discomfort or distress to your client.
- Serious localised skin infections: risk of cross-infections and exacerbating the condition.
- Ear lobe infections: as above.

- Haemophilia: due to a lack of blood clotting, the skin is unlikely to heal as well, or as quickly as it should.
- Nervous client: your client might panic or jump, which could result in incorrect placement of the studs.

13 List all the equipment needed for an ear piercing treatment.

- an ear piercing gun such as
  - a disposable gun (these are intended for single use only and are pre-loaded with studs)
  - a re-usable gun (this doesn't come into contact with the ear at all)
- hand disinfectant
- a selection of hypo-allergenic studs (pre-sterilised and pre-packed by the manufacturer)
- pre-packed alcohol-based sterile wipes
- a small bowl of cotton wool pads
- disposable gloves (ideally powder-free, nitrile/vinyl gloves to prevent sensitisation)
- aftercare solution
- a sterile skin marker pen
- a headband
- a mirror
- a small towel
- a medium towel
- client record card
- aftercare advice leaflet

14 Why are pre-packed studs recommended?

Because they've been pre-sterilised to reduce the risk of cross-infection.

15 Why is it important to use the recommended piercing gun for this treatment?

Because it doesn't come into contact with the ear at all.

16 Explain the correct procedure for ear piercing.

- Cleanse the ears thoroughly using the pre-packed alcohol-based sterile wipes. These often come as part of a starter kit and are recommended or produced by the gun manufacturer. This will minimise waste and reduce the risk of cross-infection.
- Take the mirror and discuss where your client would like the piercing.

- While your client holds the mirror, use the surgical marker pen to mark where the piercings will be. Recommend a central location as it will appear balanced and symmetrical.
- Check that the packaging of the studs isn't damaged, damp, wet or out of date as the studs will no longer be sterile and must be thrown away in the appropriate hazardous waste bin. If there's no identification of the pre-sterilised package, you'll need to contact the manufacturer before using them as they might need to be sent back and replaced.
- On each packet of studs, there's a red spot identifying they've been sterilised. If this red spot isn't present, don't use the studs as they'll need to be sent back to the manufacturer.
- Remove the backing paper of the stud pack.
- Pull back the plunger knob on the back of the gun until you here it click.
- Hold the plastic cartridge by its plastic mount and remove from its packaging, ensuring you don't touch the backing clasp or stud to avoid cross-infection.
- There are two parts of the cartridge to be separated; do this by positioning the part with the backing clasp into the slot of the gun, pushing it down until it doesn't go any further. The part holding the stud is positioned against the stud barrel of the gun, placing a protective ring around the stud.
- Hold the ear in your non-working hand and keep the gun in a horizontal position. Bring the stem of the stud in line with the mark on the ear lobe.
- Squeeze the trigger gently until it stops and check the stem of the stud is still in line with the mark on the ear lobe. Squeeze the trigger again so the ear is pierced with the backing clasp placed on the back of the stud.
- Hold the ear gently and move the gun down and away from the ear lobe.
- Discard the plastic ring into the waste bin by holding the gun upside down.
- Pull back the plunger knob.
- Remove the backing clasp holder from its slot, invert and replace.
- Repeat on the second ear.

- Show your client their pierced ears using a hand mirror.
- Provide home care and aftercare advice and product recommendations.

17 What aftercare advice should you give to each client and why is it important they adhere to this for 6–8 weeks?
- Don't remove the studs.
- Cleanse the area twice a day using a suitable disinfectant aftercare solution applied with a clean cotton ball.
- Prior to cleansing the ears, wash your hands with soap and warm water for at least 30 seconds.
- Don't touch the ears unless it's to cleanse or rotate the earrings.
- Take care when shampooing and applying perfume and hair spray to avoid sensitisation and the risk of infection.
- Rotate the studs with your index finger and thumb once each day to prevent them from sticking as the skin heals (remember to wash your hands thoroughly beforehand).
- Avoid using any other cleansing solutions than those recommended by the salon and the manufacturer. This includes essential oils, such as tea tree, because sensitisation can occur.
- Don't have any other ear lobe piercings as the skin is healing and scar tissue will be present. This means the lobes will be swollen and the process will not only be painful but also there's an risk of cross-infection.
- It's important your client follows this advice to allow the skin and cartilage to heal properly, without risk of infection developing.

18 Why is it important for your client to use the recommended aftercare solution?
To keep the ears, and the studs, clean and hygienic.

19 What are the possible contra-actions to ear piercing?
- piercings close up
- infection
- keloid scarring.

20 How would you deal with these contra-actions?

Removing studs before the skin has healed and not replacing with other earrings will cause the holes to close up. If this occurs and your client doesn't want the holes to heal up, they will need to book in for another treatment.

If the skin isn't cleansed at least twice a day, infection is likely to occur as dirt, shampoo and other products build up around the area. If infection does occur, the skin will appear erythemic, swollen and inflamed with pus or a serum-like fluid weeping from the hole. In this instance, your client should contact the therapist who will remind them of the aftercare advice and cleansing techniques to use. In severe cases, advise your client to contact their GP.

Keloid scarring might also occur after the ear lobe has been pierced due to the amount of collagen produced as the skin heals. Advise your client not to have any other ear lobe piercings as it's likely further keloid scarring might occur. For clients who are prone to keloid scarring but are determined to have their ears pierced, make it clear that there's an increased risk of this and that only one piercing is recommended.

B10 Enhance appearance using skin camouflage

1 Give the reasons why a client might book in for skin camouflage treatment.

To conceal birthmarks, erythemic conditions, hypo/hyper-pigmentation and tattoos.

2 Explain what is meant by the term hypo-pigmentation.

This is where the melanocytes stop producing melanin and the skin looks lighter in places.

3 What is vitiligo?

This is a condition of hypo-pigmentation where the melanocytes stop functioning or die and create lighter patches of skin. It's more common in Afro-Caribbean skin.

4 Why is lighting important in relation to skin camouflage?

Because it needs to look as natural as possible, therefore, natural or white light is ideal.

5 As a guide, how long should skin camouflage services take?

Up to 75 minutes, as if it were a make-up lesson.

6 Why is it important to ask your client to identify their area(s) of concern?

To avoid embarrassment and humiliation for your client and to avoid being insensitive.

7 Explain why it's important to remain empathetic and reassuring when you're dealing with a client during skin camouflage services.

To ensure your client relaxes in your company and feels confident in you as their therapist.

8 Why is important to ensure your client's expectations are realistic and achievable?

So that they leave satisfied with the results.

9 Which contra-indications to skin camouflage require medical referral and why?

- Structural changes to the area to be camouflaged: because of the risk of pain and discomfort or an underlying medical condition you're unaware of.
- Suspicious moles: a mole could be malignant so it's important you don't work over it until your client's GP has given a proper diagnosis.
- Skin infections: risk of cross-infection.

10 What skin camouflage products are available and how are they used?

- Camouflage cream: these are mixed and applied after any necessary colour corrections to rebalance the skin colour. They tend to contain no or very little oil to make them durable and waterproof. Apply camouflage creams with clean fingers in a patting motion as this gives even coverage.
- Camouflage powder: this is applied to set the camouflage cream and provide a waterproof finish. Apply with a velour puff and leave to set for roughly ten minutes. Brush off any excess with a large powder brush or a damp cotton pad.
- Setting products: setting sprays can be applied after powder to provide sun protection and make the finished results last even longer.

11 Why is important to use these products in a logical order?

To ensure an even and natural finish that's durable and waterproof.

12 What is it that makes the finished result waterproof?

The setting product.

13 How long should skin camouflage be left on the skin and why?

No longer than 24 hours to avoid clogging the skin.

14 Why is it important to understand how different lighting can affect the appearance of skin camouflage?

Because products contain ingredients that have reflective and refractive qualities and these can affect their appearance under flash photography. Always apply skin camouflage under natural light to ensure it appears as natural as possible.

15 Explain what titanium dioxide is and why it's used in skin camouflage.

This is an organic mineral that has high refractive qualities, making it a suitable SPF. It's used in skin camouflage because it provides the whitest pigment available in cosmetics.

16 Why is it important to ensure your client can recreate the same effects themselves before they leave the salon?

So they leave feeling confident in themselves and in the techniques they've learnt.

17 What aftercare advice should you give to all clients after skin camouflage services?

- Avoid heat treatments, such as saunas, steam rooms and hot tubs as the temperatures could cause the make-up to run.
- Avoid overexposure to UV light as this could aggravate any pigmentation disorders.
- Avoid using oily make-up and skin care products on top of the skin camouflage as it might smudge or remove the camouflage altogether.
- Swimming is fine as the make-up is waterproof and durable. However, don't rub the skin dry with a towel; use a patting motion to prevent smudging or removing the make-up.
- Remove skin camouflage after 24 hours to avoid clogging the pores.

18 Why should you give your client product and skin care recommendations as well?

To ensure they're caring for their skin with the best products available to them; the wrong products could aggravate their skin condition.

19 What contra-action might occur as a result of skin camouflage?

An allergic reaction.

20 How should this contra-action be dealt with?

If an allergic reaction occurs during the treatment, stop immediately, remove the make-up and apply a cold compress to the area to reduce the heat in the skin and bring down any erythema. You could also apply a calamine mask made with a rose water toner to cool and soothe the skin. Advise your client to continue applying cool compresses over the next 24 hours, by which time the reaction should have gone. Recommend they seek GP assistance if it hasn't.

S1 Assist with spa operations

1 Why is it important to maintain personal hygiene, protection and appearance when you're assisting with spa operations?

You should maintain personal hygiene, protection and appearance to prevent cross-infection, illness and injury and maintain a professional image.

2 List the personal protective equipment that you should wear when you're cleaning spa facilities.

Gloves and aprons so you don't develop skin allergies, such as contact dermatitis.

3 How can you make sure your working methods reduce the risk of cross-infection and minimise the risk of harm or injury?

By wearing PPE, adhering to the manufacturer's and organisational instructions, asking for help when you need it, checking chemicals and temperature at regular intervals according to the manufacturer's instructions.

4 Explain why it's important to maintain the correct posture when you're assisting with spa operations.

To reduce the risks of injury or fatigue.

5 Why should you report any problems or difficulties to the responsible person?

Because you might not have the knowledge, experience or authority to deal with every problem, and could end up making matters worse.

6 Why is it important to check you're using the correct cleaning materials for specific spa facilities?

Because certain facilities are made from specialist materials. For example, saunas are made from timber and spa baths/rooms are made from ceramic. Both can be easily damaged and stained so you must take care when you're cleaning these facilities.

7 Explain why tools and equipment must be sterilised or disinfected before they're used.
To reduce or eliminate the risk of cross-infection.

8 Why should you clean spa facilities and work areas at regular intervals?
To reduce the risk of cross-infection, make sure they're clean and hygienic at all times and maintain the salon's professional image.

9 How can you create and maintain the correct environmental conditions for your client?
By maintaining the appropriate temperatures for each facility, ensuring that there are no hazards or risks, making sure your client is comfortable at all times and checking all air vents are open and free from obstruction.

10 Why is it important to explain all safety requirements and put them on display?
To ensure clients don't forget what you've told them and so they cannot blame you or the business if they fail to follow your advice. Clients need to get the most from the spa facilities without the risk of injury or harm.

11 What are the general effects of dry and wet heat treatments?
- stimulates blood circulation
- stimulates lymphatic flow
- produces erythema
- disperses accumulated lactic acid
- eases tension in the muscles
- promotes a feeling of wellbeing
- decreases blood pressure
- stimulates sebaceous and sudoriferous glands.

12 What are the possible contra-actions to dry and wet heat treatments?
- dehydration
- dramatic decrease in blood pressure
- breathing difficulties
- fainting
- nausea
- headaches
- cramp
- scalding/burning of the skin
- nosebleed
- allergic reaction to the chemicals in spa pools.

13 What test is used to check the water's pH, hardness and temperature in a spa pool?
The Langlier Index or Palintest Balanced Water Index.

14 Why is it important to make sure these tests are recorded and kept up to date?
Because the local authority could conduct an audit of spa facilities at any time and failure to maintain or produce maintenance records could result in a fine or the salon could lose its licence.

15 How would you deal with any chemical concentration problems or temperature fluctuations?
By reporting it to the responsible person.

16 Explain why clients shouldn't be left unattended for too long during dry and wet heat treatments?
Because they might experience a contra-action, which could cause them to panic and make the symptoms worse. It's vital you're available should anything untoward happen as you'll need to calm your client down and make sure they're OK.

17 Why is it important to check all electrical equipment and facilities are switched off at the mains before you clean at the end of the day?
To avoid the risks of electrical faults, fires and shocks, and injury.

18 Why should you make sure the responsible person is happy with how you've shut down the equipment and facilities?
Because your duties are to assist in the operation of spa facilities and the responsible person will need to check you've done everything correctly before leaving at the end of the day.

19 Give **three** examples of dry or wet heat treatments.
- sauna
- steam bath/room
- spa pool.

20 What is Legionnaires' disease and how can you catch it?
Legionnaires' disease is a water-borne disease. It's a type of pneumonia caused by the inhalation of water droplets contaminated with the Legionella pneumophila bacterium.

INDEX

THE CITY & GUILDS TEXTBOOK